HORSE BREEDING IN IRELAND

LIMITED EDITION

COLIN A. LEWIS

Horse Breeding in Ireland

AND THE ROLE OF

The Royal Dublin Society's Horse Breeding Schemes 1886–1903

J. A. ALLEN & CO. LTD.
London and New York

First published in 1980
by J. A. Allen & Co. Ltd.
1 Lower Grosvenor Place
London SW1W 0EL

British Library Cataloguing in Publication Data

Lewis, Colin Andrew
    Horse breeding in Ireland.
    1. Horse ·breeding – Ircland
    I. Title
    636.1'08'209415   SF290.I/

    ISBN 0–85131–315–9

Typeset by Inforum Ltd, Portsmouth
in 10 on 12 point Times (VIP)
Printed in the UK by
Redwood Burn Ltd, Trowbridge and Esher
and bound by Robert Hartnoll of Bodmin

*To Cecil Wedgwood, in
appreciation of his friendship and
inspiration in years past*

Acknowledgements

This book could not have been written without the unfailing help and courtesy of Mr Eager and his staff in the Library of the Royal Dublin Society. Mr John O'Keefe of Bord na gCapall also helped greatly with the provision and verification of recent statistics. Professor T. Jones Hughes and Dr Kevin Danaher of University College Dublin, Miss Mary McGrath, and Mr Michael Osborne (Manager of the Irish National Stud), kindly read and commented upon the original manuscript, as did the publisher's anonymous reader, although the errors that remain are the responsibility of the author alone. Mrs Ursula Love and Mrs Dorothy O'Connor typed what must have seemed to them to be a most unusual manuscript, and Mrs Dianne Large prepared the final maps. Mr E. Buckmaster reproduced many of the photographs and Mr Foley graciously provided a photograph of his parents. The Royal Dublin Society graciously allowed the use of many photographs from the Society's archives. The Hon. Desmond Guiness, Mr C Sutton and Bord na gCapall also kindly supplied illustrations.

Permission to quote from Siegfried Sassoon's poem, *The Old Huntsman*, was provided by G.T. Sassoon, and Martin Brian and O'Keeffe Ltd, Publishers, and Mrs Katherine B. Kavanagh gave permission for a quotation from P. Kavanagh's *The Green Fool*. Bord na gCapall granted permission to reproduce material shown in Appendices Three and Four.

To all these people the author is most grateful, but he particularly thanks his wife for her continued support and interest in the book throughout its preparation.

Contents

List of Illustrations

Plates

Figures

Tables

Introduction

Ireland has long been renowned for the production of quality riding horses, but during the eighteenth century the horse breeding industry of the country divided into two distinctive parts. On the one hand, as in neighbouring England, much emphasis was placed upon the development of the Thoroughbred, a specialized breed that is particularly suited to racing, especially on the flat. By comparison, indigenous breeds were apparently retained, although their development is poorly documented.

During the nineteenth century, by breeding some of the less heavy native animals to Thoroughbreds, Ireland began to produce a type of riding, carriage and light harness horse that became known as the 'Irish hunter.' This type was in great demand for military, and especially cavalry use, and was widely exported to Britain and to neighbouring European continental countries until well after the end of the First World War. During the twentieth century the name given to this type gradually changed, so that, by the late 1970s, the term 'Irish Half-bred' was replacing the older 'hunter' label. Perhaps that was inevitable, since the decline of internal and British markets for hunting horses had caused the breeders of non-Thoroughbred riding horses to seek new outlets, in show jumping, eventing and ordinary pleasure riding, for their produce. Of course, in addition to riding horses Ireland also produced draught animals, although the country never engendered such a heavy breed as the English Shire or the Scottish Clydesdale. Instead, whilst importing and breeding such animals for farm and city use, Ireland developed its own indigenous draught horse, which was a much lighter and more active animal than the British draught horses. This type, during the twentieth century, was developed into the Irish Draught Horse.

Traditionally, during the nineteenth century, the production of hunters was based on putting Irish Draught mares to Thoroughbred sires. But all the evidence suggests that the Irish Draught was itself the result of the cross-breeding of Thoroughbred and other, Eastern, horses, upon the better and lighter elements of the indigenous Irish horse population, probably upon what had in earlier days been called the 'Irish hobby.'

By the beginning of the last quarter of the twentieth century heavy draught horses had become a rarity in Ireland, as mechanization and the spread of the internal combustion engine rendered them largely redundant. Even the Irish Draught had lost much of its' earlier popularity and was retained for breeding rather than for purely working purposes. The future of the horse in Ireland therefore, apparently depends upon the production of Thoroughbred racing animals, and upon the Irish half-bred riding type.

The thoroughbred industry is markedly different from the traditional hunter, or Half-bred, industry. The former is highly capitalized and highly specialized and is almost entirely dependant upon the continuation of racing for its existence. In 1976 it was estimated[1] that almost 9,000 people were employed in the racing and bloodstock industry in Ireland. Of these, almost 2,000 were fully employed in breeding Thoroughbreds. By comparison, it is doubtful whether more than a few tens of people are fully employed in breeding Half-breds. Instead it is traditional for farmers to keep one or two mares for breeding purposes, extra to their other farm stock. Additionally the mares are kept more as a hobby than as a business. By 1977 this fact had become all too apparent in the Republic of Ireland, as only 3,553 non-Thoroughbred foals were born and registered with An Bord na gCapall, the Irish Horse Board. Naturally many foals were produced that were not registered, but it is not likely that many of them would have been of great quality, since the advantages of registration were widely recognized by breeders. Thoroughbreds and non-Thoroughbreds (or Half-breds) therefore form two remarkably different groups, and their production has engendered two different and highly contrasting industries, both worthy of separate, and detailed, analyses.

This book is essentially concerned with the Irish Half-bred and with the ways in which, during the latter part of the nineteenth century, the Royal Dublin Society did much to improve the quality of such horses. It was largely upon the foundations of the Society's work that the Department of Agriculture, and now An Bord na gCapall, have been able to base their own horse breeding schemes during the twentieth century, as the state plays an active role in fostering the non-Thoroughbred breeding industry. But this is not just a book about the Royal Dublin Society's schemes. It deals with the horses themselves, describing and assessing the merits of many of the Thoroughbred sires used under the Society's schemes and noting the performances of their more illustrious progeny. The book also describes many of the stallion owners, breeders and administrators, who were involved in the industry during the hey-day of the Society's schemes. Furthermore, the spatial (and therefore geographical), patterns in the horse breeding industry of the late nineteenth and of the twentieth century are mapped and analysed. Finally, the book concludes with a description and assessment of the breeding industry associated with the production of non-Thoroughbred riding horses in Ireland in the latter part of the twentieth century.

CHAPTER ONE

Genesis

Ireland has been famous for horses for many hundreds of years yet, except for the recent past, we know almost nothing about their breeding and only a little more about their conformation. The earliest domesticated horses were probably those of around 2,000 B.C. Archaeological work at Newgrange, in the Boyne Valley, has unearthed skeletal remains of ponies of about thirteen hands.[1] More recently, in the Iron Age, the size of bits suggests that many equines in Ireland were fourteen hands or so, although there are a few bits that could have been used for animals of fifteen hands, or even more. We may therefore envisage, at around the time of Christ, a considerable variety in the sizes of horses and ponies in the country, but probably with a marked predominance of ponies.

In the early Christian period, and particularly from the eighth century onwards, many horses were depicted as carvings on High Crosses, and as marginal illustrations on some of the illuminated manuscripts. While a few of these, as on the carved pillar at Banagher in Co. Offaly, show what is apparently a full-size horse, others show ponies. The Banagher example is of a cleric seated on a large and well proportioned pacing riding horse, the type of animal that many people would be happy to ride today (although modern Irish horses seldom pace). The lower panels of the beautiful North Cross at Ahenny, on the borders of Tipperary and Kilkenny, show a team of four ponies harnessed to a two-wheeled chariot, and a led pony carrying a human headless body. These carvings probably date to the eighth century. The Bealin Cross, in Co. Westmeath, also shows a pony, but being ridden by a spear-carrying huntsman. That cross is thought to date to *circa* 810.[2] Similarly, the wonderfully illuminated Book of Kells, produced in the late eighth century, contains drawings of riders and their mounts.

One of the most interesting features of these depictions is that, in many cases, they are of ponies. This, plus much archaeological evidence, suggests that prior to the Norman invasion the Irish tended to keep ponies, rather than horses. Perhaps that is not surprising, for the excavation of Roman remains from Trimontium in Roxburghshire, Scotland, has shown that the largest horses there were only between fourteen and fifteen hands, whilst many were between twelve and thirteen hands. If the Roman cavalry, the greatest in Europe in its day, had to be satisfied with such small horses it is hardly likely that the Irish, on the edges of the known world, would have been better mounted.[3]

In 1169, at the invitation of Dermot MacMurrough, 'Lord of Hy Kinsella, King of Leinster and the Foreigners,'[4] a group of Normans led by Robert FitzStephen (whose mother was the redoubtable Welsh princess, Nesta, daughter of Rhys Tewder), invaded Ireland. They landed on the shores of Bannow Bay in Co. Wexford. The invading force was admittedly, small in numbers, but it included thirty knights and sixty cavalry-men.[5] Thus, or so it is thought, were heavy Norman cavalry horses introduced to Ireland.

Nesta's grandson, Giraldus, like his Uncle Robert and many other members of the family, also adventured in Ireland. Giraldus was a popular historian of his day and, amongst other works, wrote the famous *Conquest of Ireland* and the *Topography of Ireland*. The latter work was illustrated with marginal drawings, one of which depicts what Giraldus claimed was a typical mounted Irishman seated bareback on a cross-looking pony. As far as Giraldus was concerned there was no doubt at all: the Irish rode ponies.

Following their invasion the Normans rapidly established a colony in south east Ireland and in the Dublin area. One of their strongholds was south Wexford where they established towns and manors, and led a settled, peaceful life. The Manorial Accounts for Old Ross for the 1280s still survive, after a fashion. In 1280/81 the livestock on the Manor included 505 sheep, 316 lambs, twenty-nine cows, five pigs, nine swans, eleven peacocks and hens, and eight farm horses.[6] Although these were work horses we have no real indication of their size or shape. Yet in the same year the accounts list the expenditure of 2s.6d. as 'Expenses of Sir P. de Bocland . . . for ten bushels of oats as provendor for his horses.'[7] This suggests that the Normans kept different types of horses, work horses and riding horses, since this item is listed separately from the main accounts. Supporting evidence is afforded by the accounts for 1285 and for 1288. In the former year it cost 7s. to buy an ox and the same to buy a horse, presumably a work horse. The preceding item in the accounts was: 'For the hire of a horse to harrow the oats for twenty days, 10d.'[8] In 1288 the accounts record 'For one horse bought from Philip le Hore, 18s.'[9] One hardly imagines the expenditure of such a sum on an ordinary work-horse!

Twenty-three years later, in 1311, the Inventory of the goods of the Templars in Ireland list, as existing on their lands at Kylclogan in Co. Wexford, '. . . eight horses for three wagons, price of each horse 6s.8d; three wagons, price of each 3s.6d.' By comparison a cow was valued at 5s. and a sheep at 8d. The gentleman in charge of the lands was obviously a horseman and believed in keeping good horses for himself, which was not surprising since there was a large hunting forest in his vicinity. The Inventory lists 'In the Stable of the Preceptor one horse of the value of five marks (£3.6.8.), one horse as a hackney, value two-and-a-half marks; four colts and fillies, price of each 13s.4d.'[10]

Unfortunately, in spite of all these records, little is known of the horses themselves. For January, 1270, the *Annals of Ulster* relate that: 'The defeat of Ath-in-chip was inflicted by Aedh, son of Phelim O'Connor and the men of Connacht on the Earl Walter de Burgh and the other foreigners of Ireland. And there were abandoned one hundred horses with their saddles and armour.'[11] This evidences the existence of cavalry horses strong enough to carry armour, but nothing is known of the conformation of the horses. Incidentally, this is the first known reference to armoured horses in either Ireland or Britain.

Although we do not know just what the Norman horses in Ireland looked like in the twelfth and thirteenth centuries, there is strong evidence that the Normans were breeding horses here. The Inventory of the Templars records, at Le Croke in Co. Wexford, 'In the stable one stallion, price 30s.'[12] But such breeding as took place was organized by individual land-holders, and does not appear to have been guided by any central authority.

A manuscript in the British Museum gives us some idea of what the mounts of the Irish were like. It depicts an Irish commander, Art MacMurrough, galloping down from the mountains of Wicklow to parley with the Earl of Gloucester during the campaign of 1399. Art was seated on a grey pony that could hardly have exceeded fourteen hands. Sir Richard Credon, one of the knights in Gloucester's party, was so impressed with the pony the he commemorated it in verse:

> Un cheval ot sans sele ne arcon
> Qui lui avoit couste, ce disait on,
> Quatre cens vaches tant estoit bel et bon.

Apparently Art had paid four hundred cows for this magnificent creature: 'In coming down[13] [the mountain] it galloped so hard that I never saw in all my life hare, deer, sheep or any such animal run with such speed as it did.' In spite of the description of the wonder-horse, the fact remains that Art was mounted on no more than a pony. The Normans, by comparison, are shown seated on good solid cobs, a little thick in the jowl, perhaps, but apparently over fifteen hands high.

Almost two hundred years later, in 1581, John Derricke's *Image of Ireland* illustrates a pacing pony being held by a horseboy while its master stands in conversation. Mackay-Smith suggests that the pony belonged to the Earl of Desmond and that it was a Hobby, for which Ireland was famous. Hobbies were obviously bred with care and it is known that the Ninth Earl of Kildare (died 1539) and the Ninth Earl of Ormond and Ossory (died 1581) '. . . both kept large studs for the breeding of Hobbies which they raced also in England. Henry VIII's Privy Purse accounts include sums regularly paid out to grooms of persons who brought their horses to race against those of the King. In June 1532 there is the entry: 'a couple of hobyes . . . from my lord of Kyldare.'[14]

Hobbies from Ireland were greatly sought after in England and on the continent. On 3rd September, 1498, for example, Henry VII wrote to the Duke of Ferrara to tell him that his emissary 'The said Biasio, has now returned [from Ireland] with some amblers, which we hope are good and high couraged; but from the present turmoil and constant wars of the wild Irish amongst themselves, there is, forsooth, a great scarcity there of good horses.'[15] Thirty years later Biasio was still buying Hobbies for his master: 'In my foregoing letters I wrote that the blessed and tedious hobby-mares had arrived on this side of the sea, which I now confirm, although subsequently I have heard nothing.'[16] Poor man, one feels for him!

The breeding of Hobbies, as of all other livestock in Ireland, was a private concern. Unlike England, where Henry VIII stipulated a minimum size for stallions, there appears to have been no attempt to direct breeding by a state or governmental authority. The great Lords of the Realm, Ormond and Kildare, and even the rebellious Earl of Desmond, had their own renowned studs, but they were private ventures, not directed by the state. There is tenuous evidence, incidentally, that the Earl of Desmond's stud was to play an important role in the development of the Quarter-horse in Virginia, but that is another story and for another pen to tell.

Although careful breeding of Hobbies persisted in a few areas for much of the sixteenth century the rebellions of 1580 and 1598 did great harm to husbandry. Edmund Spenser, one-time secretary to the Lord Deputy of Ireland, wrote that '. . . notwithstanding that [Munster] was a most rich and plentiful country, full of corn and cattle, that you would have thought they should have been able to stand long, yet ere one year and a half they were brought to such wretchedness as that any stony heart would have rued the same . . . in short space . . . a most populous and plentiful country [was] suddenly left void of man and beast.'[17] Similar descriptions could have been given of many other parts of the country. Under these circumstances it was not surprising that horse-breeding fared badly, although a few blood-lines were carefully preserved and survived to better days. Nevertheless, on 9 May, 1630, Lord Ormond wrote to Viscount Dorchester that 'There is nothing in this country worthy presenting your Lordship; for the dainty breed of hobbies, which were here, are quite gone.'[18]

In 1673 Sir William Temple, Provost of Trinity College, Dublin, presented an address to the Lord Lieutenant of Ireland in which he wrote that 'Horses in Ireland are a Drug, but might be improved to a Commodity.'[19] He proceeded to suggest how the latter objective might be attained, suggesting that three days of racing, followed by a horse fair, be held annually near Dublin with the King presenting two plates. The Lord Lieutenant approved Sir William's suggestion and King Charles II duly gave two plates, to be competed for at the Curragh in April and September each year.

Plate One. *Robert Healy's painting of the Castletown Hunt, 1768, depicts a number of horses that show signs of Eastern (later to develop into Thoroughbred) blood. Horses such as these were fairly widespread in Ireland in the second half of the eighteenth century. (By courtesy of the Hon. Desmond Guinness; Photo: J. Harsch)*

The rules for the plate races stipulated that runners had to carry twelve stone each. Sir William had argued that these races, being highly prestigious, would encourage owners to breed horses of quality. 'The soil [of Ireland] is of a sweet and plentiful grass which will raise a large Breed; and the Hills, especially near the Sea coasts are hard and rough, and so fit to give them Shape and Breadth and sound Feet.'

The King's Plates, as they came to be called, were the most important attempts that had yet been made to direct horse-breeding by central government in Ireland. Of course, the direction they gave was purely voluntary, and could easily be ignored, but it was, nevertheless, a move in the right direction. Naturally there were some breeders who ran their studs on the very best lines, such as that of the Ormonds. In 1668 a letter from the Duke to his stud-manager mentions both an Arab and a Spanish stallion at his stud at Carrick-on-Suir.[20] But there were many other breeders who apparently produced horses of low quality, that were of little market value or, as Sir William had aptly said, were a 'Drug.'

During the eighteenth century there appears to have been little central guidance or control of horse-breeding in Ireland. At the end of the previous century, in 1695, the notorious Penal Laws

had prohibited any Roman Catholic from owning a horse of quality: 'No Papist, after the 20th of January, 1695, shall be capable to have or keep in his possession, or in the possession of any other, to his use, or at his disposition, any horse, gelding or mare, of the value of £5 or more.'[21] Far from helping horse breeding, the Government seemed to be discouraging it. Seen in the context of the times, however, with the Battle of the Boyne having been fought only in 1690, the Penal Laws were understandable, if a little lacking in charity. But charity was an indulgence that King William could ill afford.

In 1748 the Government took an important step in encouraging horse breeding in Ireland. Half-a-century of peace had enabled landowners to amass wealth, develop their estates and even to build many of the beautiful country houses that adorn much of the Irish landscape today. William Conolly (Speaker of the Irish House of Commons and whose son became a major race-horse owner) started to build his seat at Castletown in 1719. Westport House in far-off Mayo was built around 1730, Carton was extensively altered about 1739, and so the list continued.[22] As landlords continued to develop their lands they became increasingly interested in arable agriculture. As a result, in 1730 Parliament passed an Act for the Encouragement of Tillage and on April 18 of that year the Act was given Royal Assent.

In order to put this Act into effect Commissioners were appointed and in 1748 they offered premiums for the importation of Black Horses into Ireland. Black Horses were the foundation-stock from which English breeders were later to produce Shire Horses. The impetus for the award of these Government Premiums may have been provided by the premium of £20 given for the importation of suitable mares in 1747. That was given by the then Provost of Trinity College, 'Premium' Madden. In 1748, in addition to the Government Premiums, the Limerick and Clare Society gave premiums for the best draft filly and the best draft colt exhibited at its show. Some people also imported Eastern (or Thoroughbred) stallions, mainly for racing and breeding purposes, and by 1750 over eighty imported stallions existed in Ireland.

Throughout the remainder of the eighteenth century premiums were awarded by various bodies for the importation of livestock and crops, and even of industrial processes, into Ireland. Nevertheless, there was no real control over horse breeding, or even guidance except in the most general of senses, by any central authority. In the early nineteenth century external affairs (Napoleon and his threat to conquer Europe) were far too pressing to allow much thought to be given to controlling, developing and improving horse breeding. True, there was a tremendous need for horses for the Army, and they were bought in large numbers, but their production was still left mainly to private and largely uncontrolled enterprise. When Napoleon was finally defeated, in 1815, there was still far too much to worry about to think of controlling horse breeding.

With the end of the Napoleonic Wars came a new opening for horses in Ireland. In 1808 the Road Act had been passed, stipulating the construction of highways throughout the country. Roads, of course, had existed before, but now they were to be developed to a high standard. Furthermore, the ending of the war meant a reduction both in the price of horses and of grain to feed them. The first entrepreneur to appreciate the great possibilities of this new situation was an Italian resident in Clonmel, Charles Bianconi. On 6th July, 1815, the first 'Bianconi car' began a service from Clonmel to Cahir. It was pulled by '. . . a sturdy animal bred for hauling artillery limbers and cost £10. The vehicle was a two-wheeled Outside Car.'[23] In 1857, by which time the extension of railways was affecting Bianconi, 'I still have over 900 horses, working . . .

sixty-seven conveyances travelling daily 4,244 miles and extending over portions of twenty-two counties.'[24] Horses were still very important animals indeed.

But Government had other matters than horse breeding to attend to. The Corn Laws, passed in the emergency of the Napoleonic Wars, were not finally repealed until 1846, and were followed by the terrors of the Great Famine of 1846-8. With the population of Ireland decimated by the shortage of edible potatoes and reduced from just over eight million to just over six-and-a-half million in three disastrous years, there was far more to worry about than the guidance of horse breeding.

Following the famine and repeal of the Corn Laws (which had kept corn prices artificially high and therefore favoured tillage), agricultural production fell and tillage began to decline. In 1879 a major agricultural depression led to a further decline in the arable area and, consequently, to a decline in the need for work horses on the land. Few governments, at a time when there were surplus work horses around, would concern themselves with them. But as tillage fell in importance, so the British Empire increased in fortune and importance. Horses were needed for the Army, as in the past, to mount the men, pull the guns and move the baggage, in the greatly expanding territories overseas. Furthermore, Britain, by the 1880s, was the major industrial country in the world, and industry bred wealth. Wealthy industrialists aspired to become landed gentlemen, and wanted quality horses to haul their carriages, to carry them to covert and to ride to hounds, and many horses came from Ireland. Furthermore, the experience of stock-breeding, especially in the past hundred years, had shown that careful breeding could produce better livestock – horsemen had known that for centuries.

In April 1887 the Royal Dublin Society sent a deputation to see Lord Londonderry, the Lord Lieutenant of Ireland, to seek funds for a scheme to improve the livestock of Ireland. His Lordship was favourably inclined towards the deputation and, as a result, they pressed their case in London. In 1888 the Government granted the Society the sum of £5,000, renewable annually.[25] Thus the Royal Dublin Society was able to devise and administer a scheme, financed by the Government, '. . . for the purpose of encouraging improvement in the Breed of Horses and Cattle in Ireland.' This '. . . placed the Society in a unique position, as it became the only body in the United Kingdom administering Government Funds for improving horse and cattle breeding.'[26] It is that scheme as applied to horses, and its various changes, that is the subject of this book. And it was a most important scheme, for it laid the foundation of government involvement in horse breeding as we know it today, in the latter part of the twentieth century. It was also largely responsible for the development of the Irish Half-bred horse.

CHAPTER TWO

Class One and the Premium Stallions.

On August 24, 1886, the Annual Horse Show of the Royal Dublin Society opened at the Society's grounds at Ball's Bridge, some four miles south of the centre of the city. This was an important occasion, for it marked the height of the summer social season in Dublin (which, in effect, meant for the whole country). Until 1881 the Horse Show had been held in the grounds of Leinster House, the great mansion planned by Richard Cassels, the architect, for the Earl of Kildare and built in 1745 and succeeding years. In 1815 Leinster House was sold to the Royal Dublin Society and became the nucleus for many of the Society's activities.

The Royal Dublin Society had originated in 1731, as the Dublin Society. Its aims were to aid the development of agriculture and industry in Ireland, and to act as a scientific society. As it developed so it adopted many of the roles that, in the twentieth century, are associated with governmental and state bodies. In particular it undertook many functions that have now become the responsibility of the Department of Agriculture. These aspects of the Society's work were financed, at least in part, by the Government. During the 1880s, however, the Government were gradually assuming responsibility for some of the tasks previously undertaken by the Society. As a result the Society was, unwillingly and perhaps unfairly, forced to relinquish portions of Leinster House to the Government. Eventually, in the twentieth century, the Society moved completely to new premises acquired in Ball's Bridge and intended initially mainly for a show ground.

Although many of the participants and spectators at the 1886 Horse Show must have been interested by the recent move to Ball's Bridge, few could have foreseen the eventual importance of Class One in the development of horse breeding in Ireland. The Horse Show Committee, in its report to a Stated General Meeting of the Society on November 11, 1886, recorded that: 'Since the preceeding year the Prize List had been revised, an important alteration was made in the rules relating to the prizes for stallions . . .

The new conditions attached to the award of the prizes for stallions was designed to encourage the judicious breeding of horses by Tenant Farmers in Ireland, and it is hoped that it will have this effect. The Prizes are given on the conditions that – 'The owner of a stallion awarded any of the prizes must guarantee that his horse shall serve in Ireland during the ensuing season, and must guarantee to offer ten subscriptions for the use of *bona fide* tenant farmers' half-bred mares not exceeding four years old, at a fee not exceeding £2-10s.'[1]

Class One was limited to Thoroughbreds that had been registered in the stud book and it attracted fifteen entries. Although all were owned in Ireland, it is significant that at least five had been bred in England and one in France. Since the early eighteenth century, and possibly much earlier, Eastern-type horses had been imported into Ireland as well as into England and France, and they formed the foundation of the Thoroughbred. Horses had been interchanged between all three countries for centuries, and particularly between England and Ireland. In 1668, for example, the Duke of Ormond wrote from Kilkenny that 'I am in a great want of a couple of good stallions . . . If the King's stable can furnish me with such I could be content somebody would begg for me.'[2] The entrants in Class One epitomized this international nature of the Thoroughbred.

The three judges appointed for Class One were all noted horsemen: the Hon. T. Wentworth-Fitzwilliam of Coollattin Park in Co. Wicklow, William Dunne of Ballymanus, Stradbally, and Captain Cosby of Stradbally Hall. They awarded First Prize to *Heart of Oak,* an eleven year old bay stallion by *King of the Forest* out of *Penelope-Platwell.* This horse was owned by Captain W. H. Davis of Courtown, Kilcock. Second went, surprisingly in view of his age, to a seventeen year old dark chestnut called *York*, owned by Francis H. Power of Mallow. Third was *Pride of Prussia*, owned by R. Nihill Talbot of Grennan House, Durrow in Queen's Co. *Prescription,* owned by Aubrey Wallis of Drishane Castle, Millstreet, Co. Cork, was fourth.[3] In this unostentatious way the Royal Dublin Society's schemes for the improvement of horses were born.

Although the Society continued to hold Class One, 'the breeding class for stallions,' for many years its importance was suddenly eclipsed by an even more far-reaching development. In the Prize List for the 1887 Horse Show there appeared the following notice: 'Her Majesty's Government having promised to submit a vote to the House of Commons for a sum of money, out of which £5000 will be set apart to be administered by the Royal Dublin Society for the purpose of encouraging improvement in the Breed of Horses and Cattle in Ireland, the Royal Dublin Society is accordingly enabled to offer the sum of £3200 in sixteen equal premiums of £200 each, for Thorough-bred Sires (3 years old and upwards) suitable for getting Hunters and other Half-bred Horses, subject to the conditions that each Sire selected for a premium shall serve, if required, not less than fifty Half-bred Mares, the *bona fide* property of Farmers, at a Fee not exceeding £1 for each Mare, and shall not serve more than sixty Mares during the season of 1888, and shall travel in the district to be assigned by the Royal Dublin Society.' The notice continued, at length, to stipulate how the premiums (termed 'Service Premiums') would be paid and stated that premium stallion owners had to give a bond to the Society to ensure that the stallion would fulfil its duties. It further described how mares would be selected, by Local Committees appointed by the Royal Dublin Society, for service by the premium stallions.

£3200 might seem, and indeed was, a niggardly sum for promoting horse breeding throughout Ireland, but its expenditure stimulated much thought in the breeding industry and its effects were far greater than could reasonably be expected. The system of stallion licencing, approved stallions, and nominations for mares, which exists in Ireland in the 1970s, owes its origin to this Government grant of 1887.

The Premium Stallion class of 1887 was, like its successors, open to Thoroughbred stallions from all parts of the United Kingdom. The only qualifications were that animals should be three years old or over and that they should be registered in the stud book. Sixty stallions were entered for the class, fifty-five of them being owned in Ireland, four were owned in England and one

Plate Two. *Judging in progress at the Dublin Horse Show. C. 1900. (Photo: Courtesy of the Royal Dublin Society)*

came from Kelso, in Scotland. The Scottish entrant, *Branxholme,* was one of the sixteen stallions awarded a Service Premium, although all the other premiums went to Irish-owned horses. Six, or possibly seven, of the Irish-owned horses allotted premiums, had been bred in England. The class therefore represented the Home Countries, rather than just Ireland.

Unfortunately no record appears to exist of the heights and other characteristics of all sixty entrants, but the heights of the sixteen premium-winners is recorded. The smallest horses, *Sir Lydstone, The Marshall, Glencairne, Cleveland, Woodreeve* and *Greenfield,* measured 15.3 hands. The tallest horse was *Reckless,* measuring 16.1 hands. It seems likely, since there was no more than a two inch difference between the largest and smallest stallions, that the judges sought overall uniformity, although that can never, now, be proved.

On November 10, 1887, the Committee of Agriculture reported to the Council of the Royal Dublin Society that 'The sixteen selected Stallions have been allotted to the districts in which they are to serve during the coming season.' Furthermore 'The Committee is now engaged in arranging for the appointment of the Local Committees; they have already made considerable progress, and they will soon be in a position to submit a Report.'[4] The Report was presented to a Stated General Meeting of the Society on St. David's Day, March 1, 1888. It had been prepared by a specially appointed subcommittee of the Committee of Agriculture '. . . entrusted with carrying out the details of the Stallion Service Premium Scheme.'[5] The subcommittee reported that: 'In each of the sixteen districts into which Ireland is divided Committees have been appointed, consisting of a Chairman and not less than six other members, including at least three tenant-farmers . . . The duties of the District Committees are to fix the places at which the Stallions are to stand during the season, and also the places at which the Mares are to be assembled for inspection. On the approval of these arrangements by the Society, the District Committees will inspect the Mares, and grant nominations to the owners of such as they consider most suitable for breeding purposes, having due regard to size, age, and soundness. Other considerations being equal, the smaller tenant-farmers will be given preference in the issue of nominations.'

In fact, when the subcommittee presented its Report, the Rathkeale Committee, in County Limerick, had already completed its arrangements and inspected mares for nominations. 172 mares were submitted, all owned by farmers, for fifty nominations. The qualification for owners was that the owner must be a farmer, the '. . . aggregate tenement valuation of whose holdings does not exceed £200 per annum.' The same qualifications applied throughout Ireland. Large farmers, landowners and others were, presumably, expected to fend for themselves.

The Rathkeale Committee inspected mares at five different centres, Rathkeale, Croom, Newcastle West, Glin and Stone Hall. No centre was more than twelve miles from another centre, so that it seems likely that each centre catered for mares within a five or six mile radius. This is the only indication in the published reports of the area comprising a District. Presumably, in this first year of operation, the main concern was to see the Scheme established, rather than to spend time in the over-rigid demarcation of District limits. In any case, the Society must have wondered whether all the available nominations would be utilized in each District. If a farmer chose to travel his mare a lengthy distance in order to seek a nomination, then that was his concern. Far better to have to reject many mares in favour of the fifty best than to see nominations going unfilled. Figure One shows the Districts into which Ireland was divided, with the name of the stallion allocated to each District and, as an inset, the location of the mare inspection centres in the Rathkeale District.

Although the Rathkeale Committee had been faced with an abundance of mares to choose from, other Committees were less fortunate. In the north west of Ireland the Strabane Committee inspected only fifty-two mares, rejecting two of them. One suspects that the standard of mares in the Strabane area might have left something to be desired, but perhaps that is an unfair suspicion, for no details of the mares apparently remain. The Portadown Committee, by comparison, had a daunting task. They had to select just fifty out of a total of 258 mares submitted for inspection. The Tullow Committee were faced with problems of a different kind. Only thirty-six mares were presented for inspection, and one had to be rejected on grounds that are now unknown. To make matters worse, the stallion allotted to the Tullow District, which was *Cleveland*, died on April 23. Luckily a substitute was found, and *Harmonium* took up duty there early in May. Perhaps the lack of applications for nominations in the Tullow District had something to do with the unfortunate demise of *Cleveland*.

The Committee for the Kells District obviously were not entirely satisfied with the mares presented to them, or perhaps their arithmetic was faulty. They inspected seventy-seven mares, but allocated nominations to only forty-eight, two less than the expected number. That only

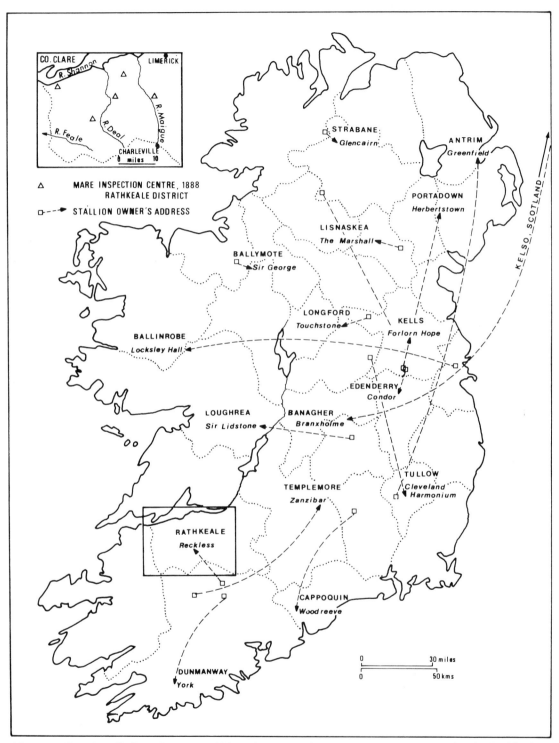

Figure 1. *Premium Stallion Districts, 1888 stud season. The mare inspection centres for the Rathkeale District are shown as an inset*

forty-eight mares suitable for nomination should have been presented in such a noted horse breeding area is amazing, but perhaps many owners of good mares decided that the Service Premium Stallion in their District was not suitable for their charges. *Forlorn Hope* had, after all, been the final stallion listed of the sixteen chosen, according to the published results, and it does not seem as if the results were given in alphabetic order, either!

In west Waterford the Cappoquin Committee decided to take full advantage of *Woodreeve,* by *King of the Forest* out of *Narino* and bred near Reading in England. Unlike other Committees, none of whom awarded more than the stipulated minimum number of nominations (fifty), and two of whom (Kells and Tullow) awarded less than the stipulated number, the Cappoquin Committee awarded fifty-seven nominations. Why other Committees did not do likewise is not at all clear. Under the Service Premium rules they could, arguably, have allocated up to sixty nominations. Possibly the majority of stallion owners interpreted the rules as meaning that they had to accept fifty nominated mares at the agreed fee of £1·00 per mare, but their horse could serve another ten mares at a fee decided by themselves. £1·00 was, even in 1888, a low fee for what were, after all, some of the best Thoroughbreds available for public service in the country.

On average, 109 mares were inspected in each District, the numbers being lowest in Tullow, Strabane, Longford, Lisnaskea, Edenderry and Banagher. The greatest numbers of mares inspected were in Portadown, Rathkeale and Ballymote. Already the centres of the hunter and half-bred industry were being reflected in the applications for nominations. Southern Ireland, south of the midland bog belt, was already noted for its hunters and other quality riding and carriage horses, as were the limestone lowlands of Sligo and the Plains of Mayo. The midlands of Ireland were, like the curate's egg, good in parts, but suffered from the physical drawbacks of bogland and ill-drainage. Quality horses were, and still are, produced there, but not to the same extent as in the better lands to the south and north west. The real surprise, however, was the vast number of applications in the Portadown District, since the north of Ireland is not generally associated with half-bred horse production. Nevertheless, in Armagh, Down and south Antrim it is known that there were, in 1877, at least eight packs of harriers, followed on horseback.[6] In the previous century Arthur Stringer, Viscount Conway's huntsman on his estates around the eastern shore of Lough Neagh, wrote a classic text entitled *The Experienced Huntsman* which was published in 1714. There was thus a strong and well-established hunting tradition in the Portadown area and, presumably, a market for half-bred hunting and riding-type horses. At £1·00 a service the chance of a nomination to *Herbertstown*, a sixteen hand horse by *Belldrum* out of *Nora,* was too good for the local farmers to miss!

In all 790 mares were selected for service and 764 of them were actually served. Three mares failed to be served in Longford, two in Kells, one in Templemore and thirteen in Tullow. No doubt the problems caused by the death of *Cleveland* were a contributory factor to the absences in the Tullow District.

Unfortunately no record was made of the number, nor scientific assessment made of the quality, of foals produced by the Service Premium stallions. Nevertheless, in his evidence before the Commissioners appointed to inquire into the horse breeding industry in Ireland, whose report appeared in 1897, Thomas Donovan of Cork stated of stallions that: '. . . when you get from Cork to the West it is in a deplorable state. I think the Government sent one horse that was worth standing for a season – a horse called 'York,' he stood, I think, at Dunmanway.'[7] *York* did, indeed, stand at Dunmanway, and in 1888, the first year of the Government Premium Scheme

Table One

Government Premiums for Stallions, 1887.[1]

District	Name of District	Stallion	Number of mares inspected	Number of mares selected for service	Number of mares served
1	Strabane	*Glencairne*	52	50	50
2	Antrim	*Greenfield*	100	50	50
3	Portadown	*Herbertstown*	258	50	50
4	Lisnaskea	*The Marshall*	66	50	50
5	Ballymote	*Sir George*	168	50	50
6	Ballinrobe	*Locksley Hall*	137	50	50
7	Longford	*Touchstone*	56	50	47
8	Kells	*Forlorn Hope*	77	48	46
9	Edenderry	*Condor*	67	50	50
10	Banagher	*Branxholme*	75	50	50
11	Loughrea	*Sir Lydstone*	82	50	50
12	Templemore	*Zanzibar*	114	50	49
13	Tullow	**Cleveland Harmonium*	36	35	22
14	Rathkeale	*Reckless*	172	50	50
15	Cappoquin	*Woodreeve*	140	57	50
16	Dunmanway	*York*	143	50	50
		Total	1743	790	764

Cleveland died on April 23, and *Harmonium* was substituted early in May.

1.   These stallions stood at stud in 1888.

for stallions. He was eighteen years old, stood 15.3½ hands, was dark chestnut in colour, and was by *Cathedral* out of *Empress*. Donovan's testimony alone bears ample witness to the initial success of the Scheme, for he was a noted horse dealer, Master of the Muskerry Foxhounds and Lord Mayor of Cork. Any man who, like Donovan, '. . . had about 120 horses which he sold annually at the Leicester Sales,'[8] and who followed both the Quorn and the Fernie for a month each hunting season, must have been extremely well qualified to talk about horses and horse-breeding.

In 1889 it was reported to the Royal Dublin Society that, for 1888, '. . . the sixteen District Committees have completed . . . (their) . . . task,' and the results of their work was presented in table form, as shown on Table One.

The Committee proceeded to report that they '. . . believe that the farmers who have participated in its benefits highly appreciate the advantages that this Grant conferred upon them.'[9] Thus ended, in what appeared to be a most satisfactory fashion, the first year of what was to become an uninterrupted and evolving scheme for '. . . encouraging improvements in the Breed of Horses' in Ireland.

CHAPTER THREE

The Queen's Premiums for Stallions

Forty-nine stallions were entered for the special show held at Ball's Bridge on February 13 and 14, 1889, to choose the Premium Stallions for the forthcoming season. All of them were owned by people living in Ireland, although at least eighteen had been bred in England. Two of the three judges also came from England: Captain Fife came from Gillingham in Dorset; J. Hume Webster lived at Marden Deer Park, Caterham Valley, Surrey. The third judge, Henry Thompson, was from Altnaveigh, Newry.

In addition to the judges there was a panel of three Veterinary Surgeons. They included the hard-working, but dreaded, Professor Pritchard, the President of the Royal College of Veterinary Surgeons in London. In his career Professor Pritchard probably felt more legs, female and male, than any other man. His probing fingers inspired awe in many owners, throughout Ireland and Britain, as he discovered sidebones and other unsoundnesses that escaped all but the expert's (and probably the owner's) attention. In April, 1878, Pritchard had spoken to a paper by Fred Street on 'The Breeding, Rearing and Management of Cart Horses,' which Street read at the Farmers' Club in London.[1] Pritchard '. . . stressed the importance of hereditary soundness,' and he later put his words into practice at many of the London Shows of the Shire Horse Society, where he was Chief Veterinary Inspector from 1880 until 1899. Between 1892 and 1899 he rejected 12.3% of the horses examined at these Shows as unsound, and most of them were faulted because of sidebones, a hereditary complaint. Other hereditary defects include certain breathing ailments, nervous disorders and some bone defects. Pritchard's two colleagues at Ball's Bridge were T. D. Lambert of Dublin and James Preston of Mallow.

The decision to hold a Premium Stallion Show had been made by the Royal Dublin Society the previous year,[2] when it had '. . . learned that it is the intention of Her Majesty's Government to propose the renewal of the vote (for the Improvement of Livestock) for the current year.' The Committee of Agriculture had '. . . appointed a Sub-Committee to consider what changes it would be desirable to make in the arrangements for the next season.'

The Sub-Committee arrived at a number of important and sometimes ingenious, conclusions. Firstly they argued that the system of paying premiums to stallion owners and giving them '. . . the full amount of the service and Groom's fees,' was somewhat wasteful. Although they did not commit their thoughts to paper the Sub-Committee obviously felt that, if owners were attracted to submit their stallions for consideration for a premium, they would not necessarily need the

27

added incentive of service and groom's fees: a sum of £1·00 per mare served, plus a lesser sum for the groom. Eventually they decided that payment of service and groom's fees should be made '. . . only in the case of Stallions sent to districts for which the Stallion is not specially entered, or in which the Owner does not reside.' They then cleverly proposed that: 'In anticipation of an additional sum being rendered available for premiums under the operation of this arrangement, it is proposed to offer two additional premiums, making a total of eighteen.'

Experience of the 1888 breeding season also led the Society to make alterations for 1889. It was decided that, in a number of cases, the Districts should be re-arranged as should certain head-quarters. Furthermore the lack of defined boundaries to the 1888 Districts must have caused concern, and possibly given rise to unrecorded problems. As a result it was now stipulated that each District should comprise the area within a twelve mile radius of the headquarters of that District. Table Two lists the headquarters of the new Districts.

The Society was also concerned that only fertile pedigree stallions, that were not too old, should be awarded premiums. The *Schedule* for the show to choose what were now termed the 'Queen's Premiums for Thorough-bred Stallions' (the Probate Duties (Scotland and Ireland) Act had been passed in 1888 which '. . . provides that the sum of £5000 shall be annually paid to the Royal Dublin Society for the improvement of the breed of Horses and Cattle in Ireland') stated that it was:

1. 'Open to competitors from all parts of the United Kingdom.'
2. 'Each Stallion must be not less than four, and not more than sixteen years old.'
3. 'All Stallions must be entered in the English Stud-book.'
4. 'Each Exhibitor of a Stallion that has been to stud must produce certificates from the owners of at least ten Mares, certifying that they are either in foal to the Stallion, or have produced foals by the Stallion during the previous year.'

Table Two

The headquarters of the 1889 Stallion Districts.

Number	Headquarter	Number	Headquarter
1	Strabane	10	Ballinrobe
2	Ballymena	11	Athenry
3	Lisburn	12	Parsonstown (i.e. Birr)
4	Dungannon	13	Baltinglass
5	Enniskillen	14	Kilkenny
6	Ballymote	15	Thurles
7	Kingscourt	16	Rathkeale
8	Mullingar	17	Fermoy
9	Roscommon	18	Bandon

5. 'Stallions selected by the Judges shall be examined by the three Veterinary Surgeons appointed by the Committee. The Certificate must be signed by two of the Veterinary Surgeons. No Stallion shall be rejected as unsound unless suffering from hereditary disease.

The Exhibitor of a Stallion passed as sound shall be entitled to a copy of the Certificate.'

There were two other conditions listed in the Schedule that dealt with administrative matters, but these five were the most important ones.

In 1888 the greatest number of mares submitted for selection for nominations in any one District had been those that confronted the Committee at Portadown, in the north of Ireland. In 1889 Mullingar in the midlands attained the honour of most mares inspected, 235, although in the Lisburn District, in northern Ireland 200 mares competed for the pleasure of being served by *Condor*, a sixteen hands horse by *Kisber* out of *Hermione* and bred by Lord Roseberry. In 1883 *Condor* had been second in the Clearwell Stakes at Newmarket, where he was beaten by only a head by *Harvester*. Since *Harvester* won the Derby it is hardly surprising that the services of his near-vanquisher should be greatly in demand.

Kingscourt, in County Cavan, had the least number of mares submitted for selection: forty-eight, all of which were deemed passable and awarded Service Tickets for the allotted stallion: *Middleman*.

As in the previous year, some committees were confronted with difficult and perplexing problems. The Dungannon Committee must have been disgusted when their stallion, *Wallingford*, '. . . sprained his shoulder early in the season, and was unable to complete the services of the mares.' When this accident happened, *Wallingford* had served only six of the forty-one mares selected for him. Whether a full complement of fifty mares would have been selected for him had he not suffered his disability, or whether the Dungannon area really was short of good mares owned by tenant farmers, we shall never know.

The least number of mares to go to the stallion, apart from those of the unfortunate farmers of the Dungannon District, were those of Athenry. Seventy mares had been submitted for inspection, fifty had been selected for service, but only thirty-seven were actually served. The mists of time have obscured the reasons for such a large number of defaulters, but obviously there were local problems. In the following year, when the Society attempted to establish how successful the scheme was by asking breeders for information on foaling, it was stated that: 'It was found impracticable to send circulars to the Owners of mares in the Athenry . . . district.'[3] The actions of the Land Leaguers at that period had gravely affected farming in the general vicinity of Athenry and had caused major problems for many landlords. The County Galway Foxhounds (immortalized as 'The Blazers') had been managed by their committee during part of 1888, and were going through very difficult times.[4] Their previous Master, Burton Persse, had stopped hunting them due to the activities of the Land League, and had hied him to England to enjoy his hunting there without the encumbrance of political disturbances. It is therefore not difficult to surmise the reasons for the high number of absentee mares at Athenry.

The Carbery Foxhounds are one of the oldest hunts in Ireland, and a record of their Masters has been kept since 1787. The Carbery are centred on the town of Bandon, west of Cork. In the 1870s and 1880s they were renowned for a number of spectacular and lengthy hunts and Carbery Masters were well thought-of in this sporting area. Dealers, such as Donovan of Cork, found a good market in the English centres of hunting for hunters acquired in this region. Thus it is hardly surprising that the tenant farmers of the Bandon District should have sought to obtain

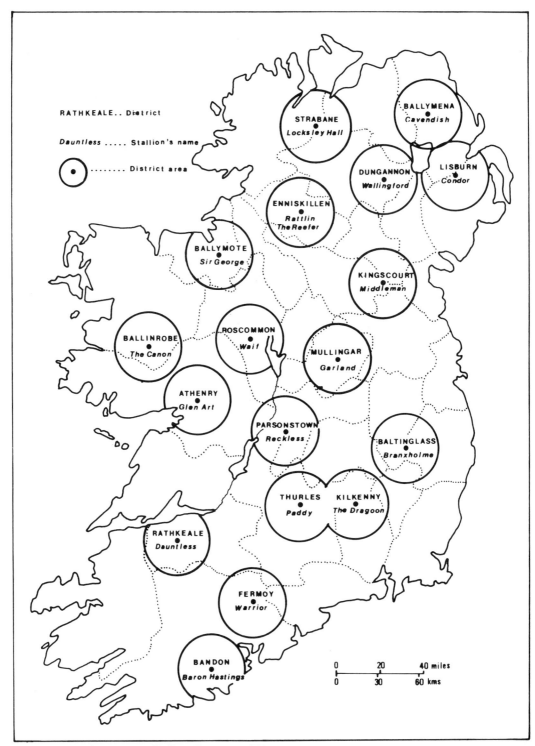

Figure 2. *Queen's Premium Stallion Districts, 1889*

the services of the Queen's Premium Stallion, *Baron Hastings*, for their half-bred mares, especially since the stallion had been a noted steeplechaser in his time, winning six races. 188 mares were submitted for inspection, all competing for one of the fifty nominations awarded in the District. Thus the Bandon Committee inspected the third largest number of mares that confronted any committee in the country.

Rathkeale District had the fourth largest number of mares to be inspected, so that the specialization in hunter and riding horse production in the southern part of Ireland, already noted for 1888, was reinforced in 1889. The leading District (in terms of numbers of mares inspected), Mullingar, east of the great bogs of midland Ireland, was part of the Meath-Kildare-Westmeath hunting area and shared many of the hunting traditions of southern Ireland. Table Three summarizes the allocations of Queen's Premiums, and the award of mare nominations, for the 1889 breeding season. (The official reports refer to the premiums as being for 1888). Figure Two shows the location and limits of the eighteen Districts in the country.

Table Three

Queen's Premiums for Stallions for the 1889 breeding season.[5]

District	Name of District	Stallion	Number of Mares submitted for inspection	Number of Mares selected for service	Number of Mares served
1	Strabane	*Locksley Hall*	not ascertained	50	50
2	Ballymena	*Cavendish*	80	50	50
3	Lisburn	*Condor*	200	50	48
4	Dungannon	*Wallingford*	not ascertained	41	6
5	Enniskillen	*Rattlin the Reefer*	119	50	50
6	Ballymote	*Sir George*	97	57	50
7	Kingscourt	*Middleman*	48	48	48
8	Mullingar	*Garland*	235	50	50
9	Roscommon	*Waif*	90	50	50
10	Ballinrobe	*The Canon*	105	50	50
11	Athenry	*Glen Art*	70	50	37
12	Parsonstown	*Reckless*	73	50	50
13	Baltinglass	*Branxholme*	117	50	50
14	Kilkenny	*The Dragoon*	77	59	44
15	Thurles	*Paddy*	112	50	50
16	Rathkeale	*Dauntless*	134	50	50
17	Fermoy	*Warrior*	not ascertained	50	50
18	Bandon	*Baron Hastings*	188	50	50

Total number of mares served – 833.

The concern of the Society that stallions should be fertile, reflected in the conditions stipulated in the *Schedule* for the Premium Stallion show, was reinforced by the attempts made in
1890 to record the number of foals produced by mares served by Queen's Premium Stallions in
1889, 'With the view of ascertaining the results of the Stallion Premium Scheme in the Season
1889, the Committee sent a circular to the Owners of 690 mares in fourteen of the eighteen
districts.'[6]

577 of the circulars were completed and returned to the Society and from these it was possible
to establish the pattern of fertility of the various stallions. Forty-eight circulars were returned
relating to the stallion that had stood in the Ballymote District, *Sir George*. Another two
circulars (*Sir George* served fifty mares) were not returned. From the returns it appeared that
the stallion had the amazingly high fertility rate of 77%, and even if the two circulars that were
not returned had related to barren mares, *Sir George*'s fertility rate would have been 74%.

Although the Society presented the fertility rate, correctly, as a 'Percentage on Returns' this
gave information that might well have been misleading. To the non-mathematically inclined it
might have seemed as if, for example, *Reckless* got 83% of his mares in foal. If, however, one
supposes that all the circulars that were *not* returned related to barren mares, then the fertility
rate of *Reckless* falls to 68%. On this latter basis, poor *Paddy* had a rate of 36%, although his rate

Table Four[7]

Foaling returns: Queen's Premium Stallions, Season 1889

District	Stallion	No. of returns from Mare owners	No. of foals			% on Returns	Worst % possible	Average %
			Colts	Fillies	Total			
Strabane	*Locksley Hall*	44	14	17	31	70	62	66
Ballymena	*Cavendish*	44	14	18	32	73	64	69
Lisburn	*Condor*	39	12	7	19	48	40	44
Enniskillen	*Rattlin the Reefer*	41	14	13	27	66	54	60
Ballymote	*Sir George*	48	20	17	37	77	74	76
Kingscourt	*Middleman*	40	16	14	30	75	63	69
Mullingar	*Garland*	42	9	18	27	64	54	59
Roscommon	*Waif*	45	20	14	34	75	68	72
Ballinrobe	*The Canon*	43	14	16	30	70	60	65
Parsonstown	*Reckless*	41	16	18	34	83	68	76
Kilkenny	*The Dragoon*	38	11	13	24	63	55	59
Thurles	*Paddy*	32	11	7	18	56	36	46
Rathkeale	*Dauntless*	40	20	12	32	80	64	72
Bandon	*Baron Hastings*	40	12	14	26	65	52	59
	Totals:	577	203	198	401	69½	58	64

on returns was 56%. Probably the true foaling rate lay somewhere between these two extremes. Assuming that the true rate lay exactly half-way between the percentage on returns, and the 'worst possible' percentage, one sees that *Sir George* and *Reckless* were the most fertile sires, with a foaling return of 76%.

Unfortunately there is relatively little information available, of a similar character, to which the foaling rates of the Queen's Premium Stallions for 1889 can be compared. Nevertheless it is apparent that fertility rates varied dramatically from horse to horse. Whether that was due to the stallion, or to the inherent fertility of the mares served, or whether it might even have reflected the skill with which services were handled, is impossible to ascertain. Thus whilst *Sir George* and *Reckless* had averaged rates of 76%, the rate for *Paddy* was 46% and for *Condor* only 44%. Table Four lists the foaling returns.

Of course, too much should not be read into foaling rates for one season, but to the scientifically inclined it must have appeared that the future use of such stallions as *Condor* and *Paddy* could hardly be justified on the grounds of fertility. Nevertheless *Condor* was selected for the Londonderry area for the 1890 season, although *Paddy* was not chosen. The stallion was, however, selected for the Thurles District for 1891 and in 1895 it was recorded that: 'Paddy's stock have taken 5 First Prizes at Clonmel Shows, and a four-year-old Gelding was Highly Commended at Dublin Show, 1894.'[8] Whether that constituted a progeny record of excellence is debatable.

CHAPTER FOUR

Decentralization.

On November 21, 1889, R. H. Borrowes presented the Royal Dublin Society with the Report of the Committee responsible for the horse breeding scheme.[1] The Report concluded by stating that 'The Committee are at present engaged in allocating the selected Stallions to the sub-districts in which they are to serve in the coming season.' Behind this bland statement lay an enormous amount of work and a major re-organisation of the whole horse breeding scheme.

1889 had been a momentous year for the Royal Dublin Society. At its Spring Show the Society had, for the first time, held horse shoeing competitions. These were badly needed, since the general standards of farriery in the country left much to be desired. Whether the best way to raise standards was by show-yard competitions, or by some other means, was arguable, but the Society did not have the financial resources to do much more than hold competitions. On November 9, 1889, the Society held the first inspections of cattle for entry into the newly formed Kerry and Dexter Herd Book, thereby initiating a herd book for the only indigenous breed of cattle in Ireland. That the Society did not lag far behind events in Britain is shown by the dates of foundation of Stud and Herd Books there. The first Book for horses, if Thoroughbreds are ignored (the General Stud Book for Thoroughbred Race Horses was opened in 1793 and included Irish as well as British entries), was formed in 1877, when Biddell's renowned work on Suffolk horses appeared as Volume I of the Suffolk Horse Society's Stud Book. The Cleveland Bay Horse Society of Great Britain and Ireland was founded in 1884, and the Yorkshire Coach Horse Society began in 1886. Developments in Ireland thus lagged only a few years after their British counterparts. Whilst the Society was in such a mood of activity and inauguration it is hardly surprising that its energetic Horse Breeding Committee should introduce a major change into the Society's horse breeding scheme: decentralization.

During the nineteenth century a number of agricultural show societies had become established in various parts of Ireland. Some of them copied the Royal Dublin Society by offering premiums for livestock, crops and even machinery, in attempts to improve standards of agriculture in their local areas. They played an important role in the dissemination of information and in the setting of standards amongst the provincial farming communities. Now the Royal Dublin Society decided to avail itself '. . . of the services which the leading Provincial Societies can offer.' Ireland, for the purposes of horse breeding, was divided into five Districts, each of which was further subdivided into a series of Sub-Districts. Shows, '. . . for the purpose of awarding

Prizes to Thoroughbred Stallions,' were to be held in each District, at which the stallions for the District were to be chosen.

The five Districts into which Ireland was divided were: Belfast, Sligo, Ballinasloe, Dublin and Cork. At Belfast the stallion show was held in co-operation with the North-East Agricultural Association of Ireland, at Sligo with the County Sligo Agricultural Society, at Ballinasloe with the Ballinasloe District Agricultural Society, at Dublin in the Society's own premises, and at Cork in conjunction with the County of Cork Agricultural Society. At each venue the Royal Dublin Society nominated a Judge and a Veterinary Surgeon to join the judges appointed by the local societies. Major Borrowes was appointed by the Horse Breeding Committee '. . . to co-operate with judges to be locally appointed for each provincial district,' and it was his duty to submit a report on the provincial proceedings.

The incentives offered to owners of stallions to encourage them to participate in the horse breeding scheme were also altered from those on offer in previous years. Instead of awarding a premium to each stallion chosen, it was decided only to offer a prize, of £20, known as the Queen's Prize. In addition the stallion was expected '. . . to serve any number of Farmer's Mares, not exceeding 50, to be nominated by the Local Committee, at a Fee (including the Groom's Fee) of £3 2s 6d. for each Mare.' All fees would be paid to stallion owners by the Society at the end of the season, the owner of each mare served contributing £1-2-6 and the Society contributing the other £2-0-0. Payment, however, was virtually guaranteed, which was hardly the case when stallion men had to try and persuade individual mare owners to pay them. Presumably it was felt that, if fifty mares were served, the fee of £156-5-0, plus the £20 prize, would be sufficient remuneration to satisfy most stallion owners. In fact, this represented a considerable reduction in income for stallion owners, since in 1889 they had at least been certain of their £200 Queen's Premium. There was, however, an important concession: 'The Owner to be permitted to keep the Stallion at his own or any other stable in the District.' But the concession was tempered by the fact that each stallion '. . . must travel to at least two places in the Sub-District, if required to do so by the Local Committee.'

Major Borrowes reported to the Society that the first District Show had been held on August 27, '. . . in conjunction with the Horse Show,' to choose stallions for the Dublin District. This District was subdivided into five Sub-Districts: Navan, Mullingar, Kilcullen, Carlow and Wexford. As in all other Sub-Districts, it was stated, in the *Schedule for the Great Irish Horse Show, 1889,* that each stallion had '. . . to stand within 10 miles of the Central Station of the Sub-District' to which it was allotted.

There were twenty-six entries at the Dublin District Show and the judges had little difficulty in finding five stallions of quality amongst the competitors. As a result *Touchstone* was allocated to the Navan Sub-District, *Locksley Hall* to Mullingar, *Greenfield* to Kilcullen, *Branxholme* to Carlow and *Waif* to Wexford. All these horses were between 15.2½ and 16.0 hands in height although, somewhat surprisingly, none of them seem to have distinguished themselves particularly on the race-course. *Branxholme*, admittedly, had won the Manchester Handicap Steeplechase, worth £380. Nevertheless the written report of the judges of the Weight-carrying Hunter Class, held at the same Show, suggests that horsebreeding in Ireland was definitely being undertaken in a professional manner. 'Class 9 we consider as fine a lot of young Horses as ever entered a Show Ring, and it is most satisfactory to find such a solid proof that Horse-breeding in Ireland is not only not deteriorating, but, if possible improving.'[2]

In contrast to the situation at Dublin, where there had been an abundance of stallions, only eight were entered for the Sligo District Show. *Sir George, Loved One* and *The Marshall* were selected, and the judges wisely nominated *Hard Lines* and *Woodman* as reserves in case any of the selected stallions dropped-out before the stud-season was over. As it happened, *The Marshall* did drop out, and was replaced by *Hard Lines. Loved One* was only 15.2½ hands high, but had been bred by the Duchess of Montrose at Newmarket and, through his great-grand-dam brought *Melbourne* blood to the mares of the Sligo Sub-District. He was later to sire the dams of *Sunstar*, winner of the 1911 Derby, and of *Sansovino*, winner of the 1924 Derby, although he had been only '. . . a moderate racer, winning three races before retiring to stud.'[3] Incidentally, *Loved One* became the maternal great great grandsire of *Hyperion*. Borrowes reported that 'The judges, in selecting these horses, felt satisfied that they were well calculated to improve the breed of horses in the Sligo District.'[4]

Stallions for the Cork District were chosen on September 25, when eleven entrants paraded before the judges in the Corn Market '. . . a large space, with sheddings most appropriate for the purpose.' *Young Speculation, Wallingford* and *Zanzibar* were the stallions selected, and they were later respectively posted to the Sub-Districts of Mallow, Rathkeale, and Dungarvan.

The Show at Ballinasloe was almost a flop. Eight stallions had been entered for it, but only five paraded before the judges. Although *Reckless, Cavendish* and *Earl Scroope* were selected, and were later sent to the Sub-Districts of Parsonstown (i.e. Birr), Athenry and Ballinasloe, the judges felt unable to select any stallions as reserves out of those on display. 'The few exhibits are to be accounted for by the fact that the closing day expired at too early a date, and that the Show was not properly advertised in the District.' None of the stallions chosen were advertised as having outstanding racing performances: *Cavendish* had managed to take third place in the Welter Handicap at The Curragh in 1888, having been fourth in the Two-Year Old Sweepstake at the same venue in 1886.

Eleven stallions were entered for the Belfast District Show, and in spite of one being absent the judges were well pleased with what they saw. *Condor, Excelsior, Purse Bearer* and *Rattlin the Reefer* were selected, and later sent to the following Sub-Districts: Londonderry, Ballymena, Belfast and Armagh. *Speculum* and *Lightfoot* were chosen as reserves, and it says much for the quality of the stallions selected that, in 1892, *Lightfoot* came first in the International Show at The Hague, in Holland.

Major Borrowes concluded his Report to the Royal Dublin Society with the opinion that: 'From what came under my observation, I think the Committee may feel satisfied that they have adopted a Scheme for the purpose of administering the public grant entrusted to them, which will have the desired effect of improving the breed of horses throughout Ireland.

The stallions selected were decidedly superior to those which have hitherto been within the pecuniary reach of the small farmers in the several districts. The farmers will, moreover, have the satisfaction of knowing that these Stallions are unquestionable as to breeding and soundness.' They had all, of course, passed a veterinary examination on the latter point.

In addition to selecting stallions to stand in the eighteen sub-districts for the 1890 season, the Horse Breeding Scheme for that year also entailed the choice of mares for service. Furthermore, it was stipulated that the Local Committee for each Sub-District should award prizes for two classes of mares. Class One was for half-bred mares under five years old, '. . . suitable for breeding Hunters or Carriage Horses, and which are certified to be in foal to a Thorough-bred

Horse, or that have produced foals during the previous year.' Class Two was for similar mares 'five years old or upwards.' Prize money totalling £20 was allocated to each class, and the Royal Dublin Society awarded a Champion Prize at each Show of £10 for the best mare in Class One and Two.

The Local Committee, in addition to selecting mares for nomination to the Sub-District stallion, and to awarding prizes for two classes of mares, had other tasks. Its members had to decide whether the Sub-District stallion should travel the area and, if so, where it should stay. Thus, for the first time since the horse breeding scheme started, the concept of travelling stallions was introduced. Figure Three shows the centres at which Sub-District stallions stood in 1890. Unfortunately the routes followed by the stallions between stopping points do not appear to have been recorded, and they probably varied to suit circumstances, but the map does show that at least some stallions were confronted with lengthy journeys. *Cavendish*, for example, stood at Athenry, Loughrea and Corofin. *Touchstone* travelled between Navan, Slane, Kilmessan and Kells.

The Local Committees were also given the unenviable task of deciding the geographic limits of their respective Sub-Districts. Obviously the rigid geometric statement of 1889: that each district comprised the area within a twelve mile radius of the headquarters of the district, had not been altogether successful.

Finally, the Local Committees were faced with the overall burden of superintending '. . . the local administration of the scheme.' They were given the added dignity in their task of being officially (and some might say 'officiously') being named the Farmers' Brood Mare Selection Committee. They had to ensure that only mares belonging to 'farmers' (defined as '. . . a person who derives his means of living from farming'), of under £200 aggregate tenement valuation per annum, were selected for service. Obviously they had a busy time and, increasingly, represented the grass-roots of the half-bred horse breeding industry.

The Horse Breeding Committee had, for the 1890 season, made ingenious use of their £3200 grant. £360 was utilized in stallion prizes. £1800 was spent on mare nominations (the detail of this section of the scheme is explained later). £720 went on ordinary prizes for shows of mares and £180 on the Royal Dublin Society Championship prizes at each mare show. This left £140 of the grant to spare, presumably to be used for administrative expenses and for covering unexpected contingencies. Only financial wizards, or a gifted committee, could have thought of such a complex, workable, and financially viable scheme.

Mare nominations were made at each Sub-District Show, held in the month of March. This was a change from the system of previous years, where a series of inspection centres for mares had been established in each stallion district. Nevertheless there were plenty of mares seeking nominations in almost all Sub-Districts. At Dungarvan the almost incredible number of 245 mares contested for the fifty nominations to *Zanzibar*, a bay horse standing 15.3½ hands, foaled in 1871 and by *Saccharometer* out of *Lady Nyassa*. In the years ahead *Zanzibar* was to become a most successful show horse, taking first place at Limerick in 1892 and in 1894, and winning at Cork in 1893. The breeders of the Dungarvan Sub-District, in which the horse stood, knew a good animal when they saw one! Goodness knows how the Farmers' Brood Mare Selection Committee managed to select just fifty mares for nomination out of the multitude presented to them.

At Mullingar 140 mares contended for the services of *Locksley Hall*, 138 were inspected at

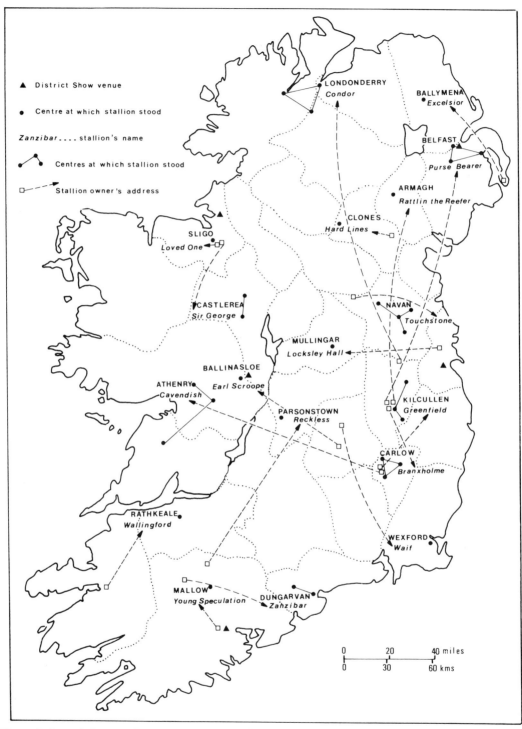

Figure 3. *Queen's Prize Stallion Districts, 1890, and the location of the five District Shows held to choose the Prize Stallions. Note how, in eight Districts, the District Stallion had to travel the District*

Belfast, and 137 at Rathkeale. On the other hand, only fifty were inspected at Sligo, although all were adjudged worthy of nomination. Sixty-two mares were inspected in the Wexford Sub-District, which was an amazingly low number for the most renowned hunter-producing area in Ireland. Perhaps the stallion there, *Waif*, was not thought highly of in the locality. In any case, only forty-two mares were finally served by him. Matters appeared better at Ballinasloe, where sixty-eight mares were inspected, but *Earl Scroope* enjoyed the pleasures of only twenty-four of them. Whether that was because most of the mares inspected were rejected, or whether there was some other reason, is not known. Table Five summarises the mare nomination situation for 1890.

Superficially the situation for 1890 was satisfactory. In 1888 only 764 mares had been served by the Premium Stallions. In 1889 the number rose to 833 and now, a year later, it had risen again, to 841. Yet all was not well. The position at Ballinasloe was most unsatisfactory, and at Mallow, and in Wexford. Yet we do not know what went wrong in these three Sub-Districts. The veils of time, and apparent lack of records, have hidden the truth from us. Equally unsatisfactory

Table Five

Mares served by Queen's Prize Stallions in 1890

Number	Name of Sub District	Name of Stallion	No. of mares submitted	No. of mares served
1	Londonderry	*Condor*	91	39
2	Ballymena	*Excelsior*	—	50
3	Armagh	*Rattlin the Reefer*	73	50
4	Belfast	*Purse Bearer*	138	49
5	Sligo	*Loved One*	50	50
6	Castlerea	*Sir George*	98	50
7	Clones	*Hard Lines*	70	49
8	Ballinasloe	*Earl Scroope*	68	24
9	Athenry	*Cavendish*	80	50
10	Parsonstown	*Reckless*	104	50
11	Navan	*Touchstone*	85	50
12	Mullingar	*Locksley Hall*	140	50
13	Kilcullen	*Greenfield*	77	50
14	Carlow	*Branxholme*	115	49
15	Wexford	*Waif*	62	42
16	Dungarvan	*Zanzibar*	245	50
17	Rathkeale	*Wallingford*	137	50
18	Mallow	*Young Speculation*	115	39

Total number of mares served: 841

was the fact that, at a number of locations, vast numbers of mares had been presented for limited numbers of nominations, so that many good mares failed to get a nomination. This must have been a worrying feature of the scheme for those who really had the good of horse breeding at heart, although it was no different to the situation in previous years.

In 1891, attempts were made to gather information about the foals produced by the Queen's Prize Stallions of 1890, as had been done in 1890 for the previous season. 648 returns were made by owners of mares served by Queen's Prize Stallions and from these it was apparent that at least 218 colts and 247 fillies had been produced, a total of 465. This was a marked increase on the 1889 season, for which at least 401 foals were known to have been born. Yet it must be admitted that a greater number of returns were made for the 1890 season, so that the increased number of foals may have been more apparent than real.

To aid breeding, and possibly to encourage the retention of young stock on the farms of the producers, the Royal Dublin Society invited each District Agricultural Society, and the Local Committee, to give prizes for the best yearling and the best two-year old, 'haltered and led,' at the Sub-District Shows. Now spectators could see the progeny of different sires, for two-year olds by Government Premium Stallions could be compared with yearling's by Queen's Premium Stallions. And the sires would, almost certainly, be different.

One excellent feature of the Horse Breeding Scheme was that it moved stallions around the country. In 1888 for example, *Condor* had served in the Edenderry District. In 1889 he stood at Lisburn, and in 1890 he travelled the Londonderry Sub-District. *Locksley Hall* had served at Ballinrobe, Strabane and now, in 1890, stood at Mullingar. Perhaps it was a relief for the horse to stand so near to his home in Co. Dublin. On the other hand, there were horses that seemed wedded to one region. *Sir George* stood in the Ballymote District in 1888 and in 1889, and in 1890 moved only to the adjacent Castlerea Sub-District. Perhaps Mr. William Alexander, of Somerton, Ballymote, owner of *Sir George*, was not too keen on having his stallion far from home.

At least one stallion was owned by a person who lived in an area that now appears most unlikely. Very few Thoroughbreds are now found in County Kerry, yet *Wallingford* was owned by Mr. Thomas J. Eager of Milltown, Killarney. Milltown is now a rather run-down little village, with an old mansion standing in walled gardens to remind one of former glories. Yet the lands around Milltown, on the limestone lowlands, are potentially highly fertile and formerly supported a well developed system of estates, great houses, gracious living and all else that the term implied, such as hounds and horses. The only hounds in Kerry today are trencher-fed foot packs, belonging to the farmers and ordinary inhabitants, and the days of the great landlord packs have long since gone.[5] The Chute Hall Hounds, three packs in Killarney, the Butler's pack at Waterville, O'Connell's Derrynane pack, all have gone. And the horses of Kerry today are draught and half-breds, with ponies and only a smattering of Thoroughbreds. Yet this was not always so, and *Wallingford* represented an era that has passed.

After the 1890 stud season had ended all that was left to do, apart from completing the assortment of administrative tasks remaining, was to decide on plans for the 1891 season, and to collect foaling details for mares served by the Queen's Prize stallions. The bare details on foaling have already been quoted: at least 465 foals were sired by Queen's Prize Stallions; but far more information than this was gathered. Table Six presents this information.

Table Six[6]

Foaling returns: Queen's Prize Stallions: Season 1890

District	Stallion	No. of returns from mare owners	No. of foals		Total	% on returns	Worst %	Average %
			Colts	Fillies				
Londonderry	Condor	28	5	9	14	50	36	43
Ballymena	Excelsior	31	9	13	22	71	44	57
Armagh	Rattlin the Reefer	39	11	11	22	56	44	50
Belfast	Pursebearer	41	10	18	28	68	57	63
Sligo	Loved One	41	16	16	32	78	64	71
Castlerea	Sir George	38	16	16	32	84	64	74
Clones	Hard Lines	34	13	13	26	76	53	65
Ballinasloe	Earl Scroope	18	5	9	14	78	58	68
Athenry	Cavendish	43	17	17	34	79	68	73
Parsonstown	Reckless	44	16	17	33	75	66	70
Navan	Touchstone	41	17	16	33	80	66	73
Mullingar	Locksley Hall	30	13	10	23	77	46	61
Kilcullen	Greenfield	44	16	14	30	68	60	64
Carlow	Branxholme	41	10	11	21	51	43	47
Wexford	Waif	32	9	11	20	62	48	55
Dungarvan	Zanzibar	43	16	19	35	81	70	76
Rathkeale	Wallingford	27	5	12	17	63	34	48
Mallow	Young Speculation	33	14	15	29	88	74	81
	Totals:	648	218	247	465	72	55	63

As for the 1889 season the Society's table ended with the 'Percentage on returns,' which, as has already been shown, could be misleading. Therefore, as for 1889, two extra columns of information have been added. The 'worst % possible' assumes that *all* returns *not* made related to barren mares. The 'average %' is the mid-figure between the 'percentage on returns' and the 'worst % possible,' and is probably a fair reflection of a stallion's fertility.

From Table Six it is clear that the great disparity in fertility between stallions, evident in the previous year, still remained. *Young Speculation*, who served thirty-nine mares, had an average % of 81, which was truly remarkable. In 1889 the highest figure had been that for *Sir George* and *Reckless*: 76%. *Condor*, with the lowest fertility of all stallions except *Paddy* in 1889: 44%, did slightly worse in 1890, with less than half his mares producing foals (43%). In fact, *Condor* had the lowest rates of all for 1890. Overall, however, there was little change. In 1889 the average

Plate Three. *T. J. Eager, the stallion owner from Milltown in Co. Kerry, lived in this unpreposessing little house.*

percentage had been 64, in 1890 it was 63. Of the seven stallions that had served in both seasons, one (*Cavendish*) had apparently improved in fertility, whilst the other six had apparently declined. The decline was marked in the cases of *Rattlin the Reefer* (from 60 to 50) and particularly of *Waif* (72 to 55). Yet whether much can be read into these figures is doubtful.

But the results of the 1890 season did cause concern. *Condor* (43%), *Branxholme* (47%) *Wallingford* (48%) *Rattlin the Reefer*, (50%), *Waif* (55%) and possibly *Excelsior* (57%) all had fertility figures that were undeniably low. Yet hunters and half-breds were, and still are, bred for performance, and one good horse is sought after far more than dozens of average animals. It is not therefore fair, nor possible, to judge horse breeding (ordinary draught horses excepted) on the same criteria as those of other animals. One good foal by a horse that had, like *Condor*, almost beaten a Derby winner, was potentially so valuable that its sire's low fertility (and the foal's consequent shortage of siblings) could be forgiven, and might even be advantageous. The problems that bothered the Royal Dublin Society's Horse Breeding Committee most were not those of fertility, but of administration. £20 Prizes for stallions had not been wholly satisfactory, and devolution, interesting though it had been as an experiment, had not been without its drawbacks. The lessons the Society learned were that the Queen's Premiums must be resurrected, and that centrality had its advantages. For the 1891 season, therefore, devolution was shelved in favour of centralization.

CHAPTER FIVE

Centralization: the Horse Breeding Scheme of 1891

By the time that the *Schedule* for the *Great Irish Horse Show, 1890,* went to the printers it had been decided to hold a show at Ball's Bridge early in the Spring of 1891 to select 'Thorough-bred Stallions for Queen's Premiums,' and a notice to that effect was included in the *Schedule*. Later we read that 'Sixteen Queen's Premiums of £200 each will be offered for Thoroughbred Stallions to serve in Ireland during the season of 1891.'[1] This represented a reversion to the number of premiums in 1888 as the financial dexterities of 1889 and 1890 were replaced by straight-forward management.

The regulations that governed the Horse Breeding Scheme for 1891 contained a number of stipulations that had not figured in previous schemes, as well as a marked tightening of the rules for soundness. Furthermore, the aggregate annual tenement valuations of farmers whose mares were eligible for nominations was reduced from £200 (which had been the upper limit in 1890) to £100. In other words, large (and therefore arguably wealthy) farmers were excluded from the nomination scheme, thus freeing nominations for suitable mares of lesser (and probably more deserving) farmers. After all, the original idea of the Horse Breeding Scheme had been that '. . . the smaller tenant-farmers will be given preference in the issue of nominations.'[2]

The Premium Show was held at Ball's Bridge on February 18 and 19, 1891, and forty-nine stallions competed for the sixteen premiums. The judges were Cecil Legard, Richard Bell and C.J. Blake, and their brief report makes interesting reading. 'In compliance with the instructions that we should write a report upon the Stallions which have been under our adjudication, we have the pleasure to state that in our opinion, they compare very favourably with any Show for the Queen's Premiums, held previously in Dublin, or in England, several of the Horses representing a high class, and being thoroughly well adapted for getting Hunters and Half-bred Stock.

We had but little difficulty in coming to a conclusion, that the sixteen selected were qualified to receive the Queen's Premiums. While it is to be regretted that two or three of the Horses selected could not receive Premiums, still at the same time, exhibitors may be congratulated on the very small percentage out of the entire number which failed to pass the Veterinary Surgeons' Examination.'[3]

In 1890 there had been no stated stipulation as to what constituted unsoundness in a stallion, although, as Major Borrowes' report showed, every stallion awarded a Queen's Prize had to be passed as sound by a veterinary surgeon. In 1889 it had been stated that 'No Stallion shall be

Plate Four. *C. J. Blake of Heath House, Maryborough (Portlaoise). Blake was one of the judges at the Premium Show of 1891 and was also a stallion owner, standing* Bel Demonio *and* St David *at stud in the 1890s. (Photo:* Dublin Horse Show Magazine)

rejected as unsound unless suffering from hereditary disease.' But what was a hereditary disease? The potential for argument, academic and otherwise, was immense, unless the hereditary diseases were named. In 1891 the Society closed any loophole that might exist and, in the *Regulations* for the Premium Stallion Show, clause 26 stated that: 'Stallions selected by the Judges shall be examined by the three Veterinary Surgeons appointed by the Committee . . . No Stallion shall be rejected as unsound unless suffering from any of the following hereditary diseases:-

Roaring-Whistling	Navicular Disease
Ringbone	Spavin
Unsound Feet	Cataract.'

Against such stipulation there could be no argument; or could there? What, exactly, were 'Unsound Feet?' Happily, however, no owner of the 'two or three' stallions that failed to pass the veterinary surgeons appears to have complained.

Each Premium Stallion, as in previous years, was allotted to a particular District, and the sixteen Districts were: Strabane, Magherafelt, Portadown, Enniskillen, Boyle, Hollymount, Roscommon, Portumna, Mullingar, Ardee, Enniscorthy, Maryborough (i.e. Portlaoise), Macroom, Listowel, Carrick-on-Suir and Thurles. Probably the most important Districts, because they lay in large regions that had never before come within the influence of the Horse Breeding Scheme, were Listowel, Macroom and Maryborough. In fact, more mares were submitted for nominations in the Macroom District than in any other District in Ireland. Strangely, in view of the intense competition for nominations in the area in the previous year, no District was established in west Waterford, although it may have been felt, (erroneously, one suspects), that Carrick-on-Suir was close enough to meet local requirements. Figure Four depicts the sixteen Districts, and shows the name of the horse allocated to each District as well as the location of its owner's address.

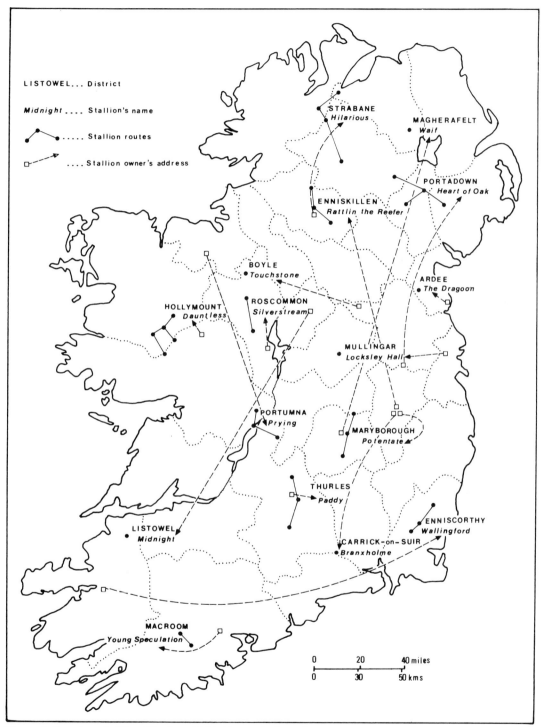

LISTOWEL... District

Midnight .... Stallion's name

●—● .... Stallion routes

□--→ ... Stallion owner's address

STRABANE
Hilarious

MAGHERAFELT
Waif

PORTADOWN
Heart of Oak

ENNISKILLEN
Rattlin the Reefer

BOYLE
Touchstone

ARDEE
The Dragoon

ROSCOMMON
Silverstream

HOLLYMOUNT
Dauntless

MULLINGAR
Locksley Hall

PORTUMNA
Prying

MARYBOROUGH
Potentate

THURLES
Paddy

ENNISCORTHY
Wallingford

LISTOWEL
Midnight

CARRICK-on-SUIR
Branxholme

MACROOM
Young Speculation

0	20	40 miles
0	30	50 kms

Figure 4. *Premium Stallion Districts, 1891. Notice the long distance travelled by such stallions as* Hilarious *(Strabane District) and* Heart of Oak *(Portadown District)*

Only seven of the Premium Stallions had been awarded Queen's Prizes in 1890, although another three had been allocated Queen's Premiums for the 1889 season. *Condor*, with his low fertility rates (43% in 1890) had finally been dropped, although *Branxholme* (47%), *Wallingford* (48%), *Rattlin the Reefer* (50%) and *Waif* (55%) were all awarded Premiums. They, with *Condor*, had the lowest fertility rates of all in 1890. *Paddy*, with an average foaling percentage of 46 in 1889 (only *Condor* had been lower), was also awarded a Premium. Show-yard appearance and the impregnation of mares bore little obvious relationship to each other. Happily, however, *Young Speculation* (with an average foaling percentage of 81 in 1890) was included in the premium list.

As in the previous season stallions were expected to travel their District, if officially requested to do so. The Portadown Committee, in particular, used this facility and *Heart of Oak* had to travel to Portadown, Armagh, Dungannon and Banbridge. His owner, Captain W.H. Davis of Courtown, Kilcock on the Kildare-Meath border, was one of the major owners of stallions in Ireland and was well used to seeing his horses travel. In the first year of the Horse Breeding Scheme, in the 1888 season, his 16.0 hand stallion, *Herbertstown*, had been assigned to Portadown. In the 1889 and 1890 seasons *Condor*, who also belonged to Davis, was located in the Lisburn and Londonderry Districts. Davis was therefore well used to dealing with Ulstermen and was obviously prepared to meet their needs.

The Strabane Committee, chaired by His Grace the Duke of Abercorn, C.B., insisted that its stallion should stand at Strabane on Mondays and Tuesdays, Londonderry on Wednesdays, Raphoe each second Friday and Omagh on Saturdays. What *Hilarious*, who was seventeen years old, thought of the arrangements is unknown. Since the horse was not included as a registered stallion in 1892 or in subsequent years it might be that the arrangements proved a little too strenuous, although *Hilarious* did put at least half his mares in foal.

Dauntless, the 'rich brown' stallion standing 16.1 hands high and who stood in the Hollymount District in Co. Mayo, travelled to even more centres than *Hilarious*. In spite of his breeding (by *Coward* out of *Dangerous*) the horse was no weakling and covered all fifty of his mares, getting at least thirty-seven of them in foal. Two years later *Dauntless* won the Connaught Cup at Galway Show, and repeated the feat the following year. His travels at stud did *Dauntless* no harm at all, and in 1894 he returned to Hollymount to compete in the local show, where he took first place.

Another stallion to travel widely was *Rattlin the Reefer*, now ten years old and owned by T. Gisborne Gordon, The Hall, Curragh, Co. Kildare. This horse was located in the Enniskillen District. The Local Committee, chaired by The Right Honourable the Earl of Enniskillen, instructed its Honorary Secretary, Mr. A. Douglas Brooke of Brookboro' in Co. Fermanagh, to inform Mr. Gordon that his horse must stand at Enniskillen, Irvinestown and Lisnaskea. *Rattlin the Reefer's* grand-dam had been sired by *Faugh-a-Ballagh*, a most successful and renowned racehorse and a valuable blood-line to introduce to the local mares. Two years previously *Rattlin the Reefer* had also stood at Enniskillen, and in 1890 he was posted to Armagh. Obviously Ulstermen thought highly of the horse, and after his second sojourn at Enniskillen the animal was sold to G. Orr, who kept the Sydenham Stud in Belfast.

The greatest number of applications for mare nominations was made in the Macroom District, where 170 vied for the attentions of *Young Speculation*. This was an outstanding show horse and a consistently fertile sire. In 1889 it took first place at Cork Show and in 1891 repeated that

Plate Five. *Lord Enniskillen, Chairman of the Enniskillen District and, in 1897, instigator of an important minority report published by the Commission of Inquiry into the horse-breeding industry. (Photo: courtesy of the Royal Dublin Society).*

Table Seven[4]

Districts, stallions and the number of mares served by
them under the Horse Breeding Scheme, 1891

District	Name of Stallion	Number of mares seeking nominations	Number of mares served
Strabane	*Hilarious*	140	49
Magherafelt	*Waif*	64	44
Portadown	*Heart of Oak*	138	48
Enniskillen	*Rattlin the Reefer*	76	50
Boyle	*Touchstone*	87	49
Hollymount	*Dauntless*	86	50
Roscommon	*Silverstream*	60	46
Portumna	*Prying*	73	50
Mullingar	*Locksley Hall*	75	50
Ardee	*The Dragoon*	65	49
Enniscorthy	*Wallingford*	68	48
Maryborough (i.e. Portlaoise)	*Potentate*	91	46
Macroom	*Young Speculation*	170	50
Listowel	*Midnight*	114	43
Carrick-on-Suir	*Branxholme*	111	50
Thurles	*Paddy*	102	50

Total number of mares served: 772

performance at the Royal Dublin Society's Show. Fifty mares were allocated nominations and were duly served by *Young Speculation*. At Strabane, where only fifty-two mares had sought nominations in the 1888 season (fifty were awarded), and where the number of mares seeking nomination in 1889 was, diplomatically perhaps, 'not ascertained' (but all fifty were allocated), 140 sought the services of *Hilarious*. The Portadown Committee chose their fifty mares from 138 that were submitted to them (forty-eight were finally served by *Heart of Oak)*, and at Listowel 114 sought nominations, with 111 at Carrick-on-Suir and 102 at Thurles. The established geographical pattern: that half-bred horse production centred on the south of Ireland and the Belfast lowland hinterland, was therefore substantiated by the pattern of applications in 1891, the Strabane area excepted. Why there should suddenly be such a great demand for nominations in the Strabane District is unknown, but perhaps the composition of the Local Committee had something to do with it. Table Seven lists the Districts, stallions and numbers of mares served by them, in 1891.

The number of services in 1891 was the lowest since the first year of the Scheme, in 1888, yet it was not in itself cause for concern. In both 1889 and 1890 the financial jugglings of the Horse

Breeding Committee had enabled eighteen Districts to be established, each with its own stallion. Thus it is hardly surprising that the number of mares served was greater in 1889 and 1890 than in 1891, when only sixteen Districts existed.

On average the number of services per stallion was higher in 1891 than in any previous year. In 1888 each stallion served an average of 47.75 mares (which was a surprisingly high average, considering that only twenty-two mares were served in the Tullow District). In 1889 the average fell to 46.27, mainly because *Wallingford* served only six mares in the Dungannon District and because of the problems that beset the Athenry District. In 1890 the average rose marginally, to 46.72, although there were still problems in Co. Galway, as reflected in the low number of mares served (twenty-four) in the Ballinasloe District. The Londonderry, Mallow and Wexford Districts had also fared badly that year. The low number of mares served in some of these Districts might even reflect political conditions and rural unrest in some localities. Land League agitation had been at its height in the early 1880s and agrarian unrest continued, sporadically, for the rest of the century. In Co. Waterford, for example, hunting was affected and between 1884 and 1900 '. . . no county pack existed owing to agrarian troubles.'[5] In 1884 in Co. Wexford '. . . hounds were poisoned on five different occasions while drawing covert,' and in 1885-6 the local hunt decided not to hold any more meets: it was too dangerous to do so.[6] Three years later conditions were far quieter, but still not entirely peaceful.

In 1891 the average number of services per stallion rose to 48.25, the highest since the inception of the Scheme. The lowest number of mares served per District was forty-three, at Listowel. Since 114 had sought nomination in that District it is unlikely that the eventual absentees were missing for political reasons. Mares, like humans, are frail, and illness, disability and unplanned love-matches inevitably caused the absence of a few mares. The Royal Dublin Society must have felt well pleased with the number of mares covered in 1891, especially if, as does not seem likely, its members pondered the stated averages.

The Society must also have felt pleased with the fertility rates of the Premium Stallions. In 1889 the average foaling percentage was 64. This fell to 63 in 1890, but for the 1891 season the percentage rose to a record of 65. The most fertile sires, as far as one can tell from the incomplete foaling returns that were made, were *Dauntless* and *The Dragoon*. Both averaged an amazing 83, and their foaling percentage on the returns made by mare owners was 92. The record established *Young Speculation* in 1890 (88% on returns, 81% on average) was therefore short-lived. If account is taken of the major distances travelled by *Dauntless* in his journeys around the Hollymount District in Co. Mayo his performance will be all the more appreciated. (Figure Four). *The Dragoon*, by comparison, apparently did not travel for his mares, but stood at Ardee in Co. Louth, where forty-nine of them visited him. Table Eight summarises the foaling returns for each stallion.

Comparison of Table Eight with Table Four shows that *Paddy* was far more successful as a sire in 1891 than in 1889. In the former year the horse had achieved an average foaling percentage of only 46, yet in 1891 his average was 74. These figures alone illustrate the dangers inherent in statistics referring to one year's performance, so perhaps the Society had been right in relying on the decisions of its judges in the show-yard, rather than on what might have seemed more scientific and reliable statistics. No doubt there were those who rejoiced in the situation, arguing that statistics could prove anything that their manipulators desired! Yet *Condor*'s fertility had been consistent, and consistently low (44% and 43%) in two successive years, and that could

Table Eight[7]

Foaling returns: Queen's Premium Stallions: Season 1891

District	Stallion	No. of returns from mare owners	No. of Foals			% on returns	Worst % possible	Average %
			Colts	Fillies	Total			
Strabane	Hilarious	40	8	16	24	60	49	54
Magherafelt	Waif	40	9	18	27	67	61	64
Porta-down	Heart of Oak	45	15	12	27	60	56	58
Ennis-killen	Rattlin the Reefer	39	17	15	32	82	64	73
Boyle	Touchstone	46	13	19	32	69	65	67
Hollymount	Dauntless	40	15	22	37	92	74	83
Roscommon	Silver-stream	35	17	10	27	77	59	68
Portumna	Prying	5	2	2	4	80	8	44
Mullingar	Locksley Hall	37	13	11	24	64	48	56
Ardee	The Dragoon	39	20	16	36	92	73	83
Enniscorthy	Walling-ford	42	14	15	29	69	60	65
Maryborough	Potentate	26	13	7	20	76	43	60
Macroom	Young Speculation	16	8	4	12	75	24	49
Listowel	Midnight	32	10	13	23	71	53	62
Carrick-on-Suir	Branxholme	34	16	14	30	88	60	74
Thurles	Paddy	44	17	18	35	79	70	74
	Total:	560	207	212	419	75	54	65

hardly have been an unreliable pointer to the horse's true worth as a sire. The lesson must be that show-yard success should be considered in relation to stock-getting performances in choosing stallions. Yet other criteria also needed consideration, particularly the value of the stallions' progeny. And how could that be related to the sire if the breeding of his mares was unknown?

The problems facing the Society in choosing stallions were immense, and almost impossible to solve scientifically, except in the very long term. For three seasons the Horse Breeding Committee had collected data on foaling returns assiduously and members of the Committee were only too well aware of the problems facing them. Yet before the returns for 1891 were available to them, before, in fact, the foals from 1891 matings had even been born, the Committee had recommended an entirely new course of action to the Society.

The Government in Ireland and the Royal Dublin Society had long been renowned for their various premium schemes. In 1748, for example, the Commissioners appointed '. . . to put into execution an act entitled an Act for the Encouragement of Tillage,' offered premiums for the importation of Black Horses (the stock from which the Shire Horse was to descend) into Ireland.[9] The purpose of such premiums was to stimulate interest in the object, thereby, it was hoped, leading to further developments in the hands of private enterprise. But the Horse Breeding Schemes now in operation could not possibly develop in such a manner. Admittedly, owners might be stimulated to stand stallions at public stud that might otherwise have been retained solely for private use, but that was of little value unless the stallion was of acceptable quality and soundness. The great problem was to devise some scheme whereby stallions could be subjected to veterinary examination and only those found sound and of good quality to be made available for public service. Providing sixteen, or even eighteen, Premium Stallions per year, spread throughout the whole of Ireland, was only playing with an immense problem. When, as at Dungarvan in 1890, 245 mares should compete for fifty nominations, or, as in 1889 at Mullingar, 235 vie for the same number, or 170 at Macroom in 1891, something was radically wrong. What was urgently needed was a scheme whereby a large number of suitable stallions would be available for service throughout Ireland. And it was such a scheme that the Horse Breeding Committee proposed for 1892.

CHAPTER SIX

1892: the year of the sound stallions.

In the Report of the Council of Agriculture to the Royal Dublin Society in the autumn of 1892, full details of that year's Horse Breeding Scheme were given.[1] Unlike previous years, in which Premium Stallions had been located at a very limited number of centres in Ireland, the 1892 Scheme entailed the potential registration of all Thoroughbred stallions that satisfied the Society's requirements. Mares that were approved by appointed Local Committees as suitable for breeding '. . . having due regard to size, age and soundness,' were awarded nominations to these stallions. Clause One of the Scheme describes its essence:

'The sum of £3,200 shall be divided amongst the 32 Counties in Ireland . . . for allotment in Nominations to Thoroughbred Stallions Registered for the purposes of this Scheme for approved Mares, the property of Farmers, the tenement valuation in aggregate of whose holdings does not exceed £150 a-year . . . the term Farmer to be understood to mean a person who derives his means of living from farming.'

All Thoroughbred stallion owners in Ireland were invited to submit their stallions for registration. Before a stallion was registered, however, it had to be '. . . duly entered in Weatherby's Stud Book,' be over three and under eighteen years of age, '. . . must be passed free from any hereditary disease by the Society's Veterinary Surgeon, and if he has been to Stud his Owner must produce satisfactory evidence as to his fruitfulness.' These were not onerous conditions, but they did ensure that only fertile and sound stallions would be registered. Furthermore, when a stallion owner applied for registration, he had to state '. . . the Fee for which he is prepared to give the Service of the Stallion to Nominated Mares – the Fee in no case to exceed the Fee he advertises for Farmers' Half-Bred Mares, and the Owner to send to the Royal Dublin Society his . . . list of Fees, for the Stallion. The Owner shall also state the number of Nominated Mares he is prepared, if asked, to accept for Service at the Fee named.' The Society, in return, '. . . shall have the power to secure all, or as many of that number of services as may be required.'

One hundred-and-forty-seven stallions* were submitted for registration and all were subjected to veterinary inspection. These inspections were carried out at the various stallion

---

* The Society's officers apparently miscounted by one, and 102 stallions were actually registered, so probably 148 were inspected. Two of the Registered Stallions had the same name, which probably caused the confusion.

owners' stables, free of charge to the owner. Furthermore, the Society reserved the right '. . . to have the Stallion inspected . . . by one or more qualified Judges, as to his general merit and fitness for the purposes of the Scheme.' As a result of these inspections 29 stallions were rejected on veterinary grounds and 'Seventeen could not be Registered for other reasons.' This was probably a diplomatic way of saying that they were poor specimens, hardly calculated to improve the breed of horses in Ireland.

The Report stated that: 'Special importance was attached to the test of soundness. The Veterinary inspections were carried out by the Royal Dublin Society's Veterinary Surgeons . . . This work involved a considerable outlay, but it was felt that the advantages to the public of having so large a number of Stallions passed through a searching Veterinary examination would amply justify the expenditure.

Every one of the 101 Stallions entered in the Register has, by the Royal Dublin Society's Veterinary Surgeons, been declared free from all hereditary diseases. This fact is regarded as of importance to many beside the fourteen hundred odd farmers who have this year received direct benefit from the grant for promoting improvement in horse breeding in Ireland.'

The Society issued strict instructions to its Veterinary Surgeons as to the hereditary diseases: 'If the Stallion suffers from one or other of the following hereditary diseases, viz.: Roaring-Whistling, Ringbone, Unsound Feet, Navicular Disease, Spavin and Cataract, the Certificate is to be marked *Unsound*.' These, however, were the same hereditary diseases as had been listed in 1891, although the Veterinary Surgeon was now requested '. . . to make the inspection of the Horse most careful and searching.' It was also stipulated that the veterinarian '. . . is in particular to thoroughly test the Horse as to the soundness of his wind,' and he was advised '. . . to carry with him a large rope, not less than 36 feet long, as in some cases owners of Stallions may not have such a rope conveniently at hand.'

In some ways the list of hereditary diseases was surprising. Professor Pritchard, who had acted as a Veterinary Surgeon for the Society at its Queen's Premium Show in 1889, had considered that sidebones were a grave unsoundness, and hereditary. Admittedly they occur most commonly in draught horses, but as Lyon says,[2] they are '. . . also found in lighter breeds.' Yet no mention of them was made in the list of hereditary diseases. Neither was any mention made of shivering, stringhalt, defective genital organs, curb, or a number of other unfortunate disabilities that are nowadays considered major defects, to be avoided in a stallion. Perhaps it was felt that such defects were too obvious to be worthy of mention, or perhaps they were the sort of things that could be dealt with by the 'qualified Judges' appointed by the Society to inspect stallions.

As a result of the veterinary inspections it was discovered that '. . . the prevailing ailments with which the unsound horses were found to be affected' were 'Roaring, Whistling and Cataract.' Cataract is an opacity of the lens of the eye which can cause blindness if it becomes large enough. Nowadays it is considered that cataracts '. . . may be hereditary, caused by a blow or a sequel to any other disease of the eye.'[3] Unfortunately, it is virtually impossible to tell whether one is dealing with a 'hereditary cataract' or a 'blow-cataract,' and it was therefore wise of the Society to stipulate that cataract be considered an unsoundness. Whistling is a high-pitched noise made by a horse that is suffering from paralysis of the left vocal chord. This paralysis decreases the available area for inhalation '. . . and the actual noise is caused by the forcible passage of air through a restricted aperture.'[4] Eventually whistling normally develops into the deeper and more pronounced noise known as roaring. When this occurs it may become impossible to work the horse at speed because the poor animal may not be able to inhale sufficient air to keep going.

In previous years the Premium Stallions had been allocated to the various Districts into which the Society had divided the country, but this was changed for the 1892 season. The Registered Stallions were allowed to stand anywhere in Ireland, at their owners' direction and expense. The only stipulation was that the owner, in applying for registration, should give full details of where his stallion was to stand. There was therefore no attempt to place stallions, or to ensure that Registered Stallions were available for service throughout the country. Instead it was left to private enterprise, and the dictates of economic forces, to decide where stallions should be located. Admittedly, in the Congested Districts (which in effect meant the western seaboard and adjoining areas), the Government-established Congested Districts Board kept its own stallions for the service of local mares. It would therefore, arguably, have been superfluous for the Society to ensure that stallions were located in those regions. In 1892 the Board stood seventeen stallions at stud in counties Donegal, Mayo, Galway, Cork, Kerry and Leitrim.[5]*

Figure Five shows the location of all the Registered Stallions in 1892 and, where such information is available, depicts the various stations to which they travelled. It seems, however, that there were only limited numbers of travelling stallions, and that most of them only stood at stud at their owner's home stable. In all likelihood many were used for riding and other work, as well as for stud duties.

With the exception of *Wallingford*, who travelled in north Kerry and west Limerick, the travelling stallions were essentially limited to the south east of a curving line from Drogheda to Cork, to the Plains of Mayo, to the Ballina-south Sligo-Roscommon area, to north west Co. Londonderry and to the Strangford Lough region. The best developed networks of travelling stallions lay in central and west Co. Dublin, where *Mont Cenis* and *Locksley Hall* travelled extensively for their mares. In south Kildare – north Carlow *Greenfield* and *Prince Alexander* sought trade, as did *Runnymeade* within north Carlow. The Barrow valley from New Ross to Old Leighlin was travelled by *Cavendish*, who came into competition with *Vanderhum* and *Greenfield* at either end of his travels. *Woodreeve II* and *Choubra* competed for the mares of central Kilkenny and in County Down *Holmby, Excelsior* and *Jester II* competed for at least some of their mares. Elsewhere in Ireland there was little apparent competition, although *Earl Scroope* travelled widely in Leix, as did *Marmion* in Wexford, *Wisconsin* and *Clan-na-Gael* in the lower Suir valley, and *Edlington* in west Waterford – east Cork. These, together with *Sideral* in Co. Londonderry, *Dauntless* in the Plains of Mayo – north Galway area, *Bon Warrior* around Ballina, *Prying* in south Sligo – north Roscommon, and possibly *Master Pirate* in the Banagher area, seem to have been the only 'full-time' stallions on the Register, although that can hardly have been the case.

Of the eighty-eight owners of Registered Stallions, only W. Pallin owned more than two Registered Stallions, and eleven owned two each. Pallin owned *Isleworth*, *Aintree*, *Master Ned* and *Pursebearer*, and lived at the Athgarvan Lodge Stud at the Curragh. He was to become one of the most important supporters of the horse breeding schemes, as later events would prove. Of the eleven two-horse men there were four who travelled their horses extensively. In Co. Sligo W.B. Powell, who lived at Rockfield, Tubbercurry, travelled *Bon Warrior* and *Prying*. *Prying* had been a Queen's Premium Stallion in 1891 and was now seven years old. The horse was 16.0 hands high and was a bay, with black points. To judge from the foaling returns for the season

*see Appendix Two.

Figure 5. *Registered Stallions and the centres to which they travelled in 1892. The location of mare exhibitions '. . . for the purpose of issuing Nominations' is also shown. It is likely that the information on which this map was based was incomplete, since this was the first year in which the Royal Dublin Society operated its registration scheme. Probably many other stallions, in addition to those so depicted, travelled the country*

Plate Six. *W. Pallin, F.R.C.V.S., Athgarvan Lodge Stud, Curragh, Co. Kildare, one of the most important supporters of the Royal Dublin Society's horse-breeding schemes. (Photo:* Dublin Horse Show Magazine)

Prying must have been a popular sire, and of twenty 'Returns from the Owners of Mares' served by the horse, eighteen reported that their mares had produced foals. Only three returns were made relating to *Bon Warrior*, two to those reporting foals. *Prying* continued in the *Register of Thoroughbred Stallions* until the end of the 1896 season, but thereafter neither the horse nor its owner made any further appearances. Perhaps Powell's career as a stallion owner ended in that year.

Michael Foley of Old Leighlin in Co. Carlow lasted longer as a Registered Stallion owner than W.B. Powell. In 1899, when his name was last entered in the Royal Dublin Society's *Register*, he owned *Waif*, although his name is not listed in the final volume of the *Register*, that appeared in 1900. The Foleys of Leighlin Bridge and of Old Leighlin were, without doubt, a horsey family. When the Premium Stallion scheme began in the 1888 season, P. Foley of Mensal Lodge,

Plate Seven. *Michael and Mrs Foley of Old Leighlin, Co. Carlow. Michael travelled his stallions extensively in the Barrow valley region and as far to the south east as Enniscorthy. (Photo: courtesy of Mr D. Foley)*

Leighlin Bridge, owned *Greenfield*. Now, in 1892, the horse belonged to Michael Foley, as did *Cavendish,* who first obtained a Queen's Premium for the 1889 season, when the stallion had been posted to the Ballymena District. Michael Foley obviously believed that his stallions should work for their keep, and travelled *Cavendish* as far south down the Barrow valley as New Ross, north as far as his own stables in Old Leighlin and west as far as Kilkenny city. *Greenfield* travelled a lesser distance, between Leighlin Bridge, Carlow, Athy and Arless in the Queen's County.

At New Ross *Cavendish* had to compete for his mares with Kiernan Mullins' stallion, *Vanderhum*. This was a chestnut of 16.0 hands, foaled in 1877. Mullins lived at Flemingstown in Glenmore, Co. Kilkenny, and travelled his horse between his own stables and New Ross. Judging by the information for the 1893 season it seems likely that *Vanderhum* stood in New Ross only on Saturdays, presumably the day that his master went to town! The Mullins were known locally as stallion-men, though, and in 1895 Felix replaced Kiernan as the stallion-owner. Men, like horses, do not continue indefinitely. In 1900 Felix Mullins still owned a Registered Stallion: *Lord George*.

In the Kilkenny area *Cavendish* competed with *Choubra* and *Woodreeve II* for females. These latter two stallions were owned by Robert Nicol of Dysart. Nicol's stallions stayed near home and travelled only within the fertile central lowland corridor of Kilkenny, but this had not always been the case. In the 1888 season *Woodreeve* had been located at Cappoquin as a Government Premium Stallion. Nicol continued to own at least one Registered Stallion until 1899, but his name does not appear in the 1900 *Register*.

In the south west of the country T. J. Eager continued to travel *Wallingford*, the horse that had first been awarded a Premium for the 1889 season, when he stood at Dungannon. *Wallingford* had made an inauspicious start to his career in the Horse Improvement Scheme, spraining his shoulder '. . . early in the season, and was unable to complete the services of the mares.' Luckily the shoulder recovered and *Wallingford* had done quite well as a stallion in succeeding years. Now, in 1892, the horse travelled between Listowel, Newcastle West and Tralee, well to the north of its owner's home in Milltown. Eager also owned a stallion called *Baldwin*, that he stood at Listowel. This horse was five years old, bay, and 15.3 hands high. Eager continued to stand *Baldwin* at stud until the end of the 1897 season. Thomas Stephens of Killorglin owned the horse in the following season. Eager made much of his living from horses and is still remembered as a stallion man by the older inhabitants of Milltown. His house, a two storied slated cottage, was destroyed to make room for the new cattle market in Milltown and the last of his family to survive in the little town, died in 1976.

As well as the four owners already described there were another six who kept two Registered Stallions each at stud. These were Henry Reynolds of Ballinalee, Edgeworthstown; W. Kilroy of Old Castle in Co. Meath; F. Flannery of Churchtown in Co. Cork; Captain Davis of Kilcock; R.N. Talbot who owned *Almoner* and *Derby Dick* (a horse that won five races at Lismore, Cashel, Waterford, Kells and Fermoy); and James Connolly of Rossanmore, Dundalk. Flannery travelled *Pennington* in his local area, but over such a short distance as to be hardly comparable with the travels of *Cavendish* or even of *Choubra* and *Woodreeve II*. All six owners were noted stallion-men and obviously made a considerable income from their stud horses.

Of the twenty-four stallions that were travelled appreciable distances, later *Registers* only list three of them as having been successful on the race-course. Although this is probably an incomplete summary of their performances it is startling to think that the majority of travelling stallions were undoubtedly poor performers on the Turf, or had never been raced. Furthermore, few of them appear to have been particularly successful in the show-yards, although *Mont Cenis* had been second in his class at the Royal Cornwall Show in 1885 and was to win at Bray Show in 1893. *Dauntless*, as already noted, was to win the Connaught Cup at the Galway Show in 1893 and 1894.

Edlington, the horse that travelled between Fermoy and Cappoquin, was the only travelling stallion to have performed consistently well on the race-course. Between 1883, when he won the Cobam Stakes at Camdown, and 1890 when he won the Tradesman's Plate at Bath, *Edlington* won no less than fourteen races. These included the Stewards Cup at Kempton Park in 1884, the Railway Handicap at Leicester in 1885, the Friday Plate at Manchester in 1887 and the Devonshire Plate at Carlisle in 1888. Perhaps it was appropriate that his Irish travels included sojourn in the centre of the Duke of Devonshire's Waterford estates, at Lismore, part way between Fermoy and Cappoquin. Significantly the horse was owned by Thomas Magnier of Fermoy, and Magnier is still a surname to conjour with in the bloodstock business! The farmers of the Blackwater valley were exceedingly fortunate to have the opportunity of sending their mares to such a stallion for the very reasonable fee of £3 - 0s. - 0d. per service.

The only other travelling stallion to have his race-course winnings listed in the *Registers* (apart from *Cavendish* with a third and a fourth at the Curragh) was *Jester II*. This stallion, who travelled the area around Ardglass-Downpatrick, had won the Prince of Wales Stakes at Scarborough in 1878. The horse also won the Nursery Stakes at Kelso in the same year. At £3.0.0. a service he seemed good value, although *Rattlin the Reefer*, standing at George Orr's stud at Sydenham, Belfast, commanded a fee of £5.0.0.

All the Registered Stallions were obliged, under the rules that governed registration, to appear at not less than one Exhibition of the Registered Stallions in the county in which they were to stand at stud. These Exhibitions were arranged by the County Committees and coincided with the 'Exhibitions of Mares for the purpose of issuing Nominations.' The purpose of the stallion exhibitions was to allow mare-owners to inspect the stallions that they could avail of for their mares and hence to enable them to decide upon the most suitable stallion for their mare.

By strange coincidence 101 'Exhibitions of Mares' were held throughout Ireland, the same number as the incorrectly stated total of Registered Stallions (102 were actually registered). The location of these exhibitions is shown on Figure Five. The report of the Council of Agriculture states that: 'In most of the counties the collections of mares were large and of a satisfactory character. In a few counties, notably in Ulster, difficulty was experienced in obtaining a sufficient number of suitable mares for the available nominations. This was attributed chiefly to the lack of first class stallions at convenient centres in these counties.'

The County Committees (also referred to as Local Committees) were appointed by the Royal Dublin Society and their decisions were carefully stated as: 'subject to confirmation by the Royal Dublin Society.' Their duties were, in the main, to select mares that were suitable for breeding and award them nominations, and to arrange exhibitions of stallions. There were strict rules relating to nominations. 'For a Nomination to a Registered Stallion whose Service Fee for Nominated Mares does not exceed £3, the sum of £1 shall be paid by the Owner of the Mare, and the balance by the Royal Dublin Society; for a Nomination to a Registered Stallion whose

Table Nine

Subsidies available for mare nominations, per county, in the
1892 breeding season

County	Subsidy (£)	County	Subsidy (£)
Antrim	100	Limerick	110
Armagh	80	Londonderry	90
Carlow	90	Longford	90
Cavan	90	Louth	80
Clare	110	Mayo	100
Cork	160	Meath	100
Donegal	80	Monaghan	80
Down	110	Queen's County	100
Dublin	80	Roscommon	100
Fermanagh	80	Sligo	90
Galway	100	Tipperary	140
Kerry	110	Tyrone	100
Kildare	100	Waterford	100
Kilkenny	110	Westmeath	100
King's County	100	Wexford	140
Leitrim	80	Wicklow	100

Service Fee for Nominated Mares exceeds £3, the sum of £2 shall be paid by the Royal Dublin Society and the balance by the Owner of the Mare. In addition the Farmer shall pay a Groom's Fee of 2s. 6d. for each Mare in each case.'

The amount of money available for each County Committee to spend on nominations was also stipulated and is shown in Table Nine.

The County Committees were obliged '. . . upon a day and at a place duly advertised in the local newspapers, [to] hold one or more Exhibitions of Mares for the purpose of issuing Nominations.' But the Society was careful to ensure that no charge of local favouritism could be laid by mare owners against the County Committees. The rules stipulated that 'The Mares to receive Nominations shall be selected by Judges named by the Royal Dublin Society.' This was probably a very wise regulation, since a local judge appointed by a local committee to examine local mares would have had to be a veritable Solomon not to have displayed, or been thought to have displayed, unfair bias. Furthermore, the Society stipulated that 'The Nominations issued in any one County shall not exceed in value the sum assigned . . . to that County,' and that farmers could only seek a nomination in the county in which they lived. In the case of a farmer whose lands extended into more than one county it was stated that he could apply for a nomination in any *one* of the counties in which his holding was situated. In addition 'No farmer shall this year receive more than one Nomination.'

The Society anticipated that in some cases there would be more Nominated Mares seeking services from particular stallions than were available from those stallions. To overcome this potential problem the rules stated that 'A farmer receiving a Nomination may select for his Mare any one of the Registered Stallions whose Service List is not already full.' Rather than let this selection degenerate into a scramble on a 'first come, first served' basis, the Society ruled that a ballot of all owners of Nominated Mares would be held. Mare owners would be given their choice of stallion according to their position in the ballot: '. . . the Owner of each selected Mare must inform the County Committee of the Stallion he selects immediately after the ballot of Mares takes place, and before he receives his Certificate of Nomination.'

Obviously the Horse Breeding Committee were sensible businessmen, fully aware of the difficulty of persuading owners to pay for the servicing of their mares (especially if the mare failed to conceive). They therefore stated that 'All Fees payable by the Farmer shall be paid to the County Committee. No Nominations shall be issued until the Fees have been paid.' Without nomination papers no Registered Stallion owner would accept a supposedly Nominated Mare for service, so the mare owner had no escape. No fee, no service, and that was that.

The regulations also stipulated that, once a stallion had been chosen for the service of a Nominated Mare, there could be no change of mind. 'The order on the Stallion is not transferable, and is available only for the selected Mare.' An exception was made to allow for the death or illness of either stallion or mare, but even so the frailties of human nature were guarded against: 'Cases of illness must be certified by a qualified Veterinary Surgeon.' There could be no switching of nominations just because a farmer 'thought' his Nominated Mare was ill (and wanted another of his mares to be substituted for nomination). And the final decision on transfer rested with the Society or the County Committee, and not with the mare or stallion owner.

By the time that the 1892 stud season ended it was evident that the new scheme was a great success. In all, 1449 mares had been served by Registered Stallions. Ninety-two Registered Stallions had served under the scheme, and a total of £4,794.18.0. had been paid in service fees to the owners of those stallions. In effect the Government Grant of £3,200 had been 'increased' by some 50%, without cost to the Government. Admittedly there had, effectively, been a levy on the owners of Nominated Mares in that they had to pay part of the service fees and the groom's fees, but in return they had been presented with a considerable choice of sound and quality stallions for the use of their mares. Furthermore, the owners of many other mares, that had not received nominations, had been able to consult the *Register of Thorough-bred Stallions* and, at their own cost, had availed their mares of the services of those certified horses. Thus, by its new scheme, the Royal Dublin Society had provided breeders throughout the majority of Ireland with a *Register* of incalculable value and had replaced the limited-value Premium Stallion Scheme with a *Register* of national importance.

On January 25, 1894, Robert Fowler, Chairman of the Committee of Agriculture, presented the Society with information on the number of foals produced as a result of The Horse Breeding Scheme, 1892.[6] Circulars had been sent to the owners of all mares that had received nominations, and of the 1449 mares served, owners provided details of 1056. From these returns it was evident that at least 752 foals had been fathered by Registered Stallions, 385 being colts and 367 being fillies. The fertility of the Registered Stallions, expressed as a percentage on the returns, was 71. This compared with 75% for the previous year, 72% for 1890 and 69½% for 1889. Fifteen stallions, judged solely on the returns, had a fertility rate of 100%. But these figures need to be considered cautiously, since they include such returns as that for *Woodman*, a chestnut stallion foaled in 1883, by *Xenophon* out of *The Doe*, and owned by Captain G.M. Eccles of Moneygoold in Co. Sligo. One circular was returned for a mare served by this horse, and it recorded the birth of a filly foal. There is no other information about *Woodman*. As a percentage on the circulars returned, *Woodman* was 100% fertile! *Early Bird*, *Heart of Oak* and *Middleman* had two returns each relating to them. Judged on the returns these stallions, too, were 100% fertile. Facts, figures and fantasies are sometimes difficult to detect!

The most popular stallions, judged by the number of returns relating to them, were *St. Paul*, *Dauntless*, *Sterling II*, *Carnage*, and *Dyspeptic*. *St. Paul* served at least sixty-one mares, producing forty-two foals for the fortunate farmers of Cavan, Leitrim and Longford. In 1882 the colt had won a Maiden Two-Year-Old Plate at Weymouth and in the following year won the Croxteth Handicap at Liverpool, the Craven Plate Handicap at Sandown Park and the Bead Hurst Welter Handicap (worth £700) at Lichfield. He was, undoubtedly, a valuable sire for the local mares, well tested and proven on the racecourse and of considerable ability. A colt got by him took second place at Navan Show in 1892 and two years later a mare by him won her class at the same show. The farmers of the north midlands were fortunate to secure his services and took full advantage of him.

Dauntless, soldiering on in Galway and Mayo (as in the previous year), served at least thirty-seven mares, and got all but one of them in foal. This was a remarkable performance and the horse was very popular in his area. Mrs. Tuohy, his owner, had agreed to accept up to seventy mares for the horse, and *Dauntless* doubtless paid his way for her at £3 per service. *Sterling II* stood in Longford and Westmeath and sired at least twenty-three foals. *Carnage* got at least nineteen foals for the farmers of Co. Antrim and *Dyspeptic* did better, with at least twenty for the Tyrone farmers. *Dyspeptic* worked hard for his mares, travelling between Augher, Omagh, Aughnacloy and Fivemiletown. He was a six year old, brown in colour, and 16.1 hands high, by *Young Plum Pudding* (by *Plum Pudding*) out of *The Marchioness*. Perhaps his great grand-dam's sire could have done something for his dyspepsia: his name was *Physician*.

Judged by the number of foals stated to have been produced according to the circulars returned, *Canon, Prince Alexander, Monsieur* and *Thrapston* were all more successful sires than *Dyspeptic*. *Canon* stood in the Tallow area of west Waterford – east Cork and obviously travelled the Bride Valley (although that is not specifically stated in the *Register*.) He was a most successful competitor in the show-ring and took four Firsts at Lismore Show as well as winning at Hollymount and, much more important, as a Registered Sire in the Produce class at Dublin in 1893 – but that triumph was still a year ahead and could not have been accurately foretold. *Canon* had been bred by the Rev. James Barry of Churchtown, Mallow, and one wonders if his name had any connection with clerical preferment! When the Irish Draught Horse Book was being founded, from 1917 onwards, *Canon* figured in many pedigrees.

Prince Alexander stood for the Counties of Carlow, Kildare and Queen's, and belonged to O.T. Slocock of Carlow, who travelled him in the south Kildare – east Queen's – north Carlow area. At least twenty-four foals were got by him in 1892. *Monsieur* belonged to Major Gerald Dease of Turbotstown, Coole, in north Westmeath and had been bred in France by *Saxifrage* out of *La Hague*. As a three-year-old *Monsieur* had won a Plate at Newmarket and two years later, in 1885, won further races on the flat at Manchester, Lewes, Windsor, Huntingdon and Sandown. In December, 1885, over hurdles, the horse won the December Hurdle at Sandown. At £3 a service this 16 hands chestnut was good value, and he sired at least twenty-three foals.

Plate Eight. *Colonel H. de Robeck, owner of regis-tered stallions such as* Marchaway, *and later to become Master of the Kildare Foxhounds. (Photo:* Dublin Horse Show Magazine)

In the north of Ireland, in Co. Armagh, Michael Quinn's stallion, *Thrapston*, sired no less than twenty-one foals. Quinn was a veterinary surgeon in Ballymena and in succeeding years it became apparent that many vets fancied themselves as stallion owners: the last draught stallion to be registered for stud in Co. Dublin was owned by a Member of the Royal College of Veterinary Surgeons, but that was sixty-three years away in the future and few horsemen foresaw the distant dismal destiny of their splendid steeds. Instead, people like Colonel H. de Robeck of Newlands, Naas; Captain Archdale of Castle Archdale, Irvinestown; Sir Douglas Brooke of Colebrooke, Brookeboro; even T.J. Eager of the slated cottage in Kerry, all stood their stallions at stud as if the horse would always reign supreme. de Robeck's stallion, *Marchaway*, got at least six mares in foal, and all produced fillies. With at least 752 foals produced by the Registered Stallions, the Royal Dublin Society must have felt well pleased with its new Horse Breeding Scheme, but by the time the mares had foaled the Society had already marched away and prepared the Second Volume of its *Register of Thorough-bred Stallions*, this time *for service under the Horse Breeding Scheme 1893*.

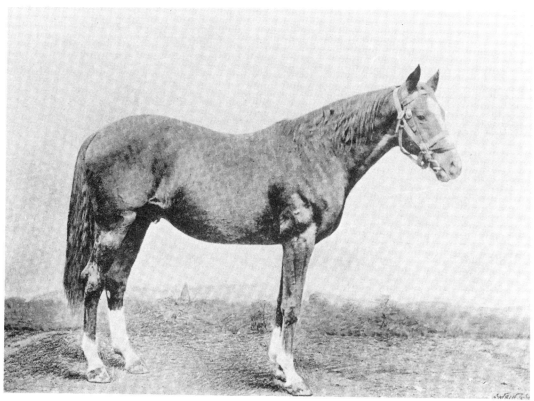

Plate Nine. Marchaway, *by* Lord Gough *out of* Away, *owned by Colonel de Robeck, winner of the Hunter Stallion class at the Royal Dublin Society's show in 1894. (Photo:* Register of Thoroughbred Stallions)

CHAPTER SEVEN

Volume Two

In March, 1893, the Royal Dublin Society published *Volume Two* of its *Register of Thorough-bred Stallions*. The volume was prefaced with a note to the effect that 137 stallions had been submitted for registration by their owners, and that 118 had been found suitable and had therefore been registered. Eleven stallions amongst those inspected had failed to pass the veterinary examination and '. . . eight could not be Registered for other reasons.' As in the previous year it was stated that all the Registered Stallions had '. . . been declared free from all hereditary diseases. This fact is of importance to many beside the sixteen hundred Farmers who will this year receive direct benefit from the grant for promoting improvement in Horse Breeding in Ireland.' Perhaps the most satisfactory note recorded in the preface, however, '. . . is that *fewer unsound* Stallions were submitted for Registration, and also that several horses, rejected last season by the Horse Breeding Committee, *have disappeared* from the Country.' Obviously the Society's message: solely sound stallions for service, was already getting across to the breeders.

The regulations governing the 1893 scheme differed only in detail from those of the preceding year. Nominations were to be awarded to suitable mares, as in 1892, and the county subsidies remained unchanged. Nevertheless, there were two important additions to the rules relating to mares. In the first case it was stipulated that, in awarding nominations, '. . . young Mares to have the preference.' In 1892 it had been stated that '. . . suitable Mares (having regard to size, age, and soundness)' should be considered for nominations, but there had been no real emphasis on the mares being young. Secondly, under Clause Six, section (c), it was categorically stated that mares to receive nominations '. . . must be passed free of any hereditary disease by the Society's Veterinary Surgeon.' This was the first time since the Horse Breeding Schemes had begun that an emphasis had been placed on the veterinary inspection of mares, and it was a highly desirable development. Just as certain unfortunate characteristics can be transmitted from a stallion to his progeny, so too can they be transmitted via the mare.

A further alteration in the regulations affords an insight into the problems that must have beset the County Committees in 1892. In that year they had to collect all fees payable by mare owners before issuing them with their nomination papers. Superficially that had seemed an excellent idea, since it ensured that the farmers paid their dues. In practice, however, many a County Committee member must have heard a hard luck story, or been promised payment 'when the crops are sold,' or 'after the fair,' and it must have been well-nigh impossible to refuse Certificates of Nomination to certain owners – even if only to get them off the doorstep! In 1893 it was ruled that 'All Fees payable by the Farmer shall be paid to the Stallion Owner, at the time of first Service, or at such other time as may be agreed upon between the Stallion Owner and the Farmer.'

The most significant difference between the 1892 and 1893 schemes, however, lay in the stallions themselves and in the routes they followed, which are shown on Figure Six. For 1892 we glimpse the glitter of a few proud horses travelling the countryside in search of mares. Now, in 1893, the *Register* recorded a multitude of widely travelling sires. In Co. Kerry T.J. Eager continued to travel a stallion, but with the bay six-year old, *Baldwin*, replacing *Wallingford*. *Baldwin* was expected to serve up to 100 mares, at £3 each, so Eager made him earn his keep. West of Cork city Mr. John Mahony's horse, *New Laund*, travelled the Bandon-Kinsale region, and Mr. Daniel Thomas Donovan from Clonakilty travelled *Narrator* between that town and Bandon. In Ulster at least thirteen stallions travelled appreciable distances and in Connaught *Dauntless* continued to tramp the limestone Plains of Mayo. But the main concentration of travelling stallions, already hinted at in the *Register* for 1892, lay in the old Anglo-Norman stronghold of the Barrow valley: Carlow, south Kildare; with extensions into Kilkenny and the Queen's County.

Michael Foley of Old Leighlin, a major travelling stallion man in previous years, continued to travel *Greenfield* and *Cavendish* extensively, but he was faced with stiff competition. O.T. Slocock travelled *Prince Alexander* between Killeen in Queen's County, Athy in Kildare, Baltinglass in Wicklow and his own stables in Carlow town. He also stood a little brown three-year-old, *Brooklands*, at stud. John Salter's bay stallion, *Earl Scroope*, also competed against Foley's horses. From his owner's stables at Coolbally, Abbeyleix, *Earl Scroope* travelled to Maryborough, Athy, Carlow, and Kilkenny, and was prepared to give up to 120 services, all at £3. Robert Keppel of Raheen, Killane (near Ballon) competed with *Runnymeade*, which he travelled between Bagnalstown, Carlow and Tullow. West of the Barrow Robert Nicol extended the route of *Choubra*, to Callan, Kilkenny and Dysart. But none of these competitors could match the aplomb of Michael Foley.

Once a fortnight, on Tuesdays, Foley sent *Cavendish* to Enniscorthy in the Co. Wexford. Thence the horse travelled to Graignamanagh where he stood on Thursdays, to Kilkenny city for Saturday, and home to Old Leighlin. The following week *Cavendish* stood at Athy on Tuesday, Carlow on Thursday, Baltinglass on Friday and Tullow on Saturday, '. . . remainder at Old Leighlin.' *Greenfield*, Foley's other stallion, also had a fortnightly programme: Tuesdays (once a fortnight) at Enniscorthy, Wednesday at New Ross, Thursday at Graignamanagh, Saturday at Kilkenny city. On the following Tuesday *Greenfield* stood at Athy, on Thursday at Carlow, on Friday at Baltinglass, on Saturday at Tullow: '. . . remainder at Old Leighlin.' Some of these itineraries must have involved both horses in daily journeys of well over twenty miles and it seems incredible that they should have been able to stand so much travelling as well as the strain of their stud duties. Both stallions were listed in the *Register* as being available to undertake up to 105 services. To misquote Alice, 'A stallion's life was terribly hard,' at least if it was owned by Michael Foley. Of course, there was a train that stopped at Milford Station, near Old Leighlin, and that, by dint of changing at Macmine Junction, could have transported the horses to Enniscorthy. Furthermore, Athy was on the direct rail route from Milford, and Kilkenny city

Figure 6. *Registered Stallions, 1893. Although more stallions are shown as travelling to a variety of centres in 1893 than in 1892, that is probably a reflection of an increased amount of information supplied to the Royal Dublin Society and not a true statement of reality. Notice the great concentration of travelling stallions in the Barrow valley region, which was a major centre of Anglo-Norman Ireland and in which there has been a long tradition of quality horse production*

could also be reached, via Bagnalstown. New Ross, similarly, could be reached, but via a change of line at Palace East. Yet there is no evidence that Foley transported his stallions by train and their timetables suggest that he expected them to rely on their own legs for transport. Foley's son, Desmond, also believes that the horses used to walk and that his father employed grooms to lead them!

Further north, in the Dublin area, *Locksley Hall's* challenge to *Mont Cenis* had ended, and the latter stallion was the only one listed as travelling the region. Yet north Co. Dublin was provided with an abundance of seemingly static stallions: *Tunis*, *Forestay*, *Studley*, *Pythias* and *Annagor*. All hailed from the fertile agricultural lowlands of the eastern seaboard (with the exception of Christopher Sherwin of Naul's horse: *Tunis*.) *Forestay* and *Studley* were both owned by A. Maxwell of Courtlough, Lusk. *Studley* had won a Nursery at Lincoln in 1883 and won both the Great Northern Handicap at York and the Lincoln Autumn Handicap at Lincoln in 1884. In 1891 the horse had been second in his class at Dublin Horse Show and he was to win at Galway Show in 1893. Maxwell valued his services at £5 each and offered fifty of them. Judged by the returns made by mare owners in the following year it seems (falsely) that *Studley* was not popular: only one reply related to him, recording the birth of a colt foal. Yet the horse won the produce class for progeny exhibited at Dublin in 1893, so his services must have been availed of. Nevertheless, Maxwell decided to sell the horse and in 1895 *Studley* belonged to W.T. Trench of Redwood, near the tiny village of Lorrha in north Tipperary.

The quality of the Co. Dublin stallions was, on the whole, satisfactory. Admittedly *Mont Cenis* was not noted on the racecourse and only won once in the show-ring, at Bray Show in 1893, but he was consistently placed. *Annagor* had won twelve races, the first being the Harbour Plate at Tipperary in 1892. *Pythias* won three races (the Nursery Handicap at the Curragh in 1887, the Belfast Plate at Down in 1888 and the Welter Handicap of the same year, at the Curragh). He was also placed twenty-two times between 1887 and 1890, so the horse was no slouch. *Tunis* (by *Mogadore* out of *Parma*) won four times at Newmarket as a two and three-year-old, including the Houghton Stakes in his triumphs. Only *Forestay* apparently won nothing, either on the racecourse or in the ring, but perhaps Mr. Maxwell was too modest to parade any successes there might have been. Between these stallions the tenant farmers of Co. Dublin had ample choice of sires to put on their nominated mares.

Adjoining Co. Dublin, in Meath, Michael Healy travelled a 15.3 hand brown stallion named *Sailor King*. At £2. 10s. a service this was the cheapest stallion in Meath and in the adjacent county of Kildare. Judged by the number of returns relating to foals, he was the most popular, too. Healy travelled *Sailor King* to Clane on Mondays, Robertstown on Tuesdays, Rathangan on Wednesdays, Edenderry on Thursdays, Carbury on Fridays and back home to Ballinaskea at Enfield on Saturdays. With the exception of the week-end poor *Sailor King* was committed to the Co. Kildare, although only forty services were expected of the horse.

James Connolly, who lived at Rassanmore near Dundalk, continued to stand the same two stallions at stud as in the previous year: *Finn Ma Coul* and *Slievegullion*. There is no indication in the 1892 *Register* that he travelled the horses, but in 1893 both stallions travelled, in a half-hearted manner. *Finn Ma Coul* stood at his owner's stables '. . . during the week; and Castleblaney, Co. Monaghan, if required.' *Slievegullion* went to Dundalk on Mondays, '. . . rest of week, Rassanmore, Co. Louth; and in Castleblaney, Co. Monaghan, if required.' Both horses were registered to accept fifty mares, at a fee of £3. 3. 0. each. Two years later Connolly

Plate Ten. *R.C. Dawson of Cloghran, Co. Dublin, was the owner of* Annagor. *He later registered* Craig Royston *as well. Photo:* Dublin Horse Show Magazine)

reduced the fees to £2 each, but by then he must have been in serious competition with the five stallions registered by J.A.S. Langan of Bellewstown House, Drogheda. According to the foaling returns *Slievegullion* and *Finn Ma Coul* both got at least nine nominated mares, and probably many others as well. *Finn Ma Coul* had won twice on the race-course, the Farmers' Plate at Ardee in 1889 and the Stewards' Plate at Dundalk. Langan, by comparison, was later to stand such quality horses as *Hominy*, winner of the Irish Grand Military at Fairyhouse in 1882 and second (beaten by a head) in the 1883 Grand Military Cup at Sandown Park, and *Wild Sherry*, winner of races at the Curragh, Sandown Park, Leopardstown (and Bellewstown), in competition. But that was in the future, and even if a winner of a Farmers' Plate at Ardee was hardly in the same class as the winner of the Irish Grand Military at Fairyhouse, that was not yet a problem for Connolly.

The Belfast area, extending into north Down, was the scene of considerable competition. Mr. Gamble Orr (a name that is distinctly suggestive of racing matters) of Strandtown, Belfast, travelled *Glencoe* to Banbridge on a Monday, Downpatrick on Tuesday, Belfast on Friday, Newtownards on Saturday, '. . . other days at his own stables at Sydenham.' At Banbridge, on alternate Mondays, *Glencoe* competed with *St. Keyne* for mares. This latter horse was owned by James Gregg of Lisburn, and had been bred by Her Majesty the Queen. *St. Keyne* stood at Lisburn and Banbridge on alternate Mondays, on Tuesdays and Wednesdays at Lisburn, on Thursdays at Ballynahinch and Lurgan, on Fridays at Belfast (competing again with *Glencoe*), on Saturdays at Dromore and Lisburn.

Glencoe also came into competition, at Newtownards, with *Excelsior*, who had been bred by Lord Falmouth in England and now belonged to Patrick M'Nabb of Parson Hall, Portaferry. In 1890 *Excelsior* had been awarded a Queen's Prize and stood in the Ballymena District, but had not been awarded a Premium in 1891. During 1892 M'Nabb travelled the horse in the Ards peninsula south of his home, to Kirkcubbin, Portaferry, Downpatrick and back to Parson Hall. Now his horse also journeyed north, to Newtownards. Two years hence, in 1895, M'Nabb had sold *Excelsior* and, owned by Alexander Browne of Corracavey, Cootehill, this stallion serviced mares of the Co. Cavan. This illustrates the continual problem that confronted stallion owners.

Few breeders wished to mate a filly with her father, since inbreeding could accentuate weaknesses and lead to degeneration. Therefore, once a stallion's progeny reached breeding age (which is normally considered to be three years old for a mare), it was imperative (unless there were a very large number of mares in the area, many of which had not yet been served by the horse), to move the stallion to another area. Obviously, by varying the routes between 1892 and 1893 M'Nabb was trying to obtain a new group of mares for his horse, without the drastic necessity of moving the beast entirely from his owner's home area. By 1895 *Excelsior* had to move, and, incidentally, M'Nabb's period as a Registered Stallion owner also came to an end.

At Downpatrick M'Nabb's stallion met the horse that belonged to Charles and John M'Namara of Ballydock, Ardglass: *Jester II*. In 1892 *Jester II* had travelled to four centres, but now the M'Namaras were more cautious, and travelled the horse only on Saturdays and Fair days to Downpatrick. For the remaining period of the stud season *Jester II* stood at home. Probably the M'Namaras had found the travelling of 1892 to be more trouble than it was worth. In any case, only four mare owners returned information to the Society relating to *Jester II*'s services in 1893, and they showed only the production of a single colt foal. One hopes that, in fact, the stallion was more successful than the returns suggest. Another Co. Down horse that had travelled widely in 1892, but that now stood at home, was *Holmby*. Joseph Perry, the owner, even reduced the stallion's fee (by 2s. 6d.) from that sought in the previous year, which tells its own story!

The only other area of Ireland in which there was considerable competition between travelling stallions lay in the Foyle valley. The farmers of the Omagh area were particularly fortunate in being able to choose between four Registered Stallions: *Cambrian*, *M.P.*, *Trespasser*, and *Dyspeptic*. Only *Dyspeptic* had apparently travelled the region in the previous year, at least as a Registered Stallion. *Cambrian* was owned by Edward Mitchell of Derryvullen, Enniskillen, and made an excursion to Omagh on Saturdays. On Thursdays the horse stood at Clones and for the remainder of the week *Cambrian* stood at home. *M.P.*, winner of two £500 Handicaps at Kempton, in 1887 and 1888, and a winner at Lincoln and Windsor, linked the Horse Improvement Schemes of Britain and of Ireland. In 1891 *M.P.* was made a Queen's Premium Stallion at Islington. From the highways of London to the byways of Co. Tyrone must have been a radical change for the horse, even though his duties were the same! *Trespasser* had been bred by an M.P., the Right Honorable H. Chaplin of Blankney in Lincolnshire and now belonged to Surgeon Captain R.J. M'Cormack, M.D., of the Army Medical Staff. Like the other three horses, *Trespasser* stood at Omagh on Saturdays. For the rest of the week the horse's time was divided between Bencham Farm, Strabane, Londonderry and Castlederg.

In the Lagan area of Co. Donegal, Thomas Hamilton's *Greenfield*, which was no relation of Michael Foley's horse of the same name, continued his stud duties. *Greenfield* stood near Raphoe on Mondays, Thursdays and Saturdays, and at Strabane on Tuesdays, Londonderry on Wednesdays and Letterkenny on Fridays. *Greenfield* had the distinction of being the most westerly Registered Stallion in Co. Donegal. The rest of the county was either too poor for quality horses and, therefore, the home of ponies and cobs, or was served by stallions belonging to the Congested Districts Board or by unregistered sires. Private enterprise obviously considered west Donegal as too poor to warrant the financial risk of travelling quality stallions there. At Strabane *Greenfield* met *M.P.* and *Trespasser* although only *Trespasser* continued north to provide competition for the mares of Londonderry.

The midlands and west of Ireland had a poor network of travelling stallions and there was no

Plate Eleven. *R. G. Carden of Fishmoyne, Temple-more, stood* Harlem *at stud in 1893. Five years later, in 1898, Carden became a member of the Stallion Registration Committee. (Photo:* Dublin Horse Show Magazine)

obvious competition between them, although some opposition was provided by 'static' stallions. William Dooley's *Cartago* traded in central King's County (Offaly) and in Westmeath and, judged by returns of foals made to the Society, seems to have been fairly successful. At Tullamore, the prosperous county town with its central square and clock-adorned buildings, *Cartago* was confronted both by the locally owned *Restraint* and by *Dulcimer*. *Dulcimer* had been bred by W. Waring of Beecham House, Reading, and was later to be advertised as having 'won many races.' For 1893 the horse travelled to Tullamore for Tuesdays, Mountmellick on Saturdays, and spent the rest of the week at Knightstown, Portarlington, where he belonged to Thomas Jones. By 1895 he belonged to O.T. Slocock and was at stud in Carlow. *Cartago* had a busy schedule, travelling as far north as Mullingar, where he stood on Thursdays.

Robert Roe, as in 1892, travelled *Master Pirate* in the Banagher-Birr area, but he also extended the route so that the horse stood at Ballinasloe on Tuesdays. Although not stated in the records it is virtually certain that *Master Pirate* crossed the Shannon at the bridge of Banagher and continued next along the narrow strip of fertile farmland, (that owes its origin to a curving mound of glacial deposition), that divides the mighty boglands of that region. The divide between fertile farmland and bleak bog is extremely striking and abrupt in this area, as anyone who has walked down the road from the tiny beautiful cathedral of Clonfert will know. Anybody who has seen the ruined Bishop's Palace there, and especially its great stables, will readily appreciate the overwhelming role that horses played in this region in the pre-motor age. That was particularly the case following 1891, when the gentlemen of East Galway decided to form their own pack of foxhounds and advertised the best centres for hunting as being 'Ballinasloe (whence meets of the Galway are accessible), Portumna and Banagher.'[2]

Master Pirate travelled through the heart of the East Galway country and must have passed Lismany on many occasions. That had been the home of J. Pollock, who kept his own private pack of hounds in the Ballinasloe area for many years prior to the formation of the subscription pack of the East Galway. On other occasions a short deviation from the direct route from Banagher to Ballinasloe would have taken Roe's stallion through Eyrecourt, past the great ruined mansion of the renowned Lords Eyre of Eyrecourt. In the *Memoirs of an Old Galway*

Nobleman it is related that 'None of the Castle windows were made to open,' which makes it all the more sad to see the great gaping gaps in the ruined walls that had formerly been closed with glass. Colonel Giles Eyre, who hunted the region from 1791 until 1829, '. . . had between thirty and forty horses in his stable, and he was believed to have spent £80,000 on a single election contest.'[3] Not surprisingly his estates were terribly encumbered on his death, but the Galway gentry of that period seem to have been a tough lot, with little thought for the morrow. 'To fit (Eyre) for the part of the country gentleman, he was encouraged to ride boldly to hounds, to shoot, to swim the Shannon, and to drive a four-in-hand.'[4] There was no emphasis on reading and writing and Eyre openly admitted that he could not read. But such minor disabilities did not prevent his Lordship from becoming Colonel of the County Galway Militia! Colonel Eyre was followed by J. Eyre as Master of Hounds, until his death in a hunting accident (he broke his neck) in 1848. Even though there was apparently no hunting thereafter in the region until Pollock started his pack there was a firm foundation of horsemanship and a great reservoir of quality mares, whose successors were later to be enjoyed by *Master Pirate*.

It would have been impossible for Parliament even to have contemplated 'schemes for the improvement of horses in Ireland' had there not already existed long standing traditions of horsemanship, an appreciation of good horses, and a vast number of good breeding stock in many areas of Ireland. The traditions of East Galway, just described, were echoed in only modified form throughout most of the fertile areas of the island. Only in the rocky or bleak blanket-bog shrouded west, and in the poor country of the north-western drumlins, were traditions of hunting, and consequently the presence of good horses, almost entirely absent, although they were understandably more pronounced in some areas than in others.

In the Galway-Athenry area Major Clarke of Graig Abbey travelled the winner of the 1887 Surrey Stakes: *Acropolis*. As a four-year-old *Acropolis* won at the Curragh, and repeated his success there the following year. Further north in the county Sebastian Nolan of Tuam travelled a chestnut stallion, 16.2 hands high, with the unfortunate name of *Prince Violet*. *Dauntless* had a far more masculine name.

In Co. Sligo W.B. Powell continued to travel *Prying*, although this stallion's route is not recorded. William Alexander's horses, *Merrylegs* and *Loved One*, must have caused him considerable competition, as did *Dalhousie* and *Ballintrae*. These latter horses, however, appear not to have travelled, except for very minor distances.

In the south of the country, on the Cork-Limerick borders, Francis Flannery travelled *Castilian* and *Pennington*. The latter stallion had been travelled, over a restricted distance, in 1892, but his route was now extended, from Charleville to Kanturk. *Castilian* stood at Church-town and Charleville, and was a useful sire for the local breeders. Bred in 1884 by T.E. Walker of Studley Castle, in Worcestershire, *Castilian* had won at Leicester, Sandown, Windsor, Epsom, Croydon and, over hurdles, at Liverpool. Yet only five foaling returns for 1893 were made relating to the horse, so that his successes were probably limited. Two years later the horse stood in Co. Louth.

Further south in the Co. Cork, around the western shores of Cork Harbour, there was an important clustering of four stallions: *Sweetheart* (second in the Derby), *Shinglass* (winner of fifteen races at venues as varied as Cork Park and Newmarket), *Kentford* (a winner at Sandown Park and Windsor), and the old campaigner: *Baron Hastings*, who had first won the Farmers Steeplechase at the local Hunt races in 1886 and, later that year, won the North Kerry Plate at

Listowel. None of these horses apparently travelled, but probably they had no need to. They were all located close enough to Cork city for city mares to be brought to them. They also served the fertile agricultural hinterland immediately south of the city, where agriculture and trade mingled generously to produce a landscape of merchants' houses set in rural surroundings, and where farming was reasonably opulent.

Canon, *Breach of Promise*, *Edlington*, and *Derby Dick* all travelled in the Bride valley-Fermoy-Dungarvan area, although there was limited competition between them. *Young Speculation*, by comparison, was restricted to his owner's stables at Blarney. Between all these horses, and others already mentioned, Co. Cork east of a line from Clonakilty to Newmarket was well provided with Registered Stallions of quality. West of that line both Cork and adjacent Kerry were devoid of Registered Stallions and only the horses of the Congested Districts Board were of acknowledged acceptable standard. Yet it would be wrong to dismiss west Cork as totally devoid of good horses. The great houses, such as that of Bantry, had fine stables, and their owners kept good horses. But, nevertheless, these areas lay, for the time being, beyond the range of the Royal Dublin Society's scheme.

In the extreme south east of Ireland, in Co. Wexford, there were four 'static' Registered Stallions. *Craigengelt*, admittedly, was travelled a mile or two, from his owner's stables to Bridgetown, but hardly far enough to be worth recording. This was still a period of rural unrest in the county, at least as far as the gentry were concerned, and the Wexford Foxhounds failed to find a Master for the 1892-3 season. Yet horses were dear to the hearts of most Wexfordmen, and The Island Hounds, hunting the north of the county, were ruled by the renowned Robert Watson, Master from 1853-1904. While Watson was in office nothing was more sure than that Wexford should provide quality horses, and the apparent paucity of Registered Stallions tells us little of the county's true status in the world of quality horse-breeding.

On the whole the Horse Breeding Scheme of 1893 was a great success. 1499 mares had been awarded nominations and 1294 of these had actually been served. £2,556.14.0. had been paid by the Society to owners of Registered Stallions. The Society later issued a circular to all owners of nominated mares seeking information on whether or not the mares had foaled, and on the sex of the foals. 873 circulars were returned and from these it was apparent that at least 628 foals had been sired by Registered Stallions. Although that was 124 less than reported in 1892, it was noted that 1056 replies had been provided in that year, so that the foaling percentage on returns had actually risen, from 71.2% in 1892 to 71.93%. The Society must have felt well pleased, and by the time that the Chairman of the Committee of Agriculture, Robert Fowler, presented the report on the 1893 results, the 1894 scheme had already been fully implemented and 1448 nominations had been awarded for that year.

The Catalogue of the Twenty-fifth annual Horse and Sheep Show, 1892, had included a new class:

'Registered Stallions. The following Prizes are offered to the owners of Thorough-bred Stallions which have been Registered with the Royal Dublin Society for service under the Horse Breeding Scheme, 1892, and whose Stock win most points in Prizes at the Horse Show of 1892, a First Prize to count seven points, a Second Prize six points, a Third Prize five points, a Fourth Prize four points, Very Highly Commended three points, Highly Commended two points, and

Commended one point:–

First Prize	£25
Second Prize	£15
Third Prize	£10
Fourth Prize	£5'

Fittingly, in view of the fact that the horse had won the historic Class One at the 1886 Annual Horse Show, that had expressly been '. . . designed to encourage the judicious breeding of horses by Tenant Farmers in Ireland,' and that had been the prelude to all the Horse Breeding Schemes, First Prize went to *Heart of Oak*. As in 1886 the horse still belonged to Captain W.H. Davis, whose horses had figured so prominently in the Premium Schemes. Second Prize went to *Studley*, owned by Mr. Maxwell of Lusk. Now, in 1893, the honours of this Produce Class fell entirely to *Studley* and he was undisputed First. The foaling returns may have suggested that he was not a popular sire, the facts of the show-ring proved otherwise. With the victory in the Produce Class of a local Co. Dublin horse that had proved himself by winning three races in England, it looked as if the Royal Dublin Society's Horse Breeding Scheme was established on firm foundations. It must have seemed to many a ring-side spectator at Ball's Bridge that the Royal Dublin Society's *Register of Thorough-bred Stallions*, updated year by year, was to last for a very long time indeed. But 1894 was the year when things almost went wrong.

CHAPTER EIGHT

1894: the year of the missing Register

The Contents page of the One-hundred-and-thirtieth volume of the Royal Dublin Society's Proceedings was, as had become the custom, adorned with a graceful engraving of Hibernia, the Irish counterpart of Britannia, and no less charming a lady. Beneath Hibernia were listed the contents, but what was listed in hope was not always the case in reality. Immediately before the details of the Spring Show the Contents page promised that one would find the *Register of Thoroughbred Stallions*, but the *Register* does not seem to have been printed. Yet the Horse Breeding Scheme for 1894 was successfully operated and, as later returns showed,[1] 1448 mares were issued with nominations and 1284 of them enjoyed the full pleasures of Registered Stallions.

Although the *Register* may not have been printed in time for the breeding season it is likely that a list of Registered Stallions was in circulation, at least to County Committees, for it is difficult to see how the Scheme could have operated without such information. In any case, the names of the 105 stallions registered for 1894, with the names and addresses of their owners and a list of the counties in which each stallion stood at stud, was printed as part of the programme for the Annual Horse Show. Unfortunately, and this remained the case for the following six years in which the Royal Dublin Society operated its *Register*, no details were given of the exact locations at which stallions stood at stud, nor of the routes they followed. It is thus impossible, for 1894 and the next six years, to reconstruct a comprehensive picture of the movements of registered travelling stallions in Ireland. To some extent newspaper advertisements and stud cards show that many horses, as in previous years, did tramp the country, but the information is too patchy and tenuous to be used for the reconstruction of events on a national scale. Henceforth it is only possible to list the base for each Registered Stallion per annum, and thereby to obtain an approximate idea of the changes that occurred from year to year.

Co. Cork had the largest number of resident Registered Stallions in 1894: ten of them. Carlow ranked next, with seven; Antrim and Sligo had six each; Dublin, Kilkenny, King's County, Limerick, Tipperary and Wexford each had five stallions. At the other extreme neither Monaghan nor Westmeath was the home county of a Registered Stallion. That did not mean that the local mares were denied the services of a Registered Stallion, for in each case Registered Stallions stood in the county, but in addition to standing elsewhere. This clue alone is sufficient to show that travelling stallions existed, and probably the pattern of travels already shown for

Plate Twelve. *Lord Rathdonnell, of Lisnavagh, Rathvilly, Co. Carlow was both an important administrator of the Royal Dublin Society's horse-breeding schemes and the owner of registered stallions. In 1894 he stood* Victoricus *at stud. This horse was a new addition to the* Register. (*Photo:* Dublin Horse Show Magazine)

1893 continued with only minor alteration in 1894. *Baldwin*, T.J. Eager's horse, continued to stand in Kerry, O.T. Slocock kept *Blue Godfrey* and *Dulcimer* in Carlow, Michael Foley travelled *Cavendish* in Carlow and Kilkenny and *Greenfield* in Carlow, Kildare and Wicklow, and so the list goes on.

As in previous years both new horses were added to the *Register* and some previously registered had their names deleted. *Blue Godfrey* was one of the new additions. Foaled in 1885 and bred by A.C. Hobman of Ludwick Hall, Hatfield (in the county of Hertfordshire), *Blue Godfrey* had won a Selling Hurdle Race at Croydon in 1888 and thereafter won another five Selling Hurdles, his last being at Kempton Park in 1892. Occasionally the horse had been tried in a handicap hurdle, and he managed to win the Hurst Handicap Hurdle at Plumpton in 1888. Although this was by no means a spectacular racing record, *Blue Godfrey* had obviously been a useful racehorse and was not to be despised. Yet Slocock only kept the horse for one season, and in 1895 this 15.3 hands chestnut belonged to Robert Stakelum of Ballinahow, Thurles. *Dulcimer*, by comparison, had belonged to Thomas Jones of Knightstown, Portarlington, in 1893, but in 1894 and 1895 he was registered as the property of O.T. Slocock. This emphasises the way in which stallions were moved, at fairly regular intervals to different areas, a pattern that has already been demonstrated for previous years.

Another addition to the *Register* was *Dalesman*, belonging to Maurice de Courcey of Dooncaha Lodge, Tarbert. As a three-year-old *Dalesman* had won the Pontefract Spring Handicap and he was later to win the Grand Military Gold Cup at Sandown Park. Later still the horse became a most useful hurdler, and carried great weights to victory on a number of occasions. At Aldershot and Croydon the horse won under 12 stone 7 lbs., and at Sandown *Dalesman* carried top weight of 12 stone 9 lbs. to victory, which was all the more astonishing since the horse was only 15.2 hands high. This was just the sort of tough little horse that must have proved invaluable for Kerry breeders. *Glen Roy*, the horse that de Courcey had stood at stud in 1893, continued in the same ownership and maintained his stud duties.

In Co. Cork Francis Flannery of Churchtown introduced *Zero* to the *Register*, and L.W.

Hendley of Ballinterry, Rathcormac, introduced *Tiercel*. The latter horse had been bred by Lord Rosslyn near Kirkaldy, Fifeshire, and was to take First Prize at Lismore Agricultural Society's Show in 1894 and, again, in 1895. *Zero* was eight years old, bay in colour, and 16 hands high. In 1891 he won the Southam Hunters' Steeplechase at Cheltenham and two steeplechases at Cardiff. He was therefore a useful sort of animal, although Flannery sold him quickly. In 1895 he belonged to John Lynch of Latoon, Newmarket-on-Fergus, where he served mares from the Co. Clare.

Although the number of stallions registered in 1894 (105) showed a reduction from those registered in the previous year, the quality (as defined by racing performances) of many of the new stallions registered was most pleasing. Horses that had won three or four races, particularly over hurdles or fences, and that had carried hefty weights to success in races of fair length, were well calculated to 'improve the breed of horses in Ireland.' Nobody could reasonably expect them to sire many Derby winners, but they were capable of producing quality riding horses, sound hunters, good carriage horses, officers' chargers and run-of-the-mill race horses. Nobody, after all, had intended that the Horse Breeding Schemes should produce the winners of Classics, but there was little reason why many of the stallions registered in 1894, given the right mares, should not sire the winners of many lesser races.

Bonnie Charlie, Michael Neary's horse, standing in Co. Galway, was already the sire of *Claverhouse*, winner of the National Hunt Juvenile Steeplechase at Derby in 1892. *Earl Scroope* had sired a horse that sold '. . . at the high price of £200,' yearlings by *Connaught* '. . . won first, second, third and fourth prizes at the Highland and Agricultural Society's Show at Edinburgh, 1893,'[2] and so the list continues. Whilst such progeny successes were particularly pleasing it was, nevertheless, apparent that many of the better quality stallions in Ireland had not been submitted for registration. Furthermore, the delay in providing a printed list of the stallions registered for 1894 caused considerable concern. After all, £2,568 of public money had been disbursed by the Royal Dublin Society to the owners of Registered Stallions. And if such sums were to be disbursed in future, should they not go to the best possible stallions? And how could the owners of such stallions be persuaded to register their horses? It was, indeed, a problem, but one that the Society was determined to solve. The Society therefore decided to issue an annual register, starting in 1895 with Volume One. Volume One of 1892 was now recognized as a useful, but false start. And the new Volume One was to be prepared by the Stallion Registration Committee, a body of important, knowledgeable and influential gentlemen who included two Lords of the Realm.

The Registration Committee, however, could do nothing about the season that had just ended, and the returns from the County Committees suggest that, as Table Ten shows, matters had not been entirely satisfactory.

The committee for Louth, for example, awarded only nine nominations, and one of those was eventually not used. In Co. Donegal, although twenty-three nominations were awarded, just seventeen were used. Yet some committees managed to award large numbers of nominations. The Wexford Committee found seventy suitable mares, sixty-four of whom were finally served. The Tipperary Committee awarded the same number, and sixty mares availed of the awards. In Kildare the situation was less satisfactory. Thirty mares qualified for nominations, but four of them did not meet a Registered Stallion. The amazing thing is that there were four Registered Stallions in Co. Kildare, but perhaps breeders felt that better, non-registered stallions were available. Perhaps the best indication that all was not well with the Horse Breeding Scheme is that twelve committees under-spent their grants by at least £20. In previous years committees apparently had no real trouble in spending all their grants, and most committees had to exercise great restraint to avoid over-spending. West Cork, Donegal, Dublin, Galway, Kerry, Kildare, Louth, Meath, Monaghan, Queen's County and Tyrone were the committees which under-spent by £20 or more. In all, £391. 18. 8. of the total grants made to the County Committees remained unspent. This was most unsatisfactory and the Society decided that, for 1895, the rules relating to the spending of the grants must be changed. Thus, at long last, the nomination system for mares was replaced, on an experimental basis, by a new system: the award of Premiums.

When the Society collected information on the foals resulting from the scheme of 1894, it was discovered that at least 628 had been produced. This was the same number as in 1893, according to the returns made by mare owners. Since thirty less returns had been made in 1894, however, it appeared that (on returns) fertility had improved, to 74.49%. In 1893 the fertility percentage on returns was 71.93%. In fact, since the Society had started collecting data in 1889, only one year had produced a better record: 1891. Yet these statistics give only a very rough guide as to actual fertility rates, and all that can reliably be stated is that at least 323 colts and 305 fillies were produced as a result of the 1894 scheme.

The most successful sire, as far as the number of foals produced and reported to the Society was concerned, was *Fife*. This stallion was owned by John Moore of Hollymount in Co. Mayo and sired at least thirty-one foals. *Fife* had been born in 1887 and was a bay horse of 16 hands. In 1892 he won at the Curragh April Meeting and in the same year was third in the Easter Plate Hurdle Race. At Hollymount Show in 1894 *Fife* also took Third Prize, but he was competing against magnificent horses, such as *Dauntless*, so that to come third was no disgrace. *Dauntless*, incidentally, won the class at Hollymount that year.

The second most successful sire, judged on the same basis as *Fife*, was Thomas Beatty's *Battle Gage*. Beatty lived near Crossdoney in Co. Cavan and neither he, nor his horse, were listed in any of the other *Registers* produced from 1892 until 1900. Nevertheless, *Battle Gage* put at least twenty-eight of his mares in foal, and they produced eighteen colts and ten fillies. *Appleton* and *Novelist* had the distinction, on returns, of being third most successful sires. They each fathered at least twenty-one foals. *Appleton* belonged to Joseph Sheehy of Rathkeale in Co. Limerick and was a dark bay four year old that had first been registered in 1893. The horse had been bred by Colonel Godman of Smeaton Manor, Northallerton, and is yet another example of the way in which breeders interchanged Thoroughbred stock between Britain and Ireland. Major Charles W. Studdert of Cragmoher, Corofin, was both the owner and breeder of *Novelist*, a 16 hand bay stallion who had been second in the Tally-ho Plate at Tipperary in 1889 and second in the Danesfort Plate at Kilkenny in 1891.

In the north of Ireland established stallions, like *M.P.* and *Cambrian*, continued to ply a steady trade, but they were joined by newly registered sires, such as John Dobson's *Fear Not*. This horse had won the Great Munster Steeplechase at Cork in 1890 and was second in both the Liverpool Hunt Steeplechase and the Hunters' Steeplechase at Manchester in 1891. Perhaps, with the horse's British winnings, it was appropriate that Dobson lived at Imperial House, Lurgan.

For practical purposes, as far as Thoroughbred sires were concerned, Ireland and Britain, (or at least Ireland and England), operated very much as one area. Of course, there was interchange with Scotland, and we have already seen how *Connaught*'s stock carried away major honours in

Table Ten[3]

Summarised accounts of the County Committees, 1894

County	No. of nominations issued	No. of mares served	Expenses of County Committee	Amount of grant	Amount paid to owners of Registered Stallions
			£ s. d.	£ s. d.	£ s. d.
Antrim	50	45	9.14.0	100.0.0	90.0.0
Armagh	40	35	8. 5.2	80.0.0	70.0.0
Carlow	45	45	7. 9.3	90.0.0	90.0.0
Cavan	45	45	7. 4.11	90.0.0	90.0.0
Clare	55	49	8. 1.6	110.0.0	98.0.0
Cork East	48	45	8.14.2	100.0.0	90.0.0
Cork West	49	35	7. 1.0	100.0.0	70.0.0
Donegal	23	17	7. 5.9	80.0.0	34.0.0
Down	55	52	9.15.0	110.0.0	104.0.0
Dublin	39	18	12. 5.3	80.0.0	36.0.0
Fermanagh	34	34	6.15.0	80.0.0	68.0.0
Galway	50	32	6. 5.0	100.0.0	64.0.0
Kerry	43	31	12. 3.2	110.0.0	62.0.0
Kildare	30	26	10.10.0	100.0.0	52.0.0
Kilkenny	55	53	7.19.0	110.0.0	106.0.0
King's County	49	46	7.12.0	100.0.0	92.0.0
Leitrim	35	33	7.14.1	80.0.0	66.0.0
Limerick	55	52	6. 1.0	110.0.0	104.0.0
Londonderry	45	43	7. 7.2	90.0.0	86.0.0
Longford	45	43	7.11.8	90.0.0	86.0.0
Louth	9	8	7.19.10	80.0.0	16.0.0
Mayo	50	50	12.17.0	100.0.0	100.0.0
Meath	25	23	10. 5.0	100.0.0	46.0.0
Monaghan	23	21	11. 3.6	80.0.0	42.0.0
Queen's County	38	33	9.11.0	100.0.0	66.0.0
Roscommon	50	49	8.13.2	100.0.0	98.0.0
Sligo	45	44	7. 6.3	90.0.0	88.0.0
Tipperary	70	60	7. 9.0	140.0.0	120.0.0
Tyrone	50	41	7.13.9	100.0.0	82.0.0
Waterford	49	48	8. 8.6	100.0.0	96.0.0
Westmeath	47	38	7. 6.0	100.0.0	76.0.0
Wexford	70	64	7. 0.0	140.0.0	128.0.0
Wicklow	32	26	8.14.3	100.0.0	52.0.0
Total:	1448	1284	£280.1.4	£3240.0.0	£2568.0.0

the Edinburgh show-yard (*Connaught* was bred at the Marden Deer Park Stud in Surrey). *Fear Not*'s neighbour, John Brady's *Tynan*, had been bred by Sir Robert Jardine, and although the *Register* lists Jardine's address as 'England' it would be very doubtful indeed whether such a noble Scottish gentleman would appreciate that address. There was also limited exchange with Wales, but the Principality was, and still is, pony and cob country, rather than horse-land. The influence of the Welsh was to be felt later, in the evolution of the Connemara pony, where the first stallion to be registered in the Connemara Pony Stud Book traces back to a Welsh Cob named *Prince Llewellyn*. But that is another story, and as far as the Royal Dublin Society was concerned, the 1894 Horse Breeding Scheme had ended, successfully, but had pointed the way towards changes that were necessary for the future.

CHAPTER NINE

1895: the year when the rules were relaxed

The Stallion Registration Committee for 1895 was composed of The Right Honourable Lord Langford, D.L., Joseph R. O'Reilly, D.L., The Right Honourable Lord Rathdonnell, H.M.L., S. Ussher Roberts, C.B., and Frederick Wrench, J.P. The copy of Volume One of the resulting Register for 1895 that now rests on the Royal Dublin Society's dusty library shelves, is appropriately signed by Wrench in his immaculate copperplate handwriting. The signature is underlined with a sweeping, almost victorious, flourish, as if to convey relief and triumph at the volume's publication.

From 1892 until 1894 stallion owners had been invited to submit their Thoroughbred sires for inspection for registration. Inspection had been rigorous, and the Society carefully appointed qualified veterinary surgeons to examine the horses, and gave them strict instructions as to what they should look for. In addition, the veterinary surgeons had been advised to carry ropes in order to lunge stallions, so that the horses' wind could be adequately tested. Now, in 1895, the rules were relaxed. Under Clause Thirteen of the Regulations for Horse Breeding in Ireland, 1895, it was stated that:

'(*a*) A Stallion, to qualify for Registration, must be Thorough-bred, and duly entered in Weatherby's Stud Book. In case of a Stallion not on the Register for 1894, his Owner must furnish a Certificate dated since February, 1894, and signed by a member of the Royal College of Veterinary Surgeons, that the Stallion is free from hereditary disease.*

Superficially it might seem that there was no relaxation in the rigour of veterinary examination, but it was one thing to have an unknown vet., paid by the Royal Dublin Society, inspect an owner's horses and quite another for the owner to ask his own vet. to undertake the examination. A horse that, in one man's perfectly honest and qualified opinion was sound might, to another man, appear to be otherwise. This must particularly have been the case with regard to wind testing. A vet. who subjected a horse to ten minutes vigorous work on the lunge was far more likely to detect roaring or whistling than a man who satisfied himself with seeing the horse run-out a few times by its groom. Both men acted honestly, but variations in thoroughness are inevitable in most walks of life. Nevertheless, of 308 stallions whose owners applied for them to be registered, eighty-nine were rejected, including a considerable number who failed their

'* The following are the hereditary diseases, viz: Roaring, Whistling, Ringbone, Unsound Feet, Navicular Disease, Spavin and Cataract.'

Plate Thirteen. *Joseph O'Reilly, vice-chairman of the Society's Committee of Agriculture and member of the Stallion Registration Committee. (Photo:* Dublin Horse Show Magazine)

veterinary examinations.

The Society did, however, attempt to safeguard standards by stipulating that the Society had '. . . the right to have the Stallion inspected as to his freedom from hereditary disease, and his general merits and fitness for the purpose of the Scheme.' Furthermore, 'The Royal Dublin Society may, without assigning any reason, or without any Veterinary or other Inspection, decline to Register any Stallion for the purpose of this Scheme.'

The Society made a major attempt to induce stallion owners to have their horses registered, and the results were excellent. The Duke of Devonshire, for example, was persuaded to register *Bacchus*, the horse that he kept primarily for the service of his own and his tenants' mares: 'Service Fee, Half-bred Mares, 5 Guineas; Thoroughbreds, 10 Guineas; Tenants on Duke's property, £3.' *Bacchus* had won many races, including the Welter Handicap at the Curragh in 1877, the November Handicap at Liverpool in 1878 and the Prince of Wales Steeplechase at Liverpool in 1880. E. Kennedy of Newtown Stud Farm, Straffan, registered *Fortunio* and *Westmoreland*. In west Cork Captain Tower Townshend registered a former winner of the Lincoln, *Controversy*. William Pallin, Fellow of the Royal College of Veterinary Surgeons, of the Athgarvan Lodge Stud on the Curragh, registered *Astrologer*, *Favonian*, *Master Ned*, *Wiseman*, *Heckberry*, *Isleworth* and *Branxholme*. In 1894 he had registered only the latter two horses. Perhaps, now that he had been appointed to the Co. Kildare Committee for the administration of the Horse Breeding Scheme in the capacity of official Veterinary Surgeon, he felt obliged to register all his horses annually.

The quality of many of the stallions newly admitted to the Register was outstanding. *Fortunio* had been bred in France by Charles Joachim Lefevre, of Haras de Chamant per Seules (Oise) and was by *Isonomy* out of *Formalité*. His racing performances had been a formality, too, as the horse was a consistent winner, being first in nineteen races, eighteen in France and one in Belgium. The Secretary of the Steeplechases Society certified that *Fortunio* had won 73,850 francs on French racecourses, and his victories included such races as The Prix d'Auteuil, and extended from 1888 until 1893. In 1894 the horse was Highly Commended at the Royal Dublin

Plate Fourteen. *Frederick Wrench, J.P., member of the Stallion Registration Committee and later a member of the committee on horse breeding of the Department of Agriculture. (Photo: courtesy of the Royal Dublin Society)*

Plate Fifteen. Fortunio, *owned by E. Kennedy of Straffan, Co. Kildare. This was one of the French-bred stallions to be registered, by* Isonomy *out of* Formalite *(by* Hermit*) and bred by Charles Joachim Lefevre at Haras de Chamant per Seules (Oise).* Fortunio *won nineteen races in France, worth 73,850 francs. In 1905 his progeny,* Delaunay, *won the All-Aged Stakes at Ascot, the King's Stand Stakes at the same venue and the July Cup at Newmarket.* Aspendale *was another noted winner in 1905, also sired by* Fortunio. *The stallion stood 15.3½ hands high, girthed 5ft 11ins and had 8½ ins of bone. (Photo:* Dublin Horse Show Magazine)

Society's Show and, as his somewhat blurred photograph shows, he was not without merit as a showhorse. Even at the relatively high fee of ten guineas a service, *Fortunio* was worth considering by owners of quality mares. Whether this was the type of horse that Parliament originally had in mind for 'Improving the Breed of Horses in Ireland' when it passed the Probate Act and in 1888 voted monies for that purpose, is debatable. Certainly there were few better horses available anywhere in the British Isles or, for that matter, in the rest of the world.

If better horses were possible, then Pallin's stallions were strong contenders. *Astrologer* had won The Peveril of the Peak Stakes, worth £1,000. *Favonian* had won the Leicestershire Handicap, also worth £1,000, and other races. *Master Ned*, already registered in 1892 and 1893, was a winner of the Irish Derby and, although bred by James Cassidy of Monasterevan, had successfully been produced in many show rings in England. He won at the Somerset County Show at Wells, the Gloucester County Show at Cirencester, the Buckinghamshire County Show at Linsdale, the Sherebourne and South of England Show, the Newport Show and the Taunton Show. *Wiseman*, now ten years old, won £5,000 in forty races, including the Lincoln Handicap. Pallin quoted a service fee of twenty guineas for the horse, but in spite of the cost it was a major achievement for the Society to have obtained the use of such a quality sire for the service of 'Farmers' Half-bred Mares.' Admittedly Pallin's other two horses were more the sort that one

Plate Sixteen. Ascetic, *owned by John M. Purdon, by* Hermit *out of* Lady Alicia, *sire of three winners of the Grand National:* Cloister, Drumcree *and* Ascetic's Silver. Ascetic *won the Croker Cup at the Royal Dublin Society's Horse Show in 1890, 1891 and 1892. The Cup is awarded for 'the best Weight-carrying Thoroughbred Stallion.' (Photo:* Register of Thoroughbred Stallions)

might associate with the service of 'Farmers' Half-bred Mares.' *Isleworth* had won the South Berkshire Steeplechase, carrying 11st 12 lbs., and the ageing *Branxholme* had won the Manchester Handicap Steeplechase. Pallin had leased *Isleworth* to John Hutchings of Thomastown, where he served local mares at a fee of £3, and *Branxholme* was leased to Patrick Colfer of The Ballagh, Enniscorthy, where he also stood at £3. *Heckberry*, (who apparently had won nothing on the racecourse), was leased to the Earl of Bessborough and stood at £4 in Piltown, Co. Kilkenny. The other stallions owned by Pallin all stood at their owner's stud, under his watchful and qualified eye.

Another fine stallion to be newly registered, although of quite a different type, was *Royal Meath*, foaled in 1884. As a four-year-old *Royal Meath* won the Foxhunters' Plate at the Meath Hunt, as was appropriate for a horse that looked every bit a hunter. But *Royal Meath* was no ordinary hunter. In 1890 he won the Grand Steeplechase de Paris, run over the course at Auteuil, and worth £4,718. And in the previous year he won the highly coveted, but far less financially valuable, Coyngham Cup at Punchestown. The horse was only slightly less successful in the show-ring, and was second in his class at Ball's Bridge in 1894.

The breeding of *Royal Meath* was most interesting. His sire was *Ascetic*, now twenty-four years old and, as his photograph shows, a venerable old gentleman. *Ascetic* was now, in 1895, entered in the Register for the first time and stood at a service fee of £40, the highest of all the Registered Stallions. Nobody could justifiably cavil at that, however, since *Ascetic* had sired '*Royal Meath*, *Roman Oak*, *The Saint*, *Aramis*, *Merry Man*, *Magic*, *Paradice*, *Novice*, *Effie*, *Anchorite*, *Cenobite*, *Elsie*, *Masseuse*, *Nancy*, *Bective*, *Cloister*, *Reflection*, *Reliance*, *Patience*, *Fanatic*, all winners, and many others.'[1] (*Cloister*, in fact, had already won the Grand National.) Neither could any reasonable person expect *Ascetic* to last much longer as a stud-horse, so that his final few services, if fertile, could fairly have been expected to be most valuable. In fact, after being included in the *Registers* for 1896 and 1897 *Ascetic*'s name appears no more, his reign had ended. Whether any tenant-farmers availed their half-bred mares of *Ascetic*'s £40 services is doubtful. One cannot help feeling that, in the inclusion of such a horse in the *Register*, the Society had gone much further than had originally been intended, and had moved away from its original aims: '. . . the provision of Thoroughbred sires suitable for getting Hunters and other Half-bred Horses,' and the aiding of '. . . the smaller tenant-farmers' in the improvement of their equine stock. Instead the Society was now adopting, perhaps unwittingly, the role of a Thoroughbred stallion licencing authority, and this was a most important development, as later events would prove.

Before 1895 all stallions of eighteen years or more were automatically excluded from the *Registers*. The rationale behind this rule is not clear, but perhaps it was felt that horses of such an age were less likely to withstand the rigours of a stud-season than their younger counterparts. Nevertheless, the rule meant that an appreciable number of sires of the highest quality, whose progeny had been fully tested on the race-course and in the show-ring, as well as in less spectacular walks of life, were automatically barred from the *Register*. That meant that no financial aid, under the terms of the Horse Breeding Schemes, could be given to mare owners who sent their mares to such stallions.

Naturally there were problems in conducting veterinary examinations of aged stallions, and it is not likely that John Purdon, the owner of *Ascetic*, or owners of valuable horses of similar age, would allow them to be lunged hard to test their wind. To overcome such difficulties the rules for 1895 stated that 'The production of a [Veterinary] Certificate may be waived in cases where evidence of soundness has been sufficiently established to satisfy the Horse Breeding Committee.'[2]

Ascetic was by *Hermit* out of *Lady Alicia*, and that mare was by *Melbourne*. *Melbourne* blood, the reader might remember, had been imparted to the mares of the Sligo District in 1890 via his little descendant, *Loved One*, and it was a valuable blood-line. It is interesting to see the same blood-line coursing through the veins of *Ascetic* and, via him, into *Royal Meath*. But John Purdon also kept stallions of less noble lineage, and stood *Bon Soir*, *Britannic*, and *Tartan* at his Cloneymore Stud, Athboy. Their fees were £5, £3 and £3 respectively, a far-cry from that of his senior stallion. None of these horses had been included in previous *Registers*, so Purdon was yet another convert to the Society's *Register*.

Royal Meath had been bred by Gordon Jackson of Rath House, Nobber, in the Co. of Meath. Now the horse belonged to Hollwey Steeds of Clonsilla House in Co. Dublin. Steeds was another newcomer to the *Register* and one wonders whether, like some other owners, he was influenced by a decision of the Royal Dublin Society that was printed, in heavy type, in their *Proceedings*:

'The Royal Dublin Society will in future make it a condition in offering Prizes in Thoroughbred Stallion Classes at any of their Shows in Dublin, or at any County or Provincial Show, that a Stallion, to be entitled to a Prize, must be entered in the Royal Dublin Society's Published Register of Stallions for the current year, or accepted for Registration.'

Royal Meath had been third in his class at Dublin in both 1892 and 1893, and his star must have seemed in the ascent.

Some counties, as in previous years, were notably deficient in Registered Stallions, as Figure Seven shows. Cavan, Donegal, King's, Leitrim and Mayo boasted only one stallion each. Monaghan, in which none were registered in the three previous years, suddenly possessed six! Three of these, *Bailsman*, *Baliol* and *Midas*, were owned by Colonel Thomson of Bushford, Rockcorry. *Bailsman* won the Glenard Plate at Galway and the Committee Plate at Killarney in 1889, the following year the horse won the Hillsborough Plate at Down Royal. At £2 10s. a service *Bailsman* seemed good value, although he was only 15.2¾ hands high. *Baliol*, who was not advertised as the winner of anything, was 1 3/4 inches taller, and commanded a fee of £6, with 10s. for the groom. Another Monaghan stallion was *Preserver*, that belonged to Charles Plunkett Kenney of Rocksavage, Inishkeen and 58, Eccles Street, Dublin.

Patrick Kavanagh, the Co. Monaghan author and poet, was born in a cobbler's dwelling near Rocksavage in 1904, and in *The Green Fool* he describes the area where '. . . the sun passed our little window completely before he went behind Rocksavage Hills.' Although Kavanagh's memories of Rocksavage and, in particular, his descriptions of the Big House, date to the war-days of 1914, they nevertheless echo the era of the stallions and the race-horses.

'Rocksavage was a big farm of three hundred acres. It lay among the small farms. It was the headquarters of a once-great estate. The house in which the two lady-owners of Rocksavage lived was known among the older folk as the Big House. During my knowledge the Big House was in poor condition. It was rich in memories of the days of fast race-horses. On the dilapidated walls of the horse-stables in Rocksavage were scrawled the names of race-horses famous in their time.

'Ah, Master Kildare was the horse,' I heard, and father told me of the time when Rocksavage was truly a Big House. When the race-horses galloped around the fields ridden by jockeys from the Curragh.

. . .During the Great War Rocksavage farm was let in con-acre [a form of temporary lease] on the eleven month's system. The letting was a godsend to the neighbourhood. Small farmers who before had only one old horse or a jennet now kept a pair of horses.

. . .Rocksavage filled a great place in our lives. Before the War there were thousands of beautiful trees on the farm . . . Then came the timber-hunger and the trees began to fall . . . Rocksavage trees were sold by auction. The man who bought one cut down five as there was nobody to stop him . . . There was no love for beauty. We were barbarians just emerged from the Penal days.'[3]

And so Rocksavage and its memories, its great horses, its riders, its Registered Stallion, passed into history. 'The Plunkets of Rocksavage were gentlemen,' wrote Kavanagh, but even in the period of the Horse Breeding Schemes the days of the gentry in Ireland were numbered. The disestablishment of the Church of Ireland in 1869 had set the process in full motion, even if few people had realized the implications at that time. Bishop Alexander of 'Derry (whose wife was the wonderful hymn writer who composed amongst many other hymns, 'All things bright and

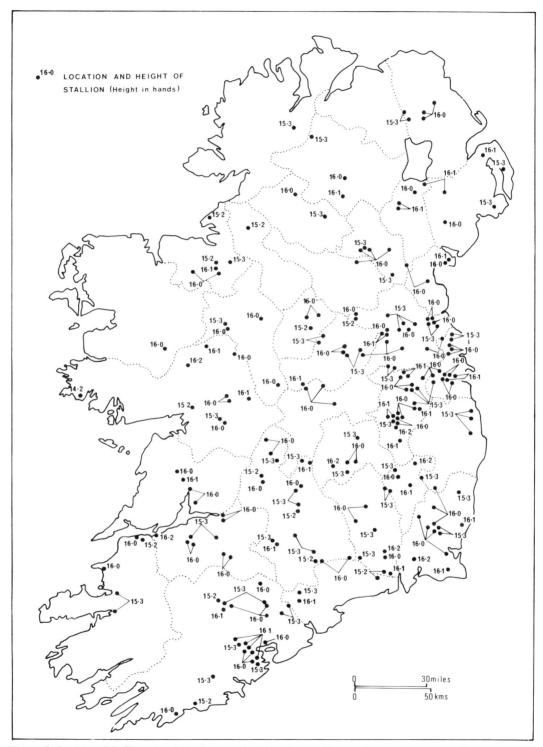

Figure 7. *Registered Stallions in 1895, showing their location and height. Notice how most stallions were 15.3 to 16.1 hands high, with no stallion exceeding 16.2 and only* Watchspring *(14.2, located in Connemara) being under 15.2*

beautiful'), recollected how, leaving the House of Lords after the second reading of the Irish church bill had been completed at 3.30 on the morning of 19 June, he could never forget '. . . the summer night just after the decision when I reeled into the cool air almost hearing the crash of a great building.'[4] Many great buildings were, literally, to crash in the years ahead as the landlord system was gradually abolished and Ireland moved towards Home Rule and later, sadly perhaps, to Independence. It must have been very hard for many of the leaders of 1916, or of the early Dails, to appreciate what the Royal Dublin Society had been doing in its Horse Breeding Schemes. One group of society was replaced by another, one set of values was subjugated to another. Yet, wonderfully, the ideals of the Society were retained in their already governmentally modified form, and still exist today. But we have run far ahead of our time, and beyond our present brief, and the Plunkets of Rocksavage were Catholics, anyway. But even Catholic landlords saw their estates crumble away and their mansions decay, unless they were very astute gentlemen, indeed.

County Londonderry had the ill-luck not to have any Registered Stallions at all within its bounds. This prompted the Society to include the following notice in the *Register*:

'Stallions are not registered for any particular County. Farmers wishing to take advantage of the benefits under the Horse Breeding Scheme for 1895 may send Mares to any registered Stallion.'

Whether that satisfied the needs of the local farmers is debatable, but it probably did not upset the Local Committee unduly. Five of its ten members had Coleraine postal addresses, and there were two Registered Stallions at Ballymena, not far from the railway station there. Coleraine and Ballymena were linked directly by rail. Another member of the committee lived at Maghera, conveniently close to William Wallace's *Derby Dick* and Patrick O'Kane's *Lismore* at Portglenone in Co. Antrim. Two members lived at Limavady and one in 'Derry itself, convenient, no doubt, to Donegal's *Greenfield*, who probably travelled to Londonderry as in previous years. Limavady was connected to the walled city of 'Derry by rail, convenient for the transport of brood mares.

In 1895, for the first time, a new note was added to the *Register*:

'Reduced Railway Rates

Owners of Mares are reminded that from April to July inclusive, all Mares travelling by rail for breeding purposes are charged for the double journey at the reduced rate of 10 per cent. over single fares.'

This concession was a great help to many of the large breeders, but the realistic attitude and the financial problems of many tenant farmers was summed up nicely by the evidence that Mr. D.A. Milward was to give two years later, to the Commissioners appointed to inquire into the horse breeding industry in Ireland. 'No farmer who works his mare can afford to send more than ten miles – it is the utmost limit; it is a day's work for a mare to travel ten miles out and back.'[5] Obviously Mr. Milward did not consider sending his mares by rail to the stallion: they had to earn their keep instead, and such a luxury as paying to transport a mare with four good legs did not enter Milward's head. To put it bluntly, many farmers could not afford to send their ordinary half-bred mares anywhere by rail, it was too expensive, in spite of all the Railway Companies' concessions. Again, as in the registration of a stallion with a £40 service fee, the signs point to a divorce between the original aims of the Horse Breeding Schemes and the developing attitudes of the Royal Dublin Society. But such a criticism is probably unjust, and concessions were concessions after all.

Westmeath, where 140 mares had sought nominations in the Mullingar District in 1890, had been without any resident Registered Stallion in 1893 and 1894. In 1892 *Monsieur* had stood at Turbotstown and *Sterling II* had made incursions to the County from adjacent Longford. The lack of Registered Stallions was all the more remarkable because Westmeath was great hunting country and noted for its quality horses. Furthermore, as the number of mares that sought nomination in 1890 suggests, there was an obvious demand from tenant farmers for the services of sound stallions at a reasonable price.

The first pack of hounds known to have hunted in Westmeath were kennelled near Killucan *circa* 1697, and belonged to Bishop Dopping. Around 1738 Thomas Packenham, M.P., kept a pack at Packenham Hall and at the turn of the century John Fetherstonhaugh hunted around Killucan and Grangemore. In 1835 Sam Reynell (who was to become an outstanding figure in the development of foxhunting in Ireland) began a pack that he hunted until the sad spectre of the Great Famine of 1848 stopped him. Then, in 1854, Sir Richard Levinge of Knockdrin started the county pack that still exists.[6]

The hunting gentry of Westmeath were quite specific about the type of hunter that was best suited to their country. Unlike many modern riders, who live in towns and seem to think that no horse is any good unless it has the height of an elephant, (and many of whom know far more about their cars than about the horses they ride), the Secretary of the Westmeath Foxhounds annually reported to *Baily's Hunting Directory* that for his country 'A short, compact horse is the best; he must have breeding.' Thus it is no surprise that when, in 1895, ten stallions were suddenly registered in Westmeath, they were all between 15.3 and 16.0$\frac{1}{2}$ hands high. On the other hand, it would be wrong to over-emphasise this uniformity of height found in Westmeath. Throughout Ireland as a whole the majority of Registered Stallions were 15.3 to 16.1 hands high as Figure Seven shows, and none exceeded 16.2. This is in marked contrast to the modern situation. In 1977 a number of Approved Stallions were 17.0 hands high or even more. *El Teide*, standing in Co. Wexford, was 17.1, *Santa's Sleigh* in Co. Tipperary was 17.0 as was *Regular Guy* in Co. Laois, and *Royoco* in Co. Kilkenny was advertised at an incredible 17.3$\frac{1}{2}$ hands.[7]

Clarendon, a brown five year old bred by Lord Ellesmere at Stechworth Park, Newmarket, belonged to Captain C. Fetherstonhaugh. Like his namesake of a century earlier the Captain lived at Killucan, where his seat was Bracklyn. C. Hannan also kept a stallion in the Killucan area, at Riverstown, where he stood *Marmiton*. This horse had been bred by Lord Roseberry and had been second in 1887 in the Champagne Stakes at Doncaster. In 1894 *Marmiton* won his class at Mullingar Horse Show. Major Gerald Dease of Turbotstown, Coole, stood *Monsieur* at stud, as in previous years. Sir Gerald Dease had been Master of the Westmeaths from 1861 until 1868 and the whole family were deeply involved with horses and hunting. The Deases were Catholics, and Sir Gerald's father, James, '. . . became in 1793, the first Catholic magistrate appointed in Ireland.'[8] Edmund F. Dease tried his hand at the writing of hunt history, and was the author of *Records of Hunting in Westmeath*. The other owners of Registered Stallions in Westmeath were: M. Ballesty (whose horse, *Bergomask*, had won the Bickerstaffe Stakes at Liverpool in 1894), Percy Maynard of Ratoath, John M. Kelly of Temple, Horseleap (his *Cornwall* won the Newmarket Plate in 1892 and the Spring Handicap at Doncaster in 1893), T. McCutchon of Rathowen (*Explorer*, a winner at the Curragh and, over hurdles, at Manchester),

Captain R.B. Irwin, John Gaynor of Moate (*Narcissus*) and Christopher Taaffe.

Captain Irwin's stallion revelled in the name of the *Marquis of Tavora*, and was by *Syrian* out of *Sword Knot*. *Syrian* was by *Mentmore*, which recalls many memories. *The Marquis of Tavora*, a 15.3 hands chestnut, was the winner of four races, at Thirsk, Derby, Liverpool and Leicester, and was already a successful sire. Irwin advertised that: '*Tavora*, *Lady Tavora*, *Keepout*, winners of Drogheda Stakes at Punchestown last year, *Lord Basil* – all are got by *Marquis of Tavora*.' The service fee for this sire of winners was not stated.

Christopher Taaffe, of Rathaspick, Rathowen, had bred his own stallion, *Piercefield*, now twenty-one years old. *Piercefield* won ten races in 1876 and 1877, including the Queen's Plate at Down Royal and the Royal Whip. Amazingly, since the horse had sired more than nine winners (including *Charming Nancy*, winner of the Baldoylc Derby), his service fee was only £3. But perhaps nine winners after a lengthy sojourn at stud failed to impress the Westmeath mareowners.

The smallest stallions registered, with the exception of *Watchspring*, were 15.2 hands or over. *Watchspring* was 14.2 hands, bay, and foaled in England in 1881. Significantly the horse stood (it would have been called a pony had it not been for its breeding) at Roundstone in Co. Galway. The area around Roundstone is the home of the Connemara Pony and many breeders of Connemaras would, today, be horrified at the thought of crossing their pedigree stock with a Thoroughbred. Mind you, the Connemara Pony Society did try just that, on an experimental basis, in the 1940s, but they soon dropped the sire involved. Yet, in 1895, *Watchspring* was imparting valuable Thoroughbred blood to the local mares. In spite of his size, *Watchspring* had a number of races to his credit. In 1885 he won a match for £100 on the Curragh. Later that year he won at Baldoyle and, in the Lady's Plate (worth £15), at Bray. The following year he won a private sweepstake of £50 each at Baldoyle and the Browncastle Plate, which was over hurdles, at Taghmon.

In addition to racing successes *Watchspring* took First Prize at the Connaught Horse Show in 1892, 1893 and 1894. Additionally, in 1892, the horse also won a Silver Medal at that Show. One wonders what the other competitors were like. The Service Fee for *Watchspring* was set by his owner, H.A. Robinson, at £2, with a Groom's Fee of 5s. Farmers of under £20 valuation were charged a fee of £1, with 2s. 6d. for the groom. In that rocky and poverty stricken area most of the fees must have been of the latter amount, but even that must have been a strain for many peasants. Surprising though it may seem, however, a rather miserable cheap novel containing a series of foxhunting scenes, was set in that area in the period around 1900. Even more surprising is that there was scope for a private-enterprise Thoroughbred stallion in what was already designated as one of the Congested Areas of Ireland. The Congested Districts Board itself owned many stallions which it stood at stud in the Congested Districts in an attempt to improve stock. These eventually included forty-one Hackneys, eight Welsh Cobs, seven Thoroughbreds, six Hunters, four Arabs, two Shires and one each of Cleveland Bay, Barb, Connemara and Norwegian, as well as a number of Spanish jackasses.[9] Finally, it appears that there must have been some sort of special pleading to allow *Watchspring* to be registered. Although his lack of stature made the horse suitable for the local mares (which were only ponies) it rendered him totally unsuited to the needs of horse breeding in most areas of Ireland. Yet the *Register*, as already quoted, stated that 'Stallions are not registered for any particular County,' so that presumably *Watchspring* could, with the Society's blessing, serve any suitable mares in Ireland.

The key to the problem, of course, lay in the word 'suitable.' *Watchspring* was suitable for the Connemara area, but most mares of premium quality elsewhere in Ireland would not be suitable for *Watchspring*. And, via Clause Twelve of the rules of the 1895 Horse Breeding Scheme, any County Committee could '. . . with the approval of the Society, refuse a Premium for any Mare . . . without assigning any reason therefor.' This clause was a safety measure that could be invoked if *Watchspring* was suddenly to be moved out of his area during the stud season. By registering the stallion the Society tacitly recognized that different areas have different needs. This instigated a regional policy in the registration of stallions that continues to operate, in far more pronounced form, in the Republic of Ireland at present. The Society was, therefore, pioneering an appreciation of geographical realities in its approach to stallion registration in at least this area. Two years later *Watchspring* belonged to Richard Berridge of Ballynahinch Castle, Toombeola, a few miles north east of Roundstone. The present Miss Berridge, of Enniskerry in Co. Wicklow, continues to be a noted and successful breeder of Connemaras.

The examples of *Watchspring* and of the Registered Stallions of Co. Westmeath all emphasize one fact: that although the Stallion Registration Committee was prepared to register a wide variety of stallions, if they suited the needs of the local mares, they were not yet prepared to play an active role in placing suitable stallions in the areas where they were needed. In some ways this was a retrogressive step, since until the *Registers of Thorough-bred Stallions* were introduced in 1892, the Society had chosen suitable stallions and posted them to selected districts. Yet the potential for active participation in a regional policy was provided for in the rules of 1895. Clause Fourteen stated that:

'In the event of a sufficient number of Stallions for this Scheme not being Registered in any County or District, the Royal Dublin Society shall have the power to provide for such County or District, either by hiring or buying one or more stallions for the purpose, or by some other means, or to employ the amount of the Grant allocated above to such County or District, in the furtherance of a similar Scheme for other Counties or Districts.'

This clause was not invoked for 1895, however, and the Committee left it to the initiative of private enterprise, and to the Congested Districts Board, to see that the country was provided with suitable stallions. Their policy, as in the three previous years, was essentially to ensure that the Thoroughbred stallions already in the country were only registered if they were sound and of reasonable conformation.

Figure Seven, in addition to demonstrating the uneven spread of Registered Stallions in Ireland, also shows important concentrations at a number of centres. These included the Curragh, where Pallin had his headquarters, the fertile grass-lands of the Liffey valley around Straffan, the rich lands of mid-Meath and coastal Co. Dublin and the Enniscorthy area of Co. Wexford. There were also important concentrations of stallions in and around the port-towns of Dublin, Cork and Waterford.

The needs of Dublin which, defined as the city itself with the adjacent urban centres of Dun Laoghaire, Howth and Bray, had a human population of 362,000 in 1891,[10] were met by a clustering of nine Registered Stallions in its immediate vicinity. Four of these: *Atheling*, *Enthusiast*, *Hackler* and *Ireland*, were owned by James Daly of Liffey Bank, Dublin. Daly also owned *Springtime*, a brown seven year old that he had leased to W.H. West of Farmley, Ferns in Co. Wexford. This horse had been bred at Newmarket and was a winner at Manchester, Hurst Park and Doncaster. The most valuable race to fall to *Springtime* was the Breeders' Foal Stakes,

Plate Seventeen. Hackler, *owned by James Daly, by* Petrach *out of* Hackness, *leading Irish sire of winners on the flat in 1900 and 1902. (Photo:* Dublin Horse Show Magazine)

worth £1,600, at Manchester.

Daly stood his horses at fees that varied from twenty guineas to five guineas, so he catered for a wide market. *Atheling* and *Enthusiast* both commanded the top fee, as was fitting for horses that had won notable races or sired notable winners. *Atheling*'s major claim to fame as a race-horse was the winning of the Scarborough Stakes, worth only £250, at Doncaster in 1886. But this mediocre result was redeemed by the siring of *Athel* who proceeded to win the Leopardstown Grand Prize of £1,000. Unfortunately, for Irish breeders, *Atheling* was eventually sold to the United States to stand at stud there. *Enthusiast* won the Two Thousand Guineas at Newmarket in 1889, and the Sussex Stakes at Goodwood. Both horses had been bred at the Yardley Stud near Birmingham. *Hackler* was by *Petrarch* and had won a Maiden Plate at Croyden in 1889. The colt was later to win three times at Newmarket, in 1890. The fee for *Hackler*, who was 16.1 hands high and a compact animal with deep chest and grand hindquarters, was ten guineas, which was good value since the horse sired many winners, both on the flat and over fences. In 1900 and 1902 *Hackler* was the leading Irish sire of winners on the turf.

Ireland was bred, as his name suggests, in Ireland by James O'C Murphy of Breemount, Trim. The horse had apparently won nothing on the racecourse and stood at the unremarkable fee of five guineas.

Mont Cenis, who has already been noted as travelling widely in the Dublin area in 1893, and who was also registered in 1894, continued to serve in the Dublin area. His fee was three guineas. The only horse with a cheaper fee was Maxwell's *Forestay*, advertised at: 'Thoroughbred Mares, £5; Half-bred Mares, £2. 10s.' Maxwell, however, lived well north of Dublin city, at Courtlough, Lusk, and that may have explained why he charged rather less than the owners of city-stallions.

Ten stallions stood in or in close proximity to Cork city. *Stratheden* belonged to Timothy Desmond of Pembroke Street and *Sweetheart* was the property of Desmond and Bateman of Conway's Yard. None of the Cork men apparently owned more than two Registered Stallions, although R.H. Hayes of Carrigaline, with *Baron Hastings* and *Kentford*, and John Reese with *Isosceles* and *Keswick* each stood two horses at stud. *Isosceles* looked good value at a fee of £5, since he had won the Visitors' Plate at Goodwood in 1888 and the Visitors' Plate over one-and-a-half miles at Ascot in 1889. In 1894 yearlings by *Isosceles* took First Prize in the Thoroughbred and Second Prize in the Half-bred classes at Cork Show. John Reese was still advertising his horse at the same fee when he last appeared in the *Register*, in 1898, although by then his progeny were firmly in command at the annual Cork Show.

In Waterford John Widger kept *Passion Flower* (by *Lord Ronald* out of *Virginia Creeper*) and *Franciscan* at stud. Although the former had won at Punchestown and Cork he only commanded a service fee of £3, whereas his companion stood at £5. Obviously the Waterford breeders were not impressed by flower-power. Martin Murphy also stood a stallion in Waterford, at the Stables, Grattan Quay. His *Koodoo* had won an Apprentices Plate at Newmarket in 1894 and had been '. . . thrice second, and once third.'

County Wexford has been noted for its horsemen for many centuries and it was there that the Norman cavalry first engaged on Irish soil. The county has also produced many great warriors, such as the Beattys of Borodale. Major David Beatty was Master of the Wexford Hounds from 1842 until 1881. His grandson was Admiral Beatty of the great Battle of Jutland of the First World War. When Major Beatty's Mastership ended his post was taken by Captain Walker of Tykillen, Wexford. Walker resigned as Master in 1890 but continued to play an active role in equestrian affairs in his county. In 1895 he was chairman of the County Wexford Committee for Horse Breeding appointed by the Royal Dublin Society.

Walker's opening meet in 1881 as Master of the Wexford Foxhounds was at Tykillen and, after many blank draws, he decided to try Saunders Court for a fox. An old woman near there directed him to rocks near the River Slaney, where she claimed that foxes abounded. Walker expressed misgivings at drawing the place, but was egged-on by Captain M.A. Maher. 'One of the best hunts ever in Wexford followed.'[11]

M.A. Maher was one of the most noted, and fearless, horsemen that Wexford has produced. His mare, *Frigate*, won the Grand National in 1889, (the year that Maher was Senior Steward of the Irish National Hunt Steeplechase Committee) and he had ridden her to hounds in Wexford. Thus it is not surprising that three of the Registered Stallions in Co. Wexford in 1895 belonged to Maher. They were *Dictator*, *Torpedo* and *Zagazig*. *Dictator* won three races and was placed on numerous occasions, both in Ireland and in England. *Torpedo* opened his account by winning

Plate Eighteen. Captain Thomas J. Walker, Tykillen, Wexford, chairman of the Co. Wexford Committee for Horse breeding in Ireland, and, from 1881
until 1890, Master of the Wexford Foxhounds.
(Photo: British Hunts and Huntsmen)

the Amateurs' Plate, which was a weight-for-age hunters' hurdle over two miles, at Tramore in
1880. He then won at Galway, Bromley and twice at Sandown Park. Maher listed *Torpedo* as the
sire of twenty-one named winners '. . . and others.' The fee for this horse was £19, with 10s. for
the groom. *Zagazig*, also a winner, stood at £5 with 5s. for the groom. Maher had registered
Zagazig in 1893 and 1894, but not the better quality *Torpedo* and *Dictator*.

    The fact that Walker and Maher were fully committed to the registration scheme shows, as do
the names of many other prominent members of Irish society, that in 1895 the Royal Dublin
Society's scheme was widely accepted amongst the horse breeding fraternity. For the first time
many of the finest Thoroughbred Stallions in Ireland had been entered in the *Register*. No longer
could one regard the Horse Breeding Schemes and the associated *Registers*, as catering just for
good country stallions. The Scheme, and the *Register*, had become socially acceptable, and
acceptable even to many of the leading breeders and racing men. But the Scheme had also
changed its character, and that was nowhere better seen than in the replacement of the
nomination system for mares by the award of Premiums.

The Regulations for 1895 state that:

'The sum allotted to each county shall be awarded in Premiums to approved Mares and Foals, the property of Farmers, the tenement valuation in aggregate of whose holdings, wherever situated, does not exceed £150 a year, except in Counties Clare, East Cork, Dublin, Kildare, Limerick, Louth, Meath, Roscommon, Tipperary and Westmeath, where the tenement valuation is fixed at £200.' The effect of this clause was to end the nomination system, although the new system was not accepted without criticism and, in 1897, County Committees were allowed to opt either for the premium or for the nomination system.

Premiums were awarded only to mares stinted to a Registered Stallion during the 1895 stud season or to foals sired by a Registered Stallion. In detail the regulations stated that:

'The Premiums shall be confined to:

(a) Two or Three-years-old Mares stinted to a Stallion on the Society's Register for 1895.
(b) Mares with Foal at foot, stinted to a Stallion on the Society's Register for 1895.
(c) Foal at foot by a Stallion on the Society's Register for 1894 or 1895.'

These regulations meant that no mare owners, in 1895, received financial subsidies when they sent mares to Registered Stallions. Instead, owners of mares and foals that were successful in the shows arranged by the County Committees were awarded Premiums of up to £5 for each mare or foal. There was, however, a variety of regulations governing the award of Premiums, in addition to those already listed. Firstly, the mare's owner had to produce a Certificate of Service by a Registered Stallion. Each Certificate, and there were printed forms supplied to all owners of Registered Stallions by the Royal Dublin Society, had to be '. . . on the Official Form,' which was fair enough, anyway. Secondly, before a mare could be awarded a Premium she had to be examined by a Veterinary Surgeon appointed by the County Committee, and had to be certified by him as free from hereditary disease. Thirdly, only owners in whose possession the mare or foal had been for at least three months before the date of award were eligible for Premiums. Finally: 'No animal to receive more than one Premium in same season.'

The Premium system removed much of the pressure caused by the former nomination system from the County Committees. Formerly, before the stud season began, County Committees had to hold shows at which mares were selected for nominations. The mare owners then had to engage in a ballot, after which, depending on their position in the draw, they chose a Registered Stallion for the service of their mare. Naturally enough, that system entailed a great deal of work and organization and some committees must have found difficulty in completing their schedules before the stud season began. Additionally, before nominations were finally paid, considerable extra paper-work was necessary. The whole business was therefore protracted and time consuming.

Under the new, or Premium system, the County Committees had only to decide on the number and value of the Premiums to be allocated, and then to hold shows in the autumn at which they selected animals and awarded the Premiums. The new system was far easier and required much less organization than the nomination system. Additionally, since it was only mares that had already been served by Registered Stallions that could be considered for Premiums, it was arguable that the new system would encourage more owners to send their mares to the horse. Under the nomination system, if a mare was not awarded a nomination, her owner could decide against breeding from her, and not lose any potential subsidy. Under the Premium system, unless he had his mare served, he stood no chance of getting a financial bonus (i.e. the Premium) from the Society. Human nature being what it is, the likelihood was that owners would gamble on getting a Premium, and have their mares serviced anyway. 'Nothing venture, nothing gain,' and in any case the mare owner knew he stood a good chance of breeding a foal, even if he did not attain the prestige of a Premium.

The Premium system was also aimed at the most fertile mares. Apart from mares that were only starting their breeding career, and were not more than three-years-old, Premiums could only be given for mares with foal at foot, that had again been stinted. In other words, the mare must already have produced a live foal that year. This regulation excluded many potentially barren and infertile mares from the system. Previously the only evidence of fertility that the Horse Breeding Schemes had demanded had been for stallions: '. . . if he has been to Stud his Owner must produce satisfactory evidence as to his fruitfulness,' stated the regulations for stallion registration in 1892. Now it was recognized that fertility depended on the mare, as well as on the stallion, and positive evidence of her fertility (in the form of a foal at foot) was demanded.

The award of Premiums for foals was, in theory at least, an excellent idea. It enabled farmers to judge the progeny of various stallions from a variety of mares, and hence helped them to decide their own future breeding policy. The competition between foal owners to exhibit good foals also led to rivalry that necessarily encouraged good feeding and management of the mare and her foal. As all horsemen know, the better an animal is cared for in its youth, the better it is likely to be as an adult. Furthermore, the older the foal the better its chances of success in the showring, other things being equal. This encouraged, or at least it would do so in the future, farmers to put their mares to the horse early in the season. Conversely it would deter them from breeding late foals, which might not thrive as well as foals that had the advantage of clement summer weather during their early weeks on earth.

Although the maximum value of any Premiums was fixed at £5, they attracted considerable competition, especially in a U-shaped area that stretched south into Waterford and east Cork from its origins on the Dublin-Meath-Louth coast, and bent northwards into east Galway and south east Mayo, Roscommon and Longford. There was far less competition in the north of Ireland, as Figure Eight shows, or in the south west and west. Surprisingly, in view of its reputation as a sporting area, there was only limited competition in Wexford, and virtually no competition in the mountainy county of Wicklow.

The greatest number of mares 'presented for Competition' for Premiums was at Rathkeale, in Co. Limerick, where sixty-four mares were on show.[12] Surprisingly, at the adjacent shows of Limerick and Bruff, only ten and twelve mares respectively were present. But Rathkeale, as has already been demonstrated, was the centre of a most important breeding region. In 1895 three Registered Stallions stood in the little town. Joseph Sheehy kept *Appleton* and *Fra Diavolo* (winner of four races including the Upleatham Welter, worth £220, at Redcar), and Peter Griffin kept *Atratus*. The Local Committee awarded Premiums worth £65.10.0. to mares and foals at Rathkeale, £28 to animals at Limerick and £16.10.0. to those selected at Bruff.

The second most popular show was at Ennis, where fifty-one mares sought Premiums, as did forty-five foals. To some extent these numbers were attributable to the policy of the Co. Clare Committee, who decided to have only one show for the whole county, at Ennis. Although this seems grossly unfair to many mare owners, it did save the Committee a lot of effort, and since all the members of the Committee were from the Fergus lowlands anyway (apart from their

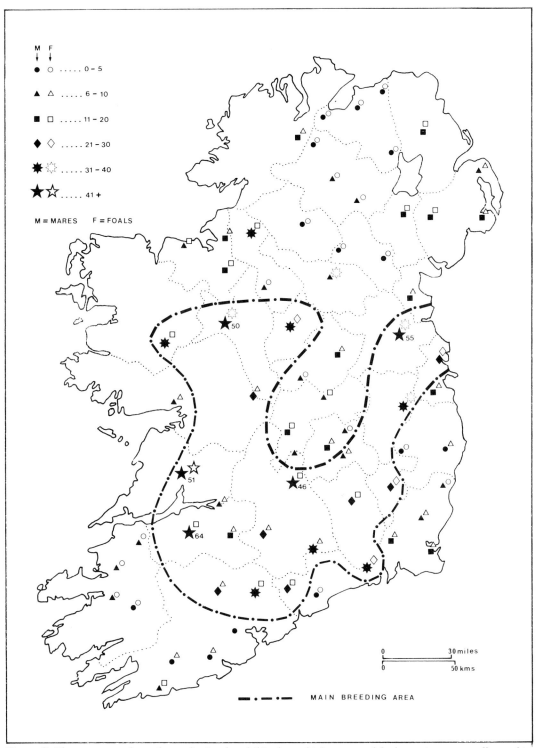

Figure 8. *The centres, and numbers of animals exhibited, at which mare and foal premiums were allocated in 1895. The key depicts the numbers of mares and foals at each centre*

appointed veterinary surgeon, E.F. Winter of Limerick), it probably seemed to them to be a very reasonable decision. Furthermore, they failed to spent all their grant, awarding £77 in Premiums out of a grant of £100.

In fact, many County Committees underspent their grants, and only Antrim, Carlow, Cavan, West Cork, Down, Dublin, Kildare, Kilkenny, King's, Limerick, Longford, Louth, Meath, Queen's, Roscommon and Tipperary disposed of all, or almost all, their grants. Whether this meant that the committees were parsimonious in their awards, or set too high a standard in the selection of Premium animals, or just that they were confronted with not enough animals or with too many mediocre specimens, is now impossible to tell. It is quite certain, however, in a county like Londonderry, where a grand total of only nine mares and eight foals were on show, that the Premium system was *not* a success.

Although, in overall terms, the Premium system in 1895 proved only moderately satisfactory, the geographical pattern resulting from the plotting of Premium shows and entrants reinforces the patterns already established. From Figure Eight it is apparent that east and north Cork, Limerick, Clare, south Tipperary, Waterford, Kilkenny, Carlow, Kildare and Meath-north Dublin, were the major breeding areas for half-breds. A subsidiary centre lay in the main lowlands of Antrim and in the lowlands of Armagh and Down. East Galway and the Plains of Mayo-Roscommon-Longford limestone-lands were also important. So, too, were the limestone pastures of central Sligo and the coastal lowlands towards the Moy estuary. The Manorhamilton area of Leitrim, another limestone region, was also surprisingly important. Central Ireland, the midlands, remained of dubious quality. Some areas were important for horse production, whilst others were just infertile bog. As the Commission of inquiry into the horse breeding industry was to report in 1897, farmers '. . . of the Southern and some parts of the Western districts make horse-breeding their staple . . . industry.'[13]

The most reassuring aspect of the Premium shows, as far as the Royal Dublin Society was concerned, must have been in the overall number of mares and foals that competed. In 1894 a total of 1448 mares were awarded nominations, and of those 1284 were actually served. For 1895, judging by the number of mares on show, at least 1106 mares had been served by Registered Stallions. This was 178 less than the number served in 1894, but it was quite certain that at least a few mares that had been served in 1895 had not, for some reason or other, been shown. There was, therefore, no significant difference in the number of mares served under the nomination system or under the Premium system. As far as foals were concerned, the Society were certain only that 628 had been produced as a result of the 1894 scheme, according to the foaling returns made by mare owners to the Society. Nevertheless, 706 foals were shown in the autumn of 1895, and all were by Registered Stallions and resulted from the 1894 breeding season. The Society were thus assured that their Horse Breeding Schemes, to date, had been successful.

The Premium shows of the autumn of 1895 ended the Horse Breeding Scheme for that year. It was a year that had seen a number of important innovations and alterations. For the Stallion Registration Committee, with the preparation and publication of Volume One of their *Register of Thoroughbred Stallions*, it had been a hard and testing year. But the real test lay in the future, in the years in which it would be seen whether or not Volume One and succeeding *Registers* became accepted in the important world of half-bred horse production in Ireland.

CHAPTER TEN

Acceptance

The title page of the Society's *Register* for 1896 states that it was: 'Printed for Her Majesty's Stationery Office By Alexander Thom and Co. (Limited), Abbey Street, The Queen's Printing Office.' The same statement had appeared on the title page of the 1895 *Register* and was to appear right until the ending of the Society's involvement in stallion registration in 1900. Her Majesty, in effect, had approved the Horse Breeding Schemes as organized by the Royal Dublin Society and, as far as she was concerned, the Schemes had her acceptance. Comparison of the 1895 with the 1896 *Register* shows that the Schemes, as represented by the *Registers*, also had the acceptance of the main breeders and stallion owners. In 1895 a total of 219 stallions had been registered. Now, in 1896, the total increased to 234, four more than the 'Prefatory Note' to the *Register* claimed. The gentlemen of the Royal Dublin Society, as we have already seen, were sometimes a little lackadaisical about arithmetic!

The Stallion Registration Committee, as formed in the previous year, was strengthened by the addition of two new members. Major R.H. Borrowes, D.L., and Major Nugent T. Everard, D.L. Major Borrowes had served as a member of the Co. Kildare Committee in 1895 (his home was Gilltown, Newbridge) but had escaped more onerous duty. Nevertheless, he had been heavily involved in the Horse Breeding Schemes of previous years and it was fitting that, with his experience, he should join the Stallion Registration Committee. He remained a member of the Committee until 1899, the penultimate year of its existence. Major Everard served on the Co. Meath Committee in 1895, which was presided over by Lord Langford who was already a member of the Stallion Registration Committee. No doubt His Lordship felt that Everard would be a valuable addition to the Committee. Everard lived at Randlestown, Navan, and continued to serve as Hon. Secretary and Treasurer of the Meath Committee. Borrowes also continued to serve on his county committee.

The pattern of distribution of stallions, as shown on Figure Nine, was little different from that of the previous year. Co. Londonderry was still without a resident Registered Stallion and, in spite of the Society's stated powers to hire or buy stallions to serve in necessitous areas, no attempt appears to have been made to locate a stallion in that county. Leitrim, where *Scotch Monk* had stood in the hill-encircled Manorhamilton area in 1895, was also stallion-less. Of course, in both areas the deficiency may have been more apparent than real, as has already been suggested for the former county, but in 1897 the Congested Districts Board moved *Uncle Sam* into Leitrim, so that there was obviously a need for a good resident stallion there.

In detail, of course, changes had taken place. Four stallions stood in Co. Fermanagh (including *Scotch Monk*, now the property of William Wilson of Derryhilla House, Enniskillen), whereas only two had stood there in 1895. The increase was mainly due to Edward Mitchell of Derryvullen, Enniskillen, registering *Masterman* and *Cordelier*. In 1895 he had not registered any stallion, although he had registered *Cambrian* in 1893 and 1894. Perhaps, with the departure of that horse from the scene, it had taken Mitchell a while to get organized again.

County Longford had three Registered Stallions in 1895; now six Registered Stallions existed there. Henry Reynolds of Ballinalee had emerged as one of the major stallion owners in Ireland, with three Registered Stallions, *Black Diamond*, *Midnight* and *Saint Paul*. C. O'Neill Kenny of Cartron Hall, Longford, had also joined the list of Registered Stallion owners, with his fancifully named *Narcissus*, a horse that had been registered as standing in Westmeath in 1894 and 1895.

But the detailed changes within counties were of less significance than the addition of new owners, and new stallions, to the *Register*. The Right Honourable The Earl of Dunraven, owner of the great mansion at Adare in Co. Limerick, built in Tudor Revival style in 1832, kept *Kirkham* at stud. This chestnut nine year old, 16.1 hands high, had been bred in Australia by The Honourable J. White in New South Wales. White was the leading owner in New South Wales and, in the 1880s, chairman of the Australian Jockey Club. He bred *Kirkham* purposely to carry his colours in the Epsom Derby, which the colt did in 1890, finishing unplaced after a good showing early in the race. It is a bit startling to think that, having been transported half-way around the world to Adare, the stallion should command a fee of only £2, with five shillings for the groom. But such fees typified the generosity of a number of landlords, at least to their own tenants. In Co. Waterford the Duke of Devonshire continued *Bacchus* at stud at £3 for tenants on His Grace's property. In Co. Wicklow *M.P.* (lately of the north of Ireland and previously of southern England), now owned by Marcus Beresford of Shelton Abbey, Arklow, served at '£2 for tenant farmers in Shelton Abbey Harriers' hunting country; £1.10s. for the Earl of Wicklow's tenants; Groom's fee, 2s. 6d.' The Earl was a considerable benefactor in the Arklow area but his former seat, now in different hands, lies dwarfed by the towers of the great fertilizer plant which employs many Arklow people. The Shelton Abbey Harriers, like many other private packs of hounds, have gone too, and few people remember them, even though parts of their territory are still hunted by the Wicklow Foxhounds.

In south west Cork, at Rosscarbery, Captain William Tower Townshend stood two horses at stud: *Beaucourt* and *Town Moor*. *Beaucourt* had been bred by Hume Webster at his Surrey stud and had been registered in 1893. Webster had been one of the three judges for the Queen's Premiums for Stallions at Dublin in 1889. *Beaucourt's* great grand-dam was by *Melbourne*, which epitomizes the way in which breeders diffused good blood-lines throughout Ireland and Britain. Although Captain Townshend did not advertise *Beaucourt* as having achieved anything on the turf, he took care to state that, in 1881, *Town Moor*, had been '. . . close 3rd to *Iroquois* and *Peregine*' in the Derby at Epsom. It was also stated that: '*Town Moor*, late the property of Her Majesty the Queen, girths 6 feet 5½ inches and is over 8 inches under the knee. *Town Moor* has sired many winners, including *Empire*, *Patchoule*, *Rosefield*, *Dartmoor*, *Dowle*, *Little Jack*, *Curly Wig*, *Mansfield*, *Rory O'More*, etc.' For breeders in the isolated district around Rosscarbery to be allowed the services of such a well-made quality horse, fully proven in one of the most prestigious races in the world, at a fee of three guineas, with two shillings and six pence for the

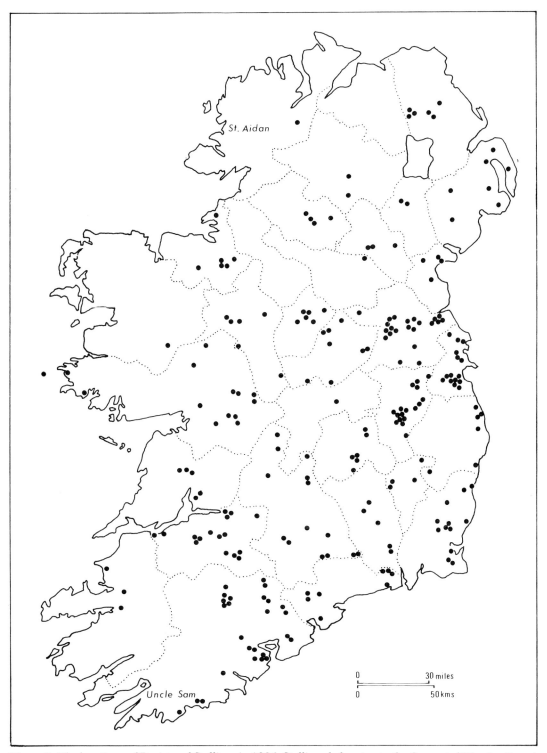

Figure 9. *The locations of Registered Stallions in 1896. Stallions belonging to the Congested Districts Board are named*

groom, was a great tribute both to Captain Townshend and to the Royal Dublin Society. *Town Moor* was eighteen years old, but the photograph of him that was printed in the *Register* depicts a handsome, compact horse, and belies his age. He was registered also during the following two years, but thereafter his name appears no more. Horses, like humans, are not everlasting.

Another west Cork horse to be fully advertised in the *Register* was *New Laund*, belonging to John Mahony of Castleack, Bandon. Mahoney had advertised the horse in the 1893 *Register* as standing at Kinsale, Bandon and at the owner's stables. In 1894 *New Laund* was not listed in the *Register*, but all the evidence suggests that the horse continued stud duties in the Bandon-Kinsale area. In 1895 *New Laund*'s stock were described in the *Register* as '. . . the leading horses at all the hunting meets in the County and command the highest prices.' Now Mahony added the prestigious information that 'At a meeting of Royal Lancers, Ballincollig, lately held here, out of a field of 150 horses, four of *New Laund*'s Gets were the first to come in for brush over a stiff country with large fences.' The Lancers, like the Hussars before them, ran the Muskerry Foxhounds from their barracks at Ballincollig. The Muskerry had been disbanded in 1881 due to agrarian troubles and hounds had been sold to the south of France. For two years the country lay unhunted, and then Colonel Mangles of the Twentieth Hussars offered to keep a pack in barracks.[1] From 1883 until 1898 the Muskerry remained, in effect, a military pack, and, as all huntsmen know, horse-soldiers ride terribly hard:

'I used to dream of Hell when I was first
Promoted to a huntsman's job . . .
And hounds were short of blood; and officers
From barracks over-rode 'em all day long
. . . good sportsmen to a man
And brigadiers by now, but dreadful hard
On a young huntsman keen to show some sport.

Ay, Hell was thick with captains . . .'[2]

A far more notable stallion newly registered as standing in west Cork was *Uncle Sam*, the property of the Congested Districts Board. This Board had been founded in 1891 to cater for those areas of Ireland in which the rateable valuation was less than £1. 10s. per head. Figure Ten depicts these areas. Throughout the Congested Districts there was widespread poverty and human misery. People tended to work small, uneconomic holdings and lived at, or very near, subsistence level. Of course, there were exceptions and in some areas, as in Valentia Island, people experienced reasonably good standards of living. There were also a number of wealthy landlords, not greatly worried by the unhappy conditions of the peasantry, but there were many more whose estates were encumbered and who were greatly in debt, or who would have liked to see a change in the social system. Much of the work of the Government-established Congested Districts Board lay in helping to alleviate poverty, develop the economic potential of the Congested Districts and change the social system.

In order to improve farming the Congested Districts Board became the greatest owner of stallions in Ireland. These ranged from jack-asses to Thoroughbreds and were made available for the service of mares in the Congested Districts at low, or even non-existent fees. *Uncle Sam* had been bred by H. Waring in England and was foaled in 1885. He proved a creditable

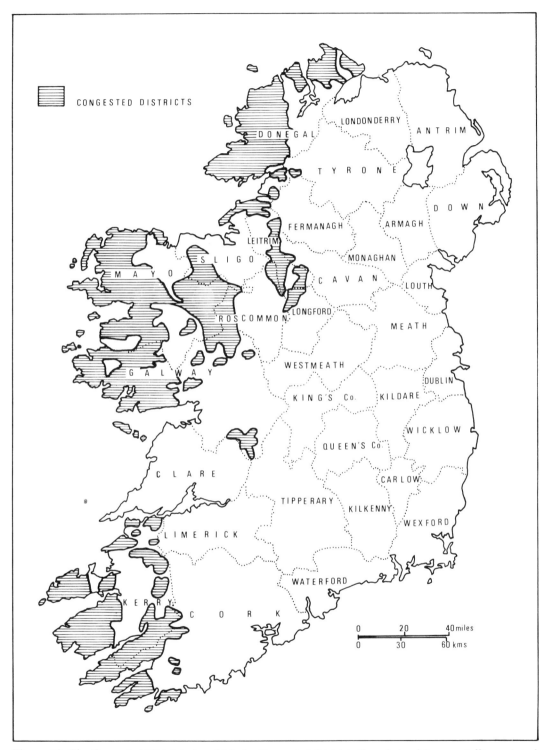

Figure 10. *The Congested Districts, in which the Congested Districts Board stood its own stallions at stud*

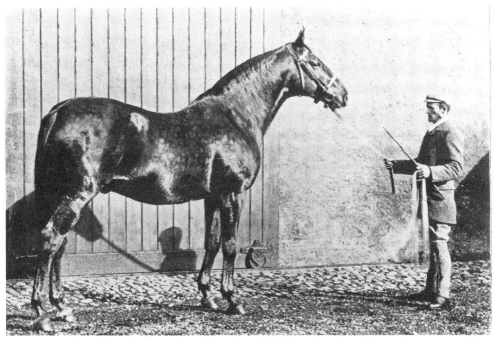

Plate Nineteen. Royal Meath, *first registered by Captain Hollwey Steeds and later the property of Sir John Arnott, Bt. Sired by* Ascetic, *out of* Catastrophe, *and bred by Gordon Jackson in Co. Meath. This horse won the Conyngham Cup in 1889 and the Grand Steeplechase de Paris at Autueil in 1890.* Royal Meath *also won the Croker Challenge Cup at the Royal Dublin Society's Horse Show in 1895 and 1896. (Photo:* Register of Thoroughbred Stallions)

performer on the turf, opening his account by winning the Grendon Juvenile Plate at Lichfield. Later successes included The Third Welter Handicap Plate at Newmarket and The New Barnes Handicap at Manchester, so the horse was a useful performer, if not outstanding. Additionally *Uncle Sam* had won in the show-ring, at Redruth in 1892, Falmouth in 1894 and Wadebridge in 1895. Now, in 1896, the horse had been bought for service in Ireland and forsook the pleasures of West Country mares for those of south west Cork.

Another Congested Districts Board stallion to be registered was *St. Aidan*. This was only a five year old, by *St. Simon* out of *St. Helena*. His grand-dam was by *Macaroni* and his dam was by *Hermit*. Both *Hermit* and *Macaroni* had won the Derby and *St. Helena* finished second in the Oaks. A better pedigree than that would have been difficult to find and *St. Aidan* himself was no slouch. In 1894 he was second in the Great National Breeders' Foal Stakes, '. . . only beaten by a neck.' *St. Simon*, as the Board advertised in the *Register*, '. . . is at present standing at a fee of 400 guineas.' One wonders if the mare owners of the Co. Donegal realized their luck when the Board stood such a horse in their midst. Even though the Royal Dublin Society might not be posting stallions to necessitous areas, the Congested Districts Board certainly were, although the Board was not without its critics.

In addition to Thoroughbreds the Congested Districts Board owned thirty-six Hackney stallions in 1896. '. . . the Hackney is not in our opinion a desirable sire,' wrote Lord Dunraven and other members of the Commission appointed to inquire into horse breeding in Ireland. Lord Enniskillen and a further group of members disagreed, however, stating that '. . . the needs of each class of breeder should be recognized,' and that the Hackney had a role to play in horse-breeding in Ireland.[3] But this argument did not concern the Royal Dublin Society, for it was now firmly committed to its *Register of Thoroughbred Stallions* and made no attempt to accommodate stallions of other breeds, although the matter was discussed, as actions four years later were to prove.

Further east, in the Dublin area, Hollwey Steeds' horse, *Royal Meath*, had at last won his class at the Dublin Horse Show: '1895, Royal Dublin Society, Ball's-bridge, 1st.' Even Mr. Ball, long since resting in his grave in St. Paul's churchyard, Bray, would have been pleased had he known, for *Royal Meath* had been placed ever since 1892, but had not previously won.

At the Curragh William Pallin had provided the Society with a difficult problem. His Irish

Plate Twenty. *J.H. Lambert, owner and lessee of many stallions, including* Ballinafad *and* Favonian, *of Redmount Hill, Ballinasloe. (Photo:* British Hunts and Huntsmen)

Plate Twenty-one. *W.H. West, Farmley, Ferns, Co. Wexford, owner, and lessee of Sires from J. Daly. (Photo:* British Hunts and Huntsmen)

Derby winner, *Master Ned*, was leased for the season to The Compton Stud, Gillingham, Dorset, England. Was *Master Ned* eligible for inclusion in the *Register* or was he not? It was nowhere stated that stallions included in the *Register* had to stand at stud in Ireland, and so *Master Ned* was duly registered under the heading of 'County Kildare'. After all, that was where his owner lived.

Pallin had also changed a number of his stallions since the previous year. *Favonian*, for example, had been sent to J.H. Lambert and now stood at Redmount Hill, Ballinasloe. *Astrologer* was leased to James Preston of Mallow, in Co. Cork. *Snowdon*, which Pallin had leased from Captain Fife of The Compton Stud in 1895, had been returned to his owner. *Heckberry*, leased to the Earl of Bessborough at Piltown in 1895 returned to his owner's stables, as did *Isleworth*, previously leased to John Hutchinson of Thomastown. *Branxholme*, however, leased to Patrick Colfer of Co. Wexford in 1895, was leased out again, to Miss Musgrave of

Tourin, Cappoquin, in the Co. Waterford. Pallin had also acquired a new stallion for his stud, *Broxton*, bred by the Duke of Westminster at Eaton Hall in Cheshire. To be successful as a stallion-man one had to ring the changes, and Pallin was expert at so doing.

Another expert owner was James Daly of Liffey Bank, Co. Dublin. He had five Registered Stallions in 1895 and six in 1896. One of these, *Springtime*, was leased in both years to W.H. West of Co. Wexford, but in 1896 Daly's new horse, *Palm Leaf*, was leased to St. George Manseragh of Friarsfield, Tipperary. *Palm Leaf* had been bred at Newmarket, where he won two plates, in 1888 and 1889. In the latter year the horse also won at Hamilton Park and at the Eglington Hunt. Daly was not only a stallion owner but a breeder and major dealer, buying '. . . hunters, chargers, harness horses, troopers and remount horses.'

The leasing of stallions was, however, very much the exception rather than the rule. Of the 234 stallions included in the *Register* only five were listed as leased, three of these belonging to Pallin and the others to Daly. Normally stallions belonged to the person who stood them at stud and it was exceptional for more than one or two to be owned by the same person. Pallin owned more Registered Stallions than anyone else in Ireland, seven; Daly owned six and J.A.S. Langan owned five.

Langan lived at Bellewstown House, Drogheda, and as has already been noted, he kept horses

Plate Twenty-two. *Captain M.A. Maher of Ballink-eele, Enniscorthy, Co. Wexford. Owner of* Torpedo *and other sires. (Photo:* Dublin Horse Show Magazine)

of considerable quality as well as less renowned animals. The service fees for his horses in 1896 ranged from as little as £3 to as much as £25. The latter fee was charged for *Brown Prince*, bred by A.J. Alexander at the Woodburn Stud in Kentucky. As Langan advertised: 'His produce won more than any sire in Ireland this year, viz., £5,056, £4,593 being in England. *Brown Prince* also secured the 1st prize of £25, presented by Royal Dublin Society, for the sire whose produce won most prizes at their Show in 1895.' Nobody could therefore cavil at the fee, although, as for the fee for *Ascetic* already noted for 1895, it could hardly have attracted the half-bred mares of ordinary tenant-farmers. But that aspect of the Horse Breeding Scheme, with the rapid break-up of the estate system, seemed fated, anyway, and its neglect could hardly be wondered at.

The other major owners of stallions were John Purdon of Cloneymore, Athboy, who owned four, including the ancient *Ascetic*; John W.A. Harris of the Victor Stud, Kilmallock in Co. Limerick (three); Captain Maher of Ballinkeele, Enniscorthy, the noted Wexford horseman (also three, his *Torpedo* was well advertised in the *Register*: 'No less than 21 of *Torpedo*'s stock were winners in England and Ireland during the year 1895.' *Torpedo*'s fee had rocketed from £19 in 1895 to £25 in 1896). Henry Reynolds of Ballinalee, Edgeworthstown and John Widger of Waterford also owned three, whilst James Preston of Mallow owned two and had another one on lease from Pallin. Preston's horses included *Ben*, first registered in 1895, and winner of such races as the Epsom Grand Prize (£2,217) in 1890 and The Rous Memorial Stakes, worth £1,327, in 1889.

Throughout the 1896 *Register* there is only one discordant note. The latter years of the nineteenth century saw an important rift in Irish racing. The racing authorities were confronted with the problem of other bodies organizing race-meetings under rules and conditions that, in some cases, left much to be desired. These meetings were called 'Illegal Meetings' and were generally frowned upon by the gentlemen of the Turf Club. Some hint of this appears in the advertisement for R. Nihill Talbot's horse, *Almoner*. '*Almoner* is sire of very good hunters, and all show quality with good-size bone, and are natural fencers. Many of them have won at the Illegal Meetings.' For the Royal Dublin Society even to allow an allusion to illegal meetings was surprising, but perhaps the gentlemen of the Stallion Registration Committee did not scrutinize all the advertisements for stallions in their *Register* with the care that one might expect. Like Nelson they were men of the world, and probably knew when to turn a blind eye.

The rules for the Horse Breeding Scheme of 1896 differed little from those of the previous year, yet the Society recognized that in one respect they needed amendment. In 1895 Premiums could only be awarded to two or three-years-old mares, or to mares with foal at foot, in both cases stinted to a Registered Stallion. Many owners considered that it was wrong to breed from a mare before she was four, and argued that it stunted the growth of the mare and, in some cases, resulted in the growth of an undersized foal. The Society therefore amended the rules so that mares of two, three or four years of age, stinted to a stallion on the Society's *Register* for 1896, were eligible for submission for a Premium.

Premium Shows were held throughout Ireland in the autumn and large numbers of mares were exhibited at many centres. Clonmel had the distinction of the highest number of competitors. Sixty-seven mares paraded before the judges and all those selected for Premiums had to undergo veterinary examination. One does not envy Mr. James Mahony, Veterinary Surgeon, the task that confronted him, but at least he was able to retreat to his home in Templemore when his duty was done. The Co. Tipperary Committee, with the exception of William Riall, all came

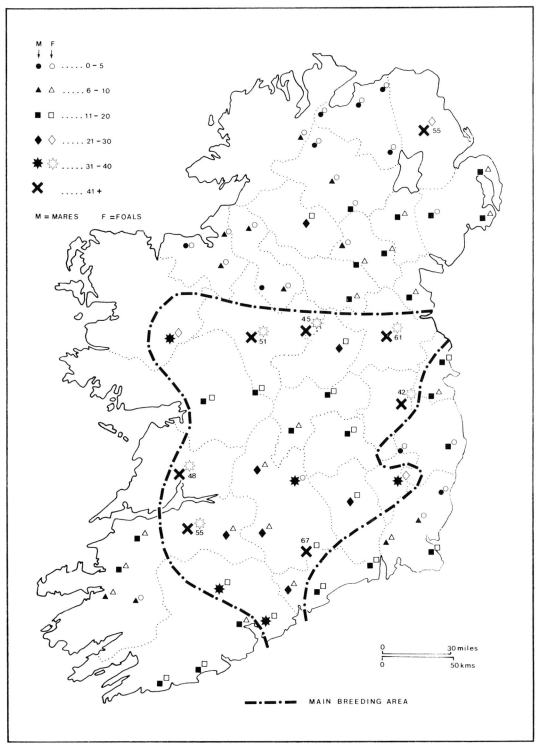

Figure 11. *The centres, and numbers of animals exhibited, at which mare and foal premiums were allocated in 1896. The key lists the number of mares and foals at each centre*

from the northern part of the shire, where horse-breeding was apparently not quite as popular as in the fertile Fethard-Clonmel-Cashel-Cahir area. Nevertheless, forty mares paraded at Templemore, twenty-eight at Tipperary and twenty-two at Nenagh, so the whole county was a most important breeding area.

The second most popular show was at Boyerstown, for Co. Meath. Sixty-one mares were present there, as well as thirty-six foals. Rathkeale and Ballymena shared third place in popularity, with fifty-five mares each, although there were more foals at Rathkeale than at the northern show. Ennis had three less mares than in the previous year, forty-eight, and the number of foals had slipped slightly, too.

The geographic pattern that Figure Eleven shows is that central and southern Ireland, and the Ballymena area, had become the main half-bred breeding areas. This is basically the same pattern that had emerged in 1895, although the midlands had seemed somewhat less important then. The Congested Districts and much of the north of Ireland, as well as Wicklow and Wexford, appear as much less important as producing regions for half-breds. To some extent this might seem odd, since Wexford has long been famous for its hunters. Yet, as studies of production patterns in the 1970s indicate,[4] Co. Wexford tends to be an area into which young horses are imported and trained before being resold. Co. Wicklow, divided by a great granite mountain mass, has never been highly renowned for horse production, although the paucity of mares at its two shows, Baltinglass and Rathdrum, is surprising. In all only eighteen mares attended the shows, but perhaps that was partly because of their location. Baltinglass and Rathdrum are hardly central to the heartland of horsey Wicklow, and a show at Carnew or Shillelagh may have produced a different entry. Since Mr. Frank Brooke of Ardeen, Shillelagh, was a member of the Co. Wicklow Committee it is surprising that he did not ensure that a show was held in his area.

As in 1895 many County Committees found themselves unable to allocate all, or almost all, their grants in Premiums. Nine committees underspent their grants (in the award of Premiums) by £20 or more. These were West Cork, Donegal, Leitrim, Londonderry, Queen's, Tyrone, Westmeath, Wexford and (with the exception of £2) Wicklow. But all was not without hope in those areas. In West Cork twelve mares had appeared at both Clonakilty and Skibbereen, with thirteen foals at each centre. Obviously Richard Connell's *Whalebone*, standing in the Skibbereen area, and Captain Tower Townshend's *Controversy*, had not been without trade in 1895.

At the other end of the country, in Co. Donegal, matters were less hopeful. Although *Greenfield* had stood in the Raphoe area, only six mares and five foals sought premiums at Raphoe show. The Co. Donegal Committee, chaired by Captain F.C. Mackay, were able only to award £31 in premiums out of the grant of £60 that had been made available to them. Mackay lived at Belmont, Londonderry, and two other members of the committee, Captain the Honourable E. Cochrane and the veterinary surgeon, E. McClay, also lived in that county. With three out of a total of nine members living outside Co. Donegal matters cannot have been too rosy for half-bred horse production there. No wonder the Congested Districts Board posted a stallion to the county during 1896.

Co. Londonderry, like Donegal, was also apparently in a bad way. Five mares were presented at Coleraine, one at Limavady, two at Londonderry and five at Magherafelt, a grand total of thirteen. Seven foals were also shown. Of course, as the Government's stallion registration scheme was to show in the twentieth century, Londonderry and adjacent counties were heavy-horse territory, dominated by feathery Clydesdales rather than by Thoroughbreds and their progeny.

But there was another, and very important, reason why the number of mares and foals exhibited in the north of Ireland was so small. Only animals belonging to tenant farmers were eligible for Premiums, and many farmers in the north of Ireland were free-holders. Yet estates did exist, and we have already seen that, in 1889 at Lisburn, for example, 200 mares had competed for 50 nominations. Thus there were plenty of premium-quality mares in Ulster belonging to tenant-farmers that were not exhibited for Premiums. The only benefit their owners derived from the Horse Breeding Scheme in 1896 was that they were able to consult the *Register*, when choosing a sire to put on their mares. As far as they were concerned, and this applied elsewhere as well, the Horse Breeding Scheme was of limited value.

Perhaps the partial failure of the Premium system was best seen in Co. Kilkenny. Five Registered Stallions were resident in the county in 1896 and a number of others must have travelled through the region for stud purposes, as in earlier years. Yet only twenty-eight mares and fifteen foals sought Premiums at the show organized for the county in 1896. The show was held at Kilkenny, which was convenient for the majority of the County Committee, all of whom lived reasonably close to the city. Whether the venue was equally suitable for mare-owners in such areas as Glenmore, where Felix Mullins kept two stallions at stud, is debatable. Yet the Co. Kilkenny Committee did manage to disburse all the money available to them for Premiums, so they probably considered the operation a success. Nevertheless, owners in areas isolated from the show venue probably held a different opinion.

Opinions elsewhere, as in Leitrim or Sligo, were not difficult to fathom. Hardly anybody presented animals for Premiums in those counties. That was partly due to a shortage of suitable animals, but Sligo had plenty of good mares, enough to encourage private enterprise to locate six Registered Stallions in the county in 1895. It was therefore apparent that the Royal Dublin Society needed to reconsider the Premium system, and perhaps replace, or modify it, for 1897.

On a more happy note, a total of 1274 mares sought Premiums in 1896, 168 more than in 1895. Furthermore, 724 foals sired by Registered Stallions were exhibited and it seemed likely that the total number of foals sired by such stallions was higher than at any previous time since the initiation of the Horse Breeding Schemes. In 1892 a total of 1449 mares were served by Registered Stallions, the highest on record. Yet for 1274 mares, all stinted to Registered Stallions, to be paraded in 1896 inevitably meant that an even greater number had been served. Whilst it was not certain that a record number of mares had enjoyed the attentions of Registered Stallions it certainly seemed as if that had probably been the case. And all the mares awarded Premiums, as in 1895, had been declared free of hereditary disease by qualified veterinary surgeons. It looked as if Ireland was set to reap a record crop of healthy half-bred foals in 1897 and the production of quality horses, saleable in the local and international markets, seemed assured. If only some means could be found whereby all tenant-farmer owners of good mares could be financially aided by the Society in hard cash for taking their mares to the horse, it seemed as if all would be well. Money talks, and the County Committees as well as the parent Society were very well aware that it was unsatisfactory for grants to remain unspent. They, like money, talked through the late autumn and winter of 1896, and as a result a typical compromise solution was arrived at, which was to be applied to the Horse Breeding Scheme of 1897.

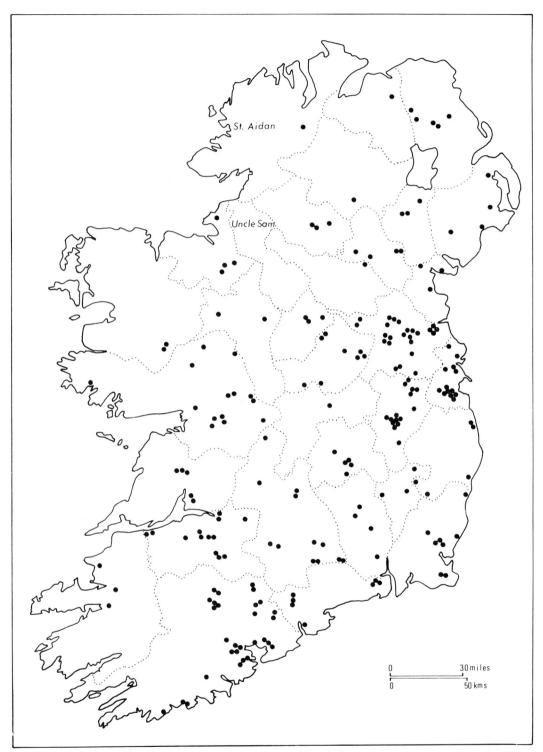

St. Aidan

Uncle Sam.

0   30 miles
0   50 kms

Figure 12. *The location of Registered Stallions in 1897. Stallions belonging to the Congested Districts Board are named*

CHAPTER ELEVEN

Compromise

Applications were made by the owners of 249 stallions for their animals to be included in the *Register* for 1897 and, '. . . after very careful inquiry, 212 were accepted.'[1] The geographical pattern of distribution of these horses was, not unexpectedly, very like that for previous years. In some areas, as in east Cork, there were slight increases in the number of Registered Stallions as compared with 1895 and 1896, and equally, in other areas there were minor decreases, as in Kerry. On the whole, however, there was little change and, as comparison of Figure Twelve with Figures Nine and Seven will show, the situation was virtually static. Admittedly the counties of Leitrim and Londonderry, that had been without resident Registered Stallions in 1896 (and 1895, in the latter case), now boasted at least one such stallion, but that hardly disturbed the established geographical pattern.

Neither was there any marked change in the actual stallions registered, nor in their owners, although fifteen stallions that had not been listed in 1896 made their appearance in the new *Register* and thirty-eight stallions formerly listed were deleted. Of the new entrants eleven were under the age of ten and, in effect, were starting or near the start of, their stud career. The four older stallions included the twenty-three-year-old *Rhidorroch* and the fourteen-year-old *Mulberry*. Both were owned by R. Graham of Balla Lodge, Donadea. For some unknown reason Graham's horses had not been registered in 1896, although both had been listed in the *Register* for 1895. They were, therefore, not newcomers to the ranks of the Registered Stallions. The thirteen-year-old, *Sweetheart*, owned by Desmond and Bateman of Conway's Yard, Cork, had also been registered in 1895, but not in 1896. *Sly Patrick*, from Kilmuckridge in Co. Wexford, was in the same position. Only *Wild Mark*, of all the horses of ten or over, was a newcomer to the *Register*. He was owned by H. Sparrow of Williamstown, Kells. In previous years only Thomas Francis Sparrow, of the same address, had registered his horses, and he continued to do so, but in competition with his namesake.

The quality of new entrants to the *Register* was, judged by their stated race-course and show-yard performances, mixed. The Harris Brothers of Mitchelstown, for example, stood *Ambergate* at stud. He had won a Maiden Plate at Leicester in 1891 and been placed in two hurdle races over two miles in 1892. *Beware*, also standing in the Co. Cork, had apparently won nothing. *Diogenes*, standing in the drumlin county of Monaghan, had won his class at the 1896 Suffolk and Cambridgeshire Joint Show on the rolling downlands of Newmarket, a far cry from the land of the little hills of clay where he was now stabled. *Holloway*, bred by Lord Roseberry and now in the Co. Down, had won the Stand Handicap Hurdle and the Town Handicap Plate at Dundalk in 1894, the Railway Plate at Leopardstown in 1895, and been placed third in Her Majesty's Plate at the Curragh in the same year, and so the list continues.

Probably the best of the new entrants to the *Register* was *Red Prince II*. This horse, now aged eight, had been bred by H.E. Linde at Eyrefield Lodge on the Curragh and was by *Kendal* out of *Empress*. His dam had won the Grand National and had been born in 1875. During his racing career *Red Prince II* won the Natural Produce Stakes, The Royal Whip (over a course of four miles), and the Lancashire Handicap of 3,000 sovereigns. Furthermore, the horse had been successful in the show-ring, taking Second Prize in his class at the Royal Dublin Society's Show at Ball's Bridge in 1896. Although Linde continued to own the horse he was a very sick man and decided to lease it for the stud season, not surprisingly, to his well-known neighbour on the Curragh, William Pallin. Sadly, on March 18, Linde died as a result of Brights' Disease. *Red Prince II* later developed into '. . . an excellent hunter 'chaser sire.'[2]

Plate Twenty-three. *Captain W.E. Holwey Steeds, Clonsilla House, Co. Dublin, former owner of* Royal Meath. *(Photo:* British Hunts and Huntsmen)

Plate Twenty-four. *Sir John Arnott, Bt, Woodlands, Cork, owner of* Royal Meath *in 1897. (Photo:* Dublin Horse Show Magazine)

On the whole the quality of the new entrants to the *Register*, probably did not equal that of those no longer listed. Charles Blake, Heath House, Maryborough, no longer registered *Bel Demonio*, winner of two races worth £1000 each, at Kempton and Sandown. Neither did he register *St. David*, winner of the Nottinghamshire Handicap of 1000 Sovereigns, carrying nine stone. *Blitz*, winner of thirteen races; *Boulevard*, winner of The Liverpool Cup; *Bruar*, a victor at Worcester; *Cairo*, winner of the Spencer Plate at Northampton in 1885; the aged *Condor*; the winner of the 1895 Baldoyle Derby, *Favoloo*; the old *Greenfield* of Michael Foley; *Guerrilla*, who took the Curragh Plate in 1880; *Lyric*, 'Winner of 23 Races in England, and placed in 20;' and many more valuable sires vanished from the *Register*. Some disappeared due to death and misfortune and some for other reasons, but they were all missed.

Inevitably old favourites, and some that were not so highly thought of, had been shifted around the country. Hollwey Steeds, having seen his horse win at Dublin, passed *Royal Meath* on to Sir John Arnott, Bart., of Woodlands, Cork, where he stood at a fee of ten guineas. *Branxholme* was home with William Pallin after his visitations to the mares of southern Ireland. His Grace, the Duke of Devonshire, had sold *Bacchus* (and it was time he did so, for the horse was twenty-three years old) to John O'Donnell. At least the venerable old stallion did not have to move far, since O'Donnell lived at the Deerpark, conveniently close to His Grace's castle at Lismore, and within sound of the bell of St. Carthage's slender-spired cathedral. His Grace now had only one Registered Stallion for the service of 'approved mares,' *Tartan*, fifteen-years-old, bay, and bred by Her Majesty The Queen.

In the Congested Districts *Uncle Sam* had been moved to the wilds of Co. Leitrim, a far cry from west Cork and further still from his west country home of two years earlier. But at least it was unlikely that *Uncle Sam* journeyed directly from Cork to Leitrim. The Congested Districts Board owned a farm on the fertile lowlands between Bray and Dublin at which they kept their stallions when the breeding season was over. Their other Registered Stallion, *St. Aidan*, still stood in Co. Donegal, sturdily serving the local female equine population.

But the most important changes were not those of the stallions, but of the rules relating to mares. Under Clause Four of the Horse Breeding Scheme, 1897, it was stated that:
'It will be optional with each County Committee to select either of the following Systems for their County:–

(a) The Nomination System as carried out by the Royal Dublin Society in 1892-1894.

(b) The Premium System as carried out by the Royal Dublin Society in 1895-1896.'

This was a typical compromise solution to the problems posed by the premium system in the previous two years. Twenty-two committees (including those of East and of West Cork) opted for the nomination system. Carlow, Cavan, Clare, Down, Fermanagh, Kildare, Londonderry, Meath, Monaghan, Queen's and Tipperary decided to retain the premium system.

During the months of March and April exhibitions to select mares for nominations were held, as shown on Figure Thirteen. Registered Stallions were paraded at these meetings. The Committee for Co. Wicklow were a bit remiss in not holding their final exhibition, at Baltinglass, until May the first. The West Cork Committee decided to get the matter dealt with as expeditiously as possible, and held exhibitions on four consecutive days: at Bandon on Tuesday, April 6th, Drinagh on Wednesday, Skibbereen on Thursday and Clonakilty on Friday. The East Cork Committee held its exhibitions on the following Monday, Tuesday and Wednesday, at Fermoy, Buttevant and Blarney. A few other committees similarly disposed of the matter speedily, but some, such as Wicklow, prolonged the business. Their exhibitions were held at Rathdrum and Newtownmountkennedy on April 6th and 7th, and at Blessington and Baltinglass on April 30th and May 1st.

The venues chosen for the exhibitions for nomination were very similar to those used in the previous year under the premium system, as comparison of Figures Eleven and Thirteen demonstrates. In Counties Kilkenny, Louth, Mayo, Westmeath and Wicklow, however, more venues were used than in the previous year, and this was fairer from the breeders' point of view. In 1896, for example, shows for premiums had been held, in Co. Wicklow, only at Rathdrum and Baltinglass. Now they were held at Newtownmountkennedy and Blessington as well. It must have been well nigh impossible for breeders in the Newtownmountkennedy area to attend either of the premium shows of 1896. Admittedly, there was a train from nearby Newcastle Station to the station at Rathdrum, but the cost of transport would hardly make the value of a premium worthwhile, especially since there was always the risk of not being awarded a premium, anyway.

In Mayo the only premium show in 1896 had been held at Hollymount, in the central southern lowlands, far removed from the Killala-Ballina breeding area in the north of the county. That had probably seemed acceptable to the County Committee, all of whom came from the south of the county and four of whom (out of a total of nine) had Hollymount postal addresses. Both the Chairman and the Hon. Secretary and Treasurer came from Hollymount. H. Lindsey Fitzpatrick lived at Hollymount House and W.E. Ruttledge lived at Carra Villa. Hollymount was near the heart of the South Mayo Harriers country and it probably seemed, to the local committee, as if the rest of the county was a wilderness. That, however, was extremely unfair to the northern breeders, although perhaps it was felt that Killala and Ballina breeders could rail their mares to Hollymount: the railway to Killala had been opened on January 2nd, 1893.[3] In 1897, however, an exhibition for nominations was held at Ballina, which must have been far more satisfactory for breeders in north Mayo than the arrangement of the previous year.

Of course it is very difficult, in the latter part of the twentieth century, to appreciate the isolation of certain areas in Ireland in the nineteenth century. Hollymount was not connected by rail until November, 1892. Achill (in the Congested Districts) had its rail link opened in May, 1895. Belmullet was never reached by the railways and was largely dependent on sea links to Sligo, Ballina and Westport. It was almost impossible even for horse-drawn vehicles to reach the

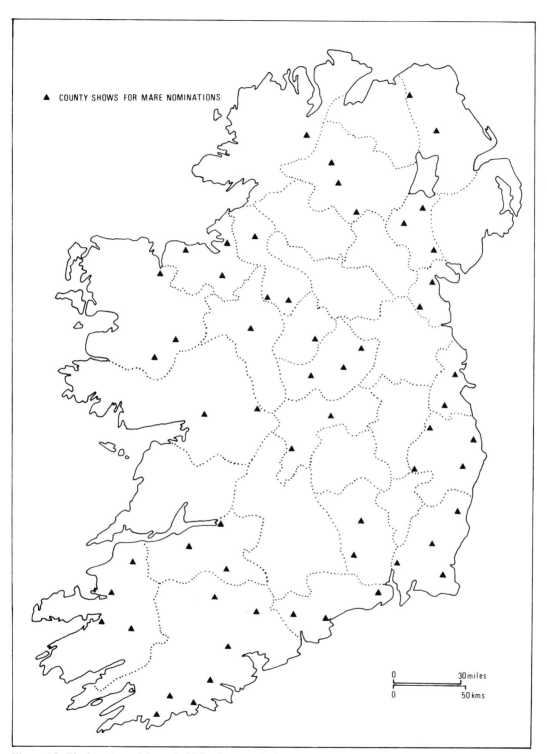

Figure 13. *The location of shows held for the award of mare nominations in 1897. The following committees opted to retain the premium system, as in 1895–96: Carlow, Cavan, Clare, Down, Fermanagh, Kildare, Londonderry, Meath, Monaghan, Queen's and Tipperary*

town from the east, since they had to traverse the desolate wastes of the great blanket bog of Erris. Transport overland, and it was thirty miles to Killala, was largely by pack-pony, '. . . endless strings of ponies, laden,' as Mrs. Pattisson described in Achill in 1896. Thomas Meleady, a Dublin dealer, recalled to the Commissioners on horse breeding, how 'When I went down there first there was a breed of ponies in it you could get up and ride them off the grass thirty miles across the mountains as I often did from Belmullet into Ballina, and they would never tire, without a feed of oats, nor did they know what the taste of oats was . . . they had necks and shoulders like thorough-breds, and the best shape you ever saw, but they are gone out of the country altogether. They used to call them Achill ponies.'[4] Although these were extreme areas of isolation, there were many other parts of Ireland that were almost as difficult to reach. Until the motor-car and the tarmacadamed road revolutionized transport, Ireland was very much dependent on the horse, and ponies with 'necks and shoulders like thoroughbreds,' were greatly to be prized.

Even in accessible areas, like Co. Kilkenny, colonized by the Anglo Normans in the 1200s and long subject to settled (or fairly settled) farming and trade, it was a great boon to breeders to have more than one exhibition to choose from. In 1896 the show for premiums had been held at Kilkenny, whereas one of the main breeding areas lay in the south of the county, around Kilmogany. Now there were two exhibitions, at Kilkenny on April 5th, and at Kilmogany on April 8th. The breeders of Louth and Westmeath must have been equally as pleased as those of Kilkenny with the increase in the number of venues in their counties.

Unfortunately the Royal Dublin Society does not seem to have printed any account either of the nomination exhibitions or of the awards of premiums. Perhaps, in the year when many of their leading horse-breeding members were busy working as Commissioners appointed by the Government to inquire into horse breeding in Ireland, there was not time to do so. The *Reports* of the Commissioners do, however, indicate the value of the Society's horse breeding schemes, and of its *Registers*. They also reflect the great economic importance of horse production in Ireland and show something of the geographical distribution of the industry.

The Commissioners reported that '. . . the number of horses now exported (from Ireland) is nearly 40,000 annually.'[5] Lord Dunraven and others believed that Ireland essentially divided into three horse-breeding regions:

(i)   West
(ii)   North
(iii)   South

They sub-divided the West into two tracts, the pony areas and Kerry and Cork, where '. . . a larger type of mare prevails, and some of the best hunters and high-class carriage horses in Ireland have been bred.' Lord Dunraven and his colleagues believed that in parts of the West '. . . it appears to us that the breeding of horses for sale can hardly be carried on with any profit by the small holders of land.' On the other hand, in parts of Galway, Mayo and Kerry '. . . a hardy breed of ponies formerly existed in considerable numbers,' and they considered that these were worthy of development. They also discovered that '. . . large numbers of foals are driven from the Western districts of Ireland to various fairs in the country, many of them being sold as far to the eastwards as Kildare, Meath, Wicklow, Wexford, and other hunter-breeding districts.' In conclusion Dunraven felt that Thoroughbred or Half-bred sires were needed in Kerry and Cork.

Plate Twenty-five. *The Fourth Earl of Dunraven, of Adare, Co. Limerick. Lord Dunraven was a member of the Commission of Inquiry into the horse-breeding industry and, with other members of the Commission, submitted a most influential report in 1897. Lord Enniskillen submitted a minority report, with support from a considerable number of members of the Commission. Dunraven was the owner of the Fort Union Stud. In association with Lord Randolph Churchill the Earl bought a filly by* Trappist *out of* Festive, *later named* L'Abesse de Jouarre. *From a mating with* St Simon *she produced* Desmond, *champion racehorse sire of the year in which he died: 1913. Lord Dunraven also stood less outstanding sires at stud, such as* Kirkham *and* Atratus, *the latter being advertised at a service fee of £5 for Thoroughbred mares, £3 for Half-bred mares, '. . .Owner's Tenants' Mares, £2.'* (Photo: History of the Turf)

Of the Northern area Dunraven found that '. . . in many parts the farmers buy horses in the South of Ireland, take them home and feed them in the same way as they would cattle, or as nearly so as circumstances permit, and eventually sell them as harness horses to London and other dealers . . . few are bought as hunters, and still fewer bred for that purpose in this division.' In Dunraven's opinion, the North should not be helped to develop breeding at the expense of Western and Southern breeders. Farmers '. . . of the Southern and some parts of the Western districts make horse-breeding their staple, and indeed in some cases, only profitable industry. Care should therefore be taken [in aiding horse breeding, not] . . . to prejudice . . . the general prosperity of the country.'

The South of Ireland, Dunraven wrote, was '. . . the chief mart in the world for high class horses for both riding and driving purposes. These horses are almost entirely the produce of thoroughbred sires, or of half-bred sires of the hunter type.' Nevertheless, His Lordship felt that '. . . many unsound, worthless stallions, are serving at low fees and are responsible for the many inferior, unsaleable animals which are exhibited in the fairs.'

'Unsaleable animals' is a phrase that rings horribly, even today, and it undoubtedly did so in 1897. The horses that fell into that category, if Dunraven was correct, were of inferior quality and the market for them had been diminished by imports of horses to Britain from America and by the spread of '. . . bicycles, tram-cars, and other means of locomotion;' the Commissioners did not degrade themselves by actually mentioning those new-fangled inventions, the motor-cars. Yet the Commissioners found that '. . . the supply of hunters and high-class carriage horses is inadequate to the demand, and could be very largely increased without lowering prices.'

As far as Dunraven was concerned the answer to Ireland's horse breeding problems was five-fold. Firstly '. . . suitable stallions, either the property of the State, or sold or leased by the State to responsible persons on easy terms, and under formulated conditions as to fees to be charged, should be distributed throughout the districts where they are needed.' Secondly, and this was a major tribute to the Society: 'We are of the opinion that it would be a very substantial benefit to the country if the registration system of the Royal Dublin Society could be largely extended.' Thirdly, '. . . we are of the opinion that the thoroughbred stallion is undoubtedly the sire most calculated to improve the breed of horses throughout the country generally' and that also certain Half-breds should be used for stud: 'In the event of a register being formed it would be well that such sires should be examined, in like manner to thoroughbred sires and should be separately registered under suitable regulations.' The fourth point, and this was a criticism largely of the breeding policy of the Congested Districts Board, was that '. . . the Hackney is not in our opinion a desirable sire.' Finally: 'Some few witnesses have advocated the establishment by Government of cart-horse stallions in certain localities; but as the main industry in Ireland consists in the breeding of a lighter class of horse, and the large proportion of the land is not adapted to the heavy draught horse, we consider the supply of such stallions may also be left to private enterprise.'[6]

Dunraven also commented on mares and foals, recommending that prizes should be given for mares in foal or with foal at foot. In addition His Lordship believed that mare nominations to registered stallions were needed: '. . .the country is . . . eminently adapted to produce hunters, high class carriage horses, and remounts,' and Dunraven unequivocally stated that State aid should be given to produce such horse-types.

Throughout much of the thinking of the Commissioners was the awareness that the military might of the United Kingdom, on land, depended very largely on the availability of horses. Horses, of hunter-type, were needed for the cavalry, for officers' chargers and so on. Slightly heavier horses were needed for the artillery, and light animals and ponies were necessary for the mounted infantry. 'No horse, no rule,' may have been a suitable dictum. As Dunraven wrote: 'We most strongly emphasize the value of the Irish horse supply for military purposes, and the serious danger that would arise should that supply fail, or the breed of horses cease to maintain the high standard which at present prevails.' His final recommendation, after criticising the niggardly financial aid given by Government to horse breeding in Ireland (£3,550 in 1897, compared with £233,333 in Hungary, £192,274 in Germany, £170,290 in Austria, and £86,152 in France) was that one Department or Body should deal with the whole horse breeding industry.

In addition to Dunraven's report, Lord Enniskillen and other Commissioners presented a minority report. This differed from Dunraven's in a number of instances. Enniskillen drew attention to the fact that there were at least 2,387 stallions '. . . in the hands of private owners' in 1896. Of these, 466 were Thoroughbred, 264 were returned as Thoroughbred but were not listed in Weatherby's Stud Book, 651 were Half-bred, 816 were pure and half-bred draught, 72 were pure or half-bred Hackneys, eleven were 'nondescript,' nine were Arab or Eastern, and 98 were so-called ponies. The Royal Dublin Society's *Register* therefore covered only a very small proportion of the stallions in Ireland, and ignored those that were not Thoroughbred. As Enniskillen stated: '. . . a very large number of horses in Ireland appear to be used for agricultural purposes, in Ulster 88%, Leinster 74%, Munster 85%, Connaught 89%.' These were virtually ignored by the Society.

Enniskillen also appreciated, like Dunraven, many of the geographical realities of Ireland. He realized that horse breeding was essentially concentrated in Leinster and Munster: stallion numbers alone showed that. In 1896 there were at least 831 stallions in Leinster, 766 in Munster, 498 in Ulster and only 292 in Connaught. (These statistics were collected by the various police authorities in the country especially for the Commissioners). 'Although Thoroughbred sires of the right stamp are to be preferred above all others *where mares are suitable,*' reported His Lordship, '. . . it is evident from the class of mares in some localities and the conditions of the people and their surroundings, that the question of encouraging other descriptions of sires must be recognized.'

The recommendations of Enniskillen and his supporters were, in the main, similar to those of Dunraven, but they concluded that '. . . the needs of each class of breeder should be recognized.' In other words, they believed that it was essential to register Thoroughbred, Hunter, Cart Horse and Hackney stallions, so as to supply the needs of all users of horseflesh. In their opinion it was wrong to neglect the needs of tillage in Ireland and to leave the breeding of draught horses completely in the hands of private enterprise, especially when such enterprise was not subject to any veterinary or other controls of quality and need. They, like the other Commissioners, accepted that the majority of horses sold in Ireland were sold for local agricultural use, and they thought this need should be catered for. Dunraven was more colonial, and military, in his outlook, considering Ireland as a great supplier of quality and military horses for export, especially to Britain.

On the whole the *Reports by the Commissioners* showed that the work of the Royal Dublin Society, though open to local criticism, was greatly appreciated. Above all, the Society's work had emphasized the need for a far more extended and comprehensive system of stallion registration and mare nomination. For the immediate future it was obviously too much to expect that the Society should handle the massive work that such comprehensive development would entail. Nevertheless, (and this would have pleased those far-sighted gentlemen who established the Society away back in 1731), the Society's work was acting as a catalyst for the future. And in the future it looked as if major developments would take place. Political developments were already pointing, strongly, to Home Rule, and it must have seemed inevitable to most politically-aware persons that the institutions of State had to be established rapidly in Ireland to cope with the new situation. On the eve of the twentieth century administration had become far too complex to be left to the gentry of the Royal Dublin Society, or to a clique in Dublin Castle. But in 1897 the Commissioners were only making their report, not opening a new and massive Department of State, such as was to be opened in 1900, when the Department of Agriculture was founded.

For the time being, now that the chairman of the Co. Fermanagh Committee (The Earl of Enniskillen) and other people could relax from their labours as Commissioners, attention swung back to the success of the Royal Dublin Society's scheme. In general terms its success had been noted by the Commissioners, but in detail it is harder to analyse. Perhaps the best way of so doing would, on a summer's day, have been to attend the annual West Carbery Show, in the fastnesses of West Cork. There, in 1896, *Whalebone* won his class. More important, 'A yearling filly by him won the Cup presented by S. [*sic.*, actually A.] C. Somerville, Esq., M.F.H., for the best filly in the Carbery Show, 1896, and a yearling by him won the first prize given by the Carbery Society, 1896, and two two-year-old colts got first and second at the Carbery Show, 1896.'[7] No matter what Dunraven might have said about there being '. . . many unsound, worthless stallions,' in Ireland, *Whalebone* was not one of them. He was a Registered Stallion for 1897, one of four that stood in County Cork (West Division). A.C. Somerville, too, came from a successful family, even if nobody had yet realized the extent of their success. In the years ahead his sister, Edith, was to become one of the most popular writers of hunting stories and, with her cousin Violet Martin (Ross), of those novels of the ascendancy life of Ireland that have never been surpassed. But *The Real Charlotte* had only been published in 1894 and, like the Royal Dublin Society's horse breeding scheme, was only gradually being appreciated for the major achievement that it was. *Some Experiences of an Irish R.M.* was not to appear until 1899, but perhaps Edith Somerville was thinking of some progeny of the Registered Stallions when she penned her tale of the green-eyed filly at Clountiss Agricultural Show. Perhaps *Whalebone* was there as well, and the Sultan, with his snowy turban! *He* wanted to buy the 'green-eyed thing' for his State carriage so it was not worthless, and hardly unsound, and probably the daughter of a Registered Stallion, even if it did cross '. . . the croquet ground, thoroughly, from corner to corner.'[8]

CHAPTER TWELVE

Continuity

The increasing prestige and importance of the Register of Thoroughbred Stallions was reflected, in 1898, by an increase in the membership of the Stallion Registration Committee, the second to have taken place. Michael Betagh, Justice of the Peace, (one hopes that position was not called into use on the Committee), R.G. Carden, D.L., and Captain C. Fetherstonhaugh, J.P., were added to the list of members, bringing the size of the Committee to twelve. The three new members were all deeply involved with horses. Richard Carden, for example, had already served on the County Tipperary Committee and, with his home at Fishmoyne, Borrisoleigh, represented the more northerly breeders in that area. Captain Fetherstonhaugh, as already noted in Chapter Nine, came of a line of hunting gentry in Westmeath and was a member of the local committee for that county.

The Registration Committee were faced with applications for the registration of 265 stallions, which was an increase of sixteen over the previous year. Of these they registered 217, an increase of five over the 1897 total. The Committee felt obliged, however, to publish a note in the *Register* stating that: 'Several Stallions, although not favourably reported upon as to conformation, have been placed on the Register after the Committee had carefully examined evidence of the high character of their produce.'

The detailed evidence of 'high character' was not disclosed, although it would be fascinating to know whether it referred to racing or show yard performance, prowess in the hunting field, or just general good looks.

Of the new entrants to the *Register*, and there were thirty of them, *The Baron* was probably of the highest quality, although *Bushey Park* was a strong second. *The Baron* was fourteen years old, dark bay, and 16.1¼ hands. He had been bred by J. Sullivan and was by *Xenophon* out of *Tantrum*. In 1886 the colt won a Maiden Plate at Newmarket and speedily followed that success by winning the Woodcote Stakes at Epsom and an International Two-year old at Kempton Park. Later in the year *The Baron*, who now had a reputation to be contended with, took the Astley Stakes at Lewes. The following year the colt opened his account with the Craven Stakes at Newmarket and then was second in both the Derby and the Grand Prix de Paris. He finished his year by winning the St. George's Stakes at Liverpool. In 1888 *The Baron* carried 12 st. 1 lb. to victory in the Southdown Club Welter Handicap. The following year he won two races at Brighton before, in 1890, again winning the Southdown Club Welter Handicap under the great weight of 12st. 6 lbs.

Plate Twenty-six. *Captain C. Fetherstonhaugh, Bracklyn, Killucan, who joined the Stallion Registration Committee in 1898 and who also stood registered stallions at stud. (Photo:* Dublin Horse Show Magazine)

Plate Twenty-seven. Bushey Park, *by* Hampton *out of* Sunshine, *bred in England by J.H. Houldsworth, a member of the Jockey Club. The horse won the Alexandra Plate at Ascot in 1893, the Great Yorkshire Handicap in 1894, the Liverpool Cup in 1895 and other races. When this photograph was taken the horse was six-years-old and at the prime of his racing career. After a brief period at stud in Cobham Mr James Daly bought the sire to stand at his Hartstown Stud near Clonsilla, Co. Dublin, where* Bushey Park *was first registered in 1898. (Photo:* Racing Illustrated)

Plate Twenty-eight. Egerton, *by* Hampton *out of* Pompeia, *winner of races at Manchester, Liverpool, Brighton, Nottingham and '. . .as a six-year-old . . . the Duchess of York Plate of £300.' In 1898, the year after his turf career ended, Colonel Thomson of Bushford, Rockcorry, Co. Monaghan, stood the horse at stud at a fee of £6.* Egerton *was typical of many registered stallions and, when this picture of him was taken, stood 15.3½ hands high, girthed 6ft 1ins and had 8 ins of bone. (Photo: courtesy of the Royal Dublin Society)*

Once his racing career was over *The Baron* was shown and used as a stallion, taking a silver medal in 1897 at the Hunters Improvement Society Show at Islington. Now, in 1898, he belonged to The Earl of Kenmare and stood at Killarney House where he imparted his potential to many Kerry mares. Mind you, one boggles somewhat at the thought of a Killarney jarvey driving a nag, by a horse that was second in the Derby, in the shafts of a jaunting car! *The Baron* stood at a fee of £10 10s. for Thoroughbred mares, 'Gentlemen's, £5; Groom 5s.; Farmers' £3; Groom 2s. 6d.; Tenants' £2 2s.; Groom, 2s. 6d.' Obviously being a gentleman was an expensive luxury.

Bushey Park had been foaled in 1889 and now stood at a height of 16.1 hands and was bay in colour. As a colt he won the Prince of Wales Stakes at Leicester, the Newmarket St. Leger, the Alexandra Plate at Ascot, the Great Yorkshire Stakes at Doncaster and the Liverpool Cup at Liverpool. It was an impressive record, especially since two of the races (at Leicester and Ascot) were each worth 1,000 sovereigns. Not surprisingly the horse had been acquired by James Daly who now owned the Hartstown Stud, Clonsilla, as well as his Liffey Bank property in Dublin.

The most interesting characteristic of the new stallions entered in the *Register* was their high quality, as evidenced by racing performances. Fourteen of the entirely new entries (some, like *Guerrilla*, had been included in earlier *Registers*), had won at least one race, and some had very lengthy and quite distinguished racing records. *Egerton*, for example, had begun his racing career as a two year old, winning at Manchester and Liverpool, and was seven years old when he retired from the turf. Even in his final year, when he ran in nine races, he was placed in three of them. Admittedly *Egerton* was no Classic hope, but he was a useful performer and must have more than earned his keep. In 1893 he won the Brighton High Weight Plate, worth £500, and in 1894 he won two races worth £600 each, as well as being second in the Nottingham Spring Handicap of £1,000. Again, in 1895, he won two races of £500 each. As a six-year-old *Egerton* took the Duchess of York Plate, of £300. Colonel Thompson of Rockcorry in Co. Monaghan was therefore doing the local breeders a decided service by placing this consistent and tough horse in their midst, and at a fee of £6 few could complain although they might have argued that it was the stallion's first stud season and that, consequently, he was an unknown quantity as a sire.

Christopher Taafe, the well-known stallion man from the Co. Westmeath, had a new horse in his stable to keep old *Piercefield* company. The newcomer was *Connaught Ranger*, bred by Joseph Blake at Ballinafad, Co. Mayo. This horse was sired by Blake's *Ballinafad*, who was foaled in 1878 and who had won his first race, as a four-year-old, at Baldoyle. *Ballinafad* later won at the Curragh (Spring Hurdle Handicap, 1881, and the International Hurdle, 1882), and again at Baldoyle (the Stewards' Plate, 1882). The horse also competed successfully in the showring and took the Twenty-Guinea Cup and Silver Medal at Ballinasloe in 1894 and the Connaught Cup at Galway in 1895, as well as various other prizes. *Ballinafad* had been entered in the *Register* in Volume One, and was still included in it. His son, *Connaught Ranger*, had a less impressive race-course record than his father, but that did not deter Taafe from standing him at stud. In 1897 he won his race at the Mullingar Hunt, Newbrook, worth £20 10s.

Taafe probably recognized a good pedigree when he saw one, and *Connaught Ranger*'s grand-dam was by *Faugh-a-Ballagh* who had been foaled in Ireland in 1841. *Faugh-a-Ballagh* won the St. Leger and sired *Leamington*, a horse that was exported to America where he begot *Iroquois*, winner of the Epsom Derby of 1881. *Faugh-a-Ballagh* was a brother of *Birdcatcher*, being by *Sir Hercules* out of *Guiccioli*, and was a member of one of the great sire families (No. 11) identified by Bruce Lowe.[1] At a fee of £3, with five shillings for the groom, his descendant, *Connaught Ranger*, probably represented good value, and only cost half as much as *Piercefield*.

By contrast with Taafe's junior stallion, with just one race to his credit, B.P.J. Mahony of Annefield, Maryboro', had an aged horse that had won twelve races, *Philammon*. This sire was twenty-four years old and had won his first race, the Strand Plate at the Curragh, in 1877. He had also been second in the Irish Derby of that year. *Philammon*'s final win was the Esher Stakes at Sandown, in 1881. Surprisingly, for a horse of his quality and seniority (he had sired at least twenty winners), he stood at the low fee of five guineas. One of his progeny, *Philomath*, was the great-grand-dam of *Papyrus*, winner of the 1923 Derby.

In the extreme south-east of Ireland, in Co. Wexford, Captain Maher had a new stallion in the *Register*: *Kentish Fire*, a son of *Torpedo*. Maher had bred this horse himself and, in 1890, had the pleasure of knowing that the colt won the Irish Derby at the Curragh and came second in the

Curragh Caesarawitch. Unlike *Torpedo*, whose fee was now still nineteen guineas, his speedy son stood at the unostentatious fee of five guineas. Maher had four Registered Stallions at stud, at fees varying from £5 to nineteen guineas.

Naturally, among the horses newly registered and re-registered (after a lapse of over a year) there were stallions who had won nothing on the race-course. *Fitz-Clifden*, for example, had twice won his class at the Royal Dublin Society's Shows, but that was all that was claimed for him. Other stallions, such as *Lyric* (now twenty-two years old) had either won nothing, or had done so such a long time ago that nobody thought of mentioning the fact.

In addition to new registrations there were also deletions from the *Register*, twenty-one in all. These included such characters as John Purdon's *Ascetic* and John Mahony's *New Laund* Perhaps they should not be mentioned in the same breath, for one sired race-horses, the other got hunters, but both were missed, in their own way. Perhaps it was fitting, with the deletion of *New Laund*, that the military should relinquish their control of the Muskerry Hounds, for had not four of his gets been '. . . the first to come in for brush over a stiff country with large fences' at a meet of Royal Lancers, the regiment that ran the Muskerrys?

There were other changes in the *Register*, too. *Marchaway*, winner of the Hunter Stallions Class at Dublin in 1894, and long the property of Colonel de Robeck of Newlands, Naas, had moved to Co. Carlow. The horse now was registered in the names of Walter Kavanagh and Denis R. Pack-Beresford, and they had increased his fees for Thoroughbreds by five shillings, to five guineas. The Colonel had not mentioned the word 'Thoroughbred,' but presumably that was what he charged the highest fees for.

Another change, and one that was regrettable, was that the Congested Districts Board only registered one horse, *Diogenes*. They had obviously acquired the stallion from Thomas McMahon of Castleblaney, and the horse was now stood in Co. Kerry. *Uncle Sam*, whom the Board had registered in 1897, disappeared entirely from the *Register* for 1898. *St. Aidan*, having changed hands, belonged to Norman Thompson of Delgany, in Co. Wicklow, which was probably a more congenial home for the grandson of a Derby winner than the windswept wilds of Co. Donegal.

Heading the list of stallion owners, for the first time, was James Daly, the Dublin man. Three of his seven stallions, *Ballynoe*, *Palm Leaf* and *Springtime* were leased out, the first two standing in the Co. Tipperary and the latter in Co. Wexford. William Pallin had six Registered Stallions and, as in previous years, also indulged in leasing. *Favonian* was again standing with John Lambert at Ballinasloe, but this was the only stallion, in the *Register*, that Pallin leased-out for the season. As in the previous year he continued to lease *Red Prince II*, still listed as belonging to Linde, although the poor man had been dead for a whole year.

On the whole the quality of the Registered Stallions for 1898 was excellent. Horses of widely different values, as was right and proper, were listed, and they varied from animals that had never even been raced to Classic winners. Captain Tower Townshend's horses were typical. His *Town Moor* (close third in the Derby), was still at stud; so was *Beaucourt* (although not listed as having won anything). Joining them was a new stallion, *Hidden Treasure*, winner of a maiden at Ascot '. . . and ran 3rd to *Surefoot* at the same meeting and has not run since.' There were many hidden treasures in the *Register*, and some that were more prominent, and the Stallion Registration Committee had good cause to congratulate itself on the publication of the 1898 *Register*. It listed sires that fulfilled many different requirements, and many of whom were ideally suited for

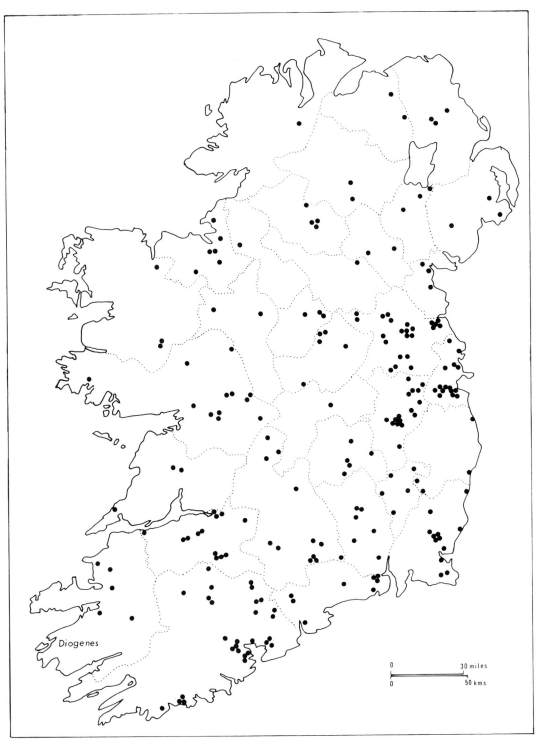

Diogenes

Figure 14. *The location of Registered Stallions in 1898. The stallion belonging to the Congested Districts Board is named*

the service of tenant-farmers' half-bred mares.

The geographical distribution of the stallions, shown on Figure Fourteen, was markedly similar to that of 1897. The poorer and more remote regions, as in previous years, were deficient in stallions, the more fertile and prosperous areas in some cases had a glut of them. West Cork, apart from the southern coastal belt, had no Registered Thoroughbred Stallion at all. Neither was there such a stallion in the Kenmare-Iveragh area, apart from the Congested Districts Board's *Diogenes*. These were the areas where, between 1891 and 1961, there was a population decrease of fifty to seventy per cent.[2] Under such conditions of human out-migration and widespread poverty there was little scope for the services of a good Thoroughbred, and it would be unfair to expect private enterprise to accept the risk of standing a stallion in such an area. Similarly there were no Registered Stallions in west Mayo and in west Donegal. Although the outward movement of the human population in those areas was not quite as severe as in the extreme south-west the conditions of poverty were every bit as bad, if not worse.

In detail, as has already partly been noted, stallions continued to be moved around the country, often from owner to owner. This was essential to prevent stallions from serving their own daughters, but it did nothing to solve the problem of the poor areas, where there were no Registered Stallions anyway. *Dulcimer*, owned by O.T. Slocock of Carlow in 1895, now belonged to Aeneas Falkiner Nuttall and stood at Cullinamore, Sligo. *Vanderbilt*, standing with Charles H.T. Reade at Donishall, Carnew, in 1895, had become the property of Charles Boyd of Castletown Manor, Ballina. At long last, however, the Royal Dublin Society appeared to have become aware of the problems of the 'empty areas,' and of a more general need to introduce really high quality horses into the country and to locate them in needy areas. This was not a criticism of the quality of many of the stallions that had been introduced, by private enterprise, to the country. Rather was it a reinforcing of the efforts of individual stallion owners.

The *Proceedings* of the Society somewhat sadly report that, for 1898, '. . . an extra grant was given to each county, *pro rata*, after the Society had failed to purchase suitable sires to bring into the country. Weeks were spent by an agent in England without his being able to recommend the purchase of even one horse.[3] It was an inauspicious start to the Society's new policy of active purchase of stallions, but at least it was a step in the right direction. On paper, according to the rules that had governed the Horse Breeding Schemes since 1895, the Society had the power to purchase suitable stallions, if the number and quality of stallions offered for registration was insufficient. For three years the Society had allowed its purchasing powers to remain dormant but now, stirred perhaps by the reports of the Commissioners on horse breeding, it was beginning to activate them.

As far as mares were concerned the schemes operated much as in 1897. County Committees had the choice of either the nomination or the premium system. Added flexibility was provided, however, by allowing committees to use a mixture of both schemes. In other words they could allocate nominations for mares and premiums for yearlings, or they could just award nominations and forgo any premiums. Twenty-two committees opted for the nomination system, in some cases with premiums for yearlings; eight chose the premiums system; two, Cos. Limerick and Tyrone, had not decided which system to use at the time when the *Register* went to press. The committees that chose the premium system were: Carlow, Clare, Fermanagh, Kildare, Londonderry, Meath, Queen's and Tipperary. To judge by the choice of system in 1899 the committees must have been reasonably satisfied with the system they adopted in 1898. Only the Co.

Plate Twenty-nine. *C.H.T. Reade of Dromishall, Carnew, Co. Wicklow, was a well-known horse man and this photograph shows his chestnut gelding that won the class for horses to carry up to 15 stone at the Dublin Horse Show of 1900. The horse was sired by John Widger's registered stallion,* Passion Flower, *a winner at Punchestown and Cork races. (Photo: courtesy of the Royal Dublin Society)*

Fermanagh Committee decided to change from the premium system, and even they hedged their decision by opting for a combination of nominations for mares and premiums for two-year-olds and yearlings. In all cases awards, either of nominations or premiums, could only be made if the animal was certified free from hereditary disease by a Veterinary Surgeon appointed by the local committee.

When all was said and done the overall impression of the 1898 scheme was that it was one of continuity. The *Register* had shown a slight increase in numbers, and the apparent decrease in quality of new entrants, which seemed apparent in 1897, had been reversed. Furthermore, the Society had appreciated that both the nomination system and the premium system had good points, and that a combination of both systems was even better. As the breeding season ended local committee members, like Captain John MacGillycuddy of Killarney, could again turn their thoughts towards the needs of their kennels (he hunted stags with his own hounds, but it was still a little early for stag-hunting to begin.) As the premium shows ended gentlemen like the Chairman of the Co. Kildare Committee, Lieut. Colonel H. de Robeck, could concentrate on their fox-hounds. And it was time to do so, for the cubbing season was almost over and de Robeck was just starting his second season as Master of the Kildares. The hunter's moon was waxing, thinly, in the night skies, and soon it would flood the Kildare countryside with its silvery, ghostly, fullsome light. The harvest, except in a few unfortunate areas, was long since saved and in their churches the Ascendancy had sung Jane Campbell's hymn-translation 'We plough the fields, and scatter,' mostly unaware that it had been composed in German. As far as many members of the Royal Dublin Society were concerned there was not too much to be worried about, and 'continuity' was a precious word.

CHAPTER THIRTEEN

The Trio

Some committees have a habit of enlarging themselves. The Stallion Registration Committee was in that category. It began with five members in 1895, increased to seven in 1896, reached a dozen in 1898 and now, in 1899, had thirteen members. Michael Betagh no longer served on it, but Lord Ashtown and Colonel de Robeck had joined its ranks. Ashtown has been described as eccentric, mainly because he chose to spend much of his time in Ireland rather than in English social society.[1] He owned a number of renowned stallions, including the fine Hackney, *Sir Augustus*, and the two Registered Stallions, *Terror* and *The Rector*, all of whom stood at Woodlawn in Co. Galway. Colonel de Robeck, who became the Baron in 1904, has already been described as Master of the Kildares, but he was an eminent gentleman in many different ways and no stranger to horses, horse-racing, horse-breeding and everything else associated with horses of quality.

As in 1898 the Register stated that the sum of money allocated to each county in Ireland to aid horse-breeding was '. . . based on the number of Horses in the several Provinces . . . the average amount offered, per County, in each of these Provinces, is as follows:- Leinster, £95; Connaught, £88; Ulster, £73; and Munster, £125.'[2] The counties with the highest grants were Wexford and Tipperary, strange though that may seem in view of the fact that only twelve Registered Stallions stood in each county; there were twenty-three Registered Stallions in East Cork, yet the grant for that area was only £100. But Wexford, in particular, was famous for its horses and its horsemen and the county was full of fine brood mares.

The owners of 275 stallions applied for their horses to be included in the *Register* and, '. . . after very careful inquiry,' 206 were registered. This was the lowest number to be listed since the *Registers* were started five years earlier, although that was not a major cause for concern. Thirty stallions listed in 1898 were no longer in the *Register*, but there were eighteen new entrants and a couple of entrants who had been listed in years prior to 1898, but not in that year. *Uncle Sam*, one of the Congested Districts Board's stallions, was listed for Co. Leitrim, making a happy return to the *Register*, and the Board also had *Diogenes* listed, for Kerry. The tiny *Watchspring*, all 14.2 hands of him, had finally disappeared from the scene, even though Thomas Meleady had told the Commissioners on horse-breeding in 1897 that '. . . it is a little thoroughbred horse we want like *Watchspring*,' as a polo pony. But stallions do not last for ever, and *Watchspring* was no exception. The sad thing was that the Society did not replace the stallion with another one of similar kind, suited to the needs of that isolated area of Connemara.

The Society did, however, introduce three new stallions to the country, *Chad*, *Laurium* and *Ground Ivy*.[3] *Chad* had been bred by Lord Roseberry and his paternal grandsire was *Hermit*. Surprisingly, in view of the fullness of the details given for many other horses, the *Register* only records the stallion's breeding, age, colour and service fee. Even *Chad*'s height was not given, and no details of any racing, show-ring or stud performances. It was a very strange introduction to an active scheme of stallion purchase, but the horse seems to have been passed on to R. Malone, a well-known veterinary surgeon in Wexford, out of the Society's hands.

Laurium had won the Meldon Welter Handicap at Newcastle, the Eglinton Stakes at Carlisle and the Diamond Jubilee Handicap (worth £232) at Hamilton Park, all in 1897. The horse stood at John Lambert's stables, Redmount Hill, Ballinasloe. Lambert had leased stallions from William Pallin in many previous years, and that was a good recommendation for him to the Society. *Laurium* was advertised at a service fee of £4, '. . . by agreement with Royal Dublin Society, twenty-five Nominated Mares at £2. 2s., including groom's fees.'

The third horse purchased by the Society, *Ground Ivy*, was not listed in the 1899 *Register*, although his name appears in 1900. In that year the horse stood at B.P.J. Mahony's establishment, Annefield, Maryborough. Like *Chad* no details of the horse's performances were given, nor was his height stated. His grand-dam was by *King of the Forest*, the sire of old *Heart of Oak*, Captain Davis's fine stallion who won the class that preceeded the inception of the Horse Breeding Schemes, Class One of the 1886 Horse Show. *King of the Forest* had also sired *Woodreeve*, the stallion that stood in the Cappoquin District in 1888, and appeared in the pedigree of other tested and quality stallions. Perhaps it was his presence in *Ground Ivy*'s pedigree that influenced the Society to acquire his brown grandson. Mahony had kept old *Philammon* at stud the previous year and was well used to stud work.

Thomas McCutchan of Streete, Co. Westmeath, owned one of the most interesting new entrants to the *Register*. This was *Sternchaser*, bred by the New Zealand Stud Company. *Sternchaser* won his first race as a four-year-old, after being second in his previous year in a Maiden Plate at the Victoria and Amateur Turf Club in Australia. He also won, at the ages of five and six, the Mordiolloc Handicap (worth £50) and the Welter Handicap (worth £100). Whilst not exactly a top quality racer, it was nevertheless grand to see a two-way trade with the colonies. Of course, Lord Dunraven was already standing an Australian-bred horse at his stud at Adare, so *Sternchaser* was by no means the first antipodean equine to savour the delights of the Irish fillies.

Captain D.D. Heather of Knockadoo, Coolaney in the Co. Sligo, owned what was arguably the best new-entrant to the *Register*. This was *Red Heart*, a grandson of *Xenophon*. Linde, the recently deceased Curragh trainer who had leased *Red Prince II* to William Pallin, had trained a son of *Xenophon*'s, *Seaman*, to win both the Conyngham Cup at Punchestown and the Grand Hurdle Race at Paris in 1881. *Xenophon* was known as a progenitor of good horses, and *Red Heart* was no exception. In 1894 he won the Twickenham Two-year-old Maiden Plate at Kempton Park, the October Nursery Handicap at Lingfield, the International Foal Stakes at Leopardstown, and the Osmaston Nursery Stakes at Derby. In 1895 *Red Heart* won two races and, in the following year, won three more, ending his run of successes by taking the Visitors' Plate at Goodwood. Half-bred mares could enjoy *Red Heart*'s attentions for five guineas, although Thoroughbreds had to pay nine guineas.

Another solid entrant to the *Register* was the fourteen-year-old *Glenvannon*, bred by Captain Archdale of Co. Fermanagh and now owned by Mrs. Cowhy of Churchtown House, near Buttevant. *Glenvannon* had been second in the Open Hunters' Race at Limerick in 1889 and had then won the Great Munster Plate at Cork. During that year he won five races, and was second on five occasions. In 1890 *Glenvannon* was second in the Great Munster Plate. This was just the sort of solid, if unspectacular, record that was needed if a horse was to have a reasonable chance of improving ordinary stock, and *Glenvannon* was fairly typical of many of the country-stallions, especially in east and north Cork.

The most interesting newcomer to the lists of stallion-owners was a Dublin medical man, Dr. Cox. In 1897 he had given evidence to the Commissioners inquiring into horse-breeding in Ireland and he had also published his own book, entitled *Notes on the history of the Irish horse*. This little volume was based on much laborious work, including the culling of stud-notices and notices of sales and premiums, from a number of eighteenth century newspapers. Now the Doctor had turned theory and learning into practice, and stood *Blâr Aodan* with E.P. Ryan at Cabra Castle, Thurles. The experiment was obviously a success, since Cox continued to own the stallion in 1900, even though the Doctor resided at 54, St. Stephen's Green, in Dublin.

The value of the *Registers*, and of many of the stallions listed therein, had already become

Plate Thirty. Crotanstown, *photographed as a three-year-old when in training at Lambourne. The colt had been bred by R. Newcomen at the Curragh and was by* Gallinule *or* Favo *out of* Lady Louisa (*by* Solon). *After winning at Baldoyle in 1894 he was placed in a number of races before being retired to stud with E.K.B. Tighe at Woodstock, Inistioge, in Co. Kilkenny, where he was first registered in 1899. This was just the sort of sire that, at a service fee of two guineas, was invaluable for the production of quality Half-breds.* Crotanstown *stood 16 hands high, girthed 6ft 1½ ins and had 7⅞ ins bone. (Photo:* Racing Illustrated)

Plate Thirty-one. *E.K.B. Tighe, owner of* Crotanstown *and other horses. (Photo:* British Hunts and Huntsmen)

apparent, but nowhere more so than in the Grand National. This great race has long dominated steeplechasing and to win it is the greatest ambition of many an owner. In 1899 a note in the *Register* recorded that *Hominy* was the sire of *Cathal*, '(2nd for Grand National).' *Hominy* was one of the many excellent stallions that J.A.S. Langan kept at Bellewstown House, and in 1899 his fee was £4, with five shillings for the groom. *Cathal* ran in the Grand National in 1895, being beaten by a length-and-a-half by another Irish horse, *Wild Man from Borneo*. The *Wild Man* was ridden by Joe Widger of Waterford and was owned by his brother, John, who has already been noted as an owner of Registered Stallions.

In 1897, when the Meath-bred *Manifesto* won the race, poor *Cathal* fell at the last fence, and appeared to be dying. Luckily '. . . a vet discovered that he had merely swallowed his tongue; and *Cathal*, having ungratefully bitten his rescuer, recovered so well as to finish second the following year, for the second time.'[4]

Two years before *Cathal*'s first second in the Grand National the race had been won by *Cloister*, bred by the Earl of Fingall. That horse was by *Ascetic*, John Purdon's venerable stallion, and a former Registered Stallion. '*Ascetic* had proved useless as a racehorse and was used to

Plate Thirty-two. *John Widger of Waterford, who owned the winner of the 1895 Grand National and who also stood many good stallions in his yard. (Photo:* Dublin Horse Show Magazine)

fetch the post from the local village.'[5] But, useless or not, *Ascetic*'s progeny were to dominate a number of Grand Nationals. As yet only *Cloister* had done so, but two other youngsters were already eating oats and preparing for the fray, even though their days were still in the future.

In Co. Limerick Joseph Sheehy continued to stand *Fra Diavolo* at stud. Although, like *Ascetic*, apparently not much of a race-horse, *Fra Diavolo* had sired *Soltaire*, the winner in 1897 of the Grand Steeplechase of Paris. Other stallions had similarly successful progeny, whilst others sired the winners of selling races or hunt races. But the fact was that many useful horses were being sired by Registered Stallions, and the lists of successful progeny printed in the *Registers* became increasingly lengthy.

The most lengthy, if not the most noteworthy, list of progeny was printed under the name of *Scene Shifter*. This beautiful horse, by *Mask* out of *Cockleshell*, belonged to John Harris of the Victor Stud, Kilmallock. *Scene Shifter* had been bred by J.A. Craven in England and was a bright bay, foaled in 1885. He was 16.0½ hands high and had been a useful racer in his day. Amongst other successes the horse won the Taplow Welter Handicap at the Western Ayr Meeting in 1891. Harris proudly produced two closely printed pages of *Scene Shifter*'s and his offsprings' feats: '. . . at Cardiff (Wales) Show, 1896, in three-year-old gelding class likely to make weight-carrying hunters, *Lorenzo*, by *Scene Shifter*, 2nd prize; at Ballinasloe Show, 1896, in two-year-old colts likely to make hunters, *Light Heart* by *Scene Shifter*, 1st prize;' and so the catalogue continued, almost *ad nauseum*. Thomas Nugent, of Carrick-on-Suir, was briefer and to the point with his progeny notice: '*Young Marden*'s stock have won more prizes at County Shows during the years 1896, 1897 and 1898, than any other Sire Horse in Ireland.' And that was that. It might not have looked as impressive as *Scene Shifter*'s notice, but it said all that was necessary and for those who read with discernment, the record obviously could hardly be bettered.

Among the stallions whose names had gone from the *Register* were *Studley*, *The Robber*, *Town Moor* and *Young Victor*. The latter horse had sired famous show-jumpers, such as *Hurrah*, winner of the Champion Wall Jump at Ball's Bridge in 1887. Show-jumping was a relatively new, but developing sport, that was to blossom in the twentieth century. *Studley* had won at the Dublin Horse Show in 1892 for his produce exhibited, and as late as 1897 (he had been foaled in

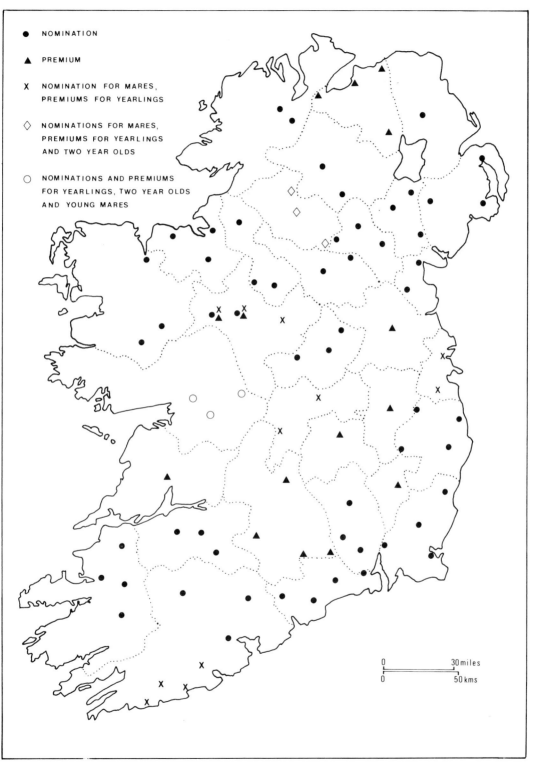

Figure 15. *The location of shows held to award mare nominations and mare and foal premiums in 1899.*

1881) was placed first in the class for stallions over twelve years old and overall Champion Sire and winner of the Croker Challenge Cup for the best weight-carrying sire. It was sad to see such horses disappear, but time, tide and age wait for no man, and for no horse, either, and it was only natural that some old favourites should fade from the scene.

As in 1898 County Committees were allowed to choose either the nomination scheme for mares, or the premium scheme, or even a combination of both. Some committees, such as that for Co. Donegal, played safe and opted for the nomination system, '. . . with Premium in the Autumn if any Surplus Funds.' The Co. Galway Committee, under the chairmanship of Howard St. George of Brackernagh, Ballinasloe, devised the most complicated (some might think 'fantastic') of schemes. They offered twelve nominations for competition at each of their three shows, (Ballinasloe, Athenry and Loughrea). 'The balance of the £100 Grant will be offered in Premiums for young Mares, Two-Year-Olds, and Yearlings at the County Galway Horse Show at Ballinasloe in August, 1899.' The Co. Westmeath Committee, who had chosen the nomination system, decided on what seemed a particularly fair way of administering it: 'The Nominations will, as far as practicable be divided as follows:- One-third for two-year-old Mares and Fillies rising two years old; one-third for Mares not over six years old, and one-third for Mares over six years.'

The distribution of all the shows held in conjunction with the award of nominations and premiums is shown on Figure Fifteen. This map is the best indication, since the Royal Dublin Society began its Horse Breeding Schemes, of the distribution of half-bred breeding mares. West Mayo, even around Clew Bay; Dingle and Iveragh; the interior of west Cork; the west of Donegal; the Sperrins; north Cavan; all emerge as showless. Although this is not proof of a lack of substantial numbers of good half-bred mares, it is reasonable to deduce that fact, especially in the light of other evidence that the map does not show. North Galway, with its glacial-drift covered swelling limestone plains, is also showless, but that was the region in which *Dauntless* and other stallions used to travel (*Prince Violet*, *Bonnie Charlie* and *Master Ned* still did so, the latter horse having moved from William Pallin's Curragh stables to those of Michael Neary, near Creggs). The Co. Galway Committee were possibly a little remiss in not allocating a show to the Tuam-north Galway region, but it was scarcely possible to hold shows everywhere. In any case, only one member of the committee came from that region, T.F. Lewin of Castlegrove, Tuam, so there could hardly have been a strong 'northern' lobby.

Co. Kerry is particularly interesting. Shows were held at Killarney, Castleisland, Listowel and Tralee. Yet Kenmare, Dingle and, to a lesser extent, Cahirciveen, were important urban centres in the county. When the *Irish Draught Horse Book* was first published, in 1918, a number of Irish Draughts were registered in those areas. They included *Justice*, a dappled-grey stallion owned by Edward McSweeney of Gerahduveen, Kenmare, and *Sunbeam*, a brown stallion belonging to Robert Casey of Ballintaggart, Dingle. There was therefore an appreciation of good horses in those areas and it is inconceivable, especially for the fertile farmlands around Dingle and Ventry, that the areas should have been barren of good half-bred brood mares. But those areas lay mainly in the domain of the Congested Districts Board, so perhaps it was appropriate to leave them to the mercy of that beneficial organization.

The interior of west Cork is also interesting. West of Macroom the landscape is dominated by rugged mountains, and is not the sort of landscape that was likely to sustain quality horses. Yet the head of Bantry Bay was entirely different, with its fertile drumlin farmland. But no attempt was made to cater for it. North Cork, beyond Kanturk, is barren bleak land too, like that beyond Macroom, though not as rocky and barren. That area was served only by the show at Kanturk, but it was hardly likely to be good horse country. A tough, rough cob was far more to the point in that region.

Co. Tipperary had an odd allocation of shows. The Golden Vale was well catered for, with shows at Carrick-on-Suir, Clonmel and Tipperary. But no attempt was made to provide for the Ormond country, that fertile region that stretched north and west from Nenagh to the county boundary. 'Dalesman' (C.N. de Courcy-Parry) has written a vivid account of social conditions in that area around 1920: '. . . everything was most formal by night, even to arming one's hostess up to the festive board,' if one moved in county society, of course. He also described the fine horses of the area, recounting how, at a hunt, 'I was on a particularly fine horse, and, putting him at a large gate into a road just to test his abilities . . . I was horrified to find two gentlemen – with horses to sell – jumping it on either side of me, quite regardless of the gate-posts.'[6] Fine horses, and horses that jump gate-posts, are not bred overnight, yet in 1899 the Co. Tipperary Committee made no attempt to accommodate the breeders of that region. Perhaps they felt that only gentry lived there, with no tenant-farmers worth bothering about; after all, 'Dalesman' did admit that when he went there he had not anticipated '. . . so much splendour.'

Other committees, like those of Waterford, Wexford, Westmeath and others, organized their shows in what now seems a more responsible manner, catering for all parts of their county's breeding-areas. In Co. Waterford shows were held at Lismore, Dungarvan, Kilmacthomas and Waterford itself. But perhaps it is not fair to judge committees now, almost eighty years later, and without the full facts and debates of the committees before us. The Tipperary Committee, in spite of the multitude of mares in its area, had only £140 to spend, the Kerry Committee had £100, the same as in Galway and East Cork, while seven committees had only £60 each at their disposal. All things considered it was amazing that the county committees managed to achieve so much with so little money, and they deserve a great deal of credit for what they did.

The main criticism of the year, if criticism is necessary when so little finance was available anyway, must surely be of the distribution of the Registered Stallions. 1899 was the first year, as far as can be discovered from the printed records, in which the Royal Dublin Society purchased stallions to stand in Ireland. The rules of the Horse Breeding Scheme specifically stated that the Society could hire or buy stallions '. . . to provide for such County or District' as should be deficient in Registered Stallions. Figure Sixteen, depicting the location of the Registered Stallions in 1899, only too clearly shows that many areas were remarkably, sadly, deficient in such horses. There was not even one Registered Stallion resident in the whole of Co. Cavan, for example, and only one in Monaghan. Yet now, when the Society were introducing stallions into Ireland, they placed them in areas where there appeared to be plenty, anyway.

Chad was located with Malone, the vet., in Wexford. There were eleven other Registered Stallions in the county already, including three within six or seven miles of Wexford town. *Laurium* went to John Lambert of Redmount Hill, Ballinasloe. Admittedly Lambert had no other Registered Stallion in 1899, but David Craig of Ochilmore Mills had *Ballinafad* and *Favonian*, C.I. Kelly of Eyrecourt had *Pythias*, and there were three Registered Stallions not too far away, at Woodlawn. One cannot help feeling that there were other areas in which *Laurium*'s services might have been more urgently needed. *Ground Ivy* was not listed in the 1899 *Register*, but in the following year he stood near Maryboro' (Portlaoise), at least that was an area that was,

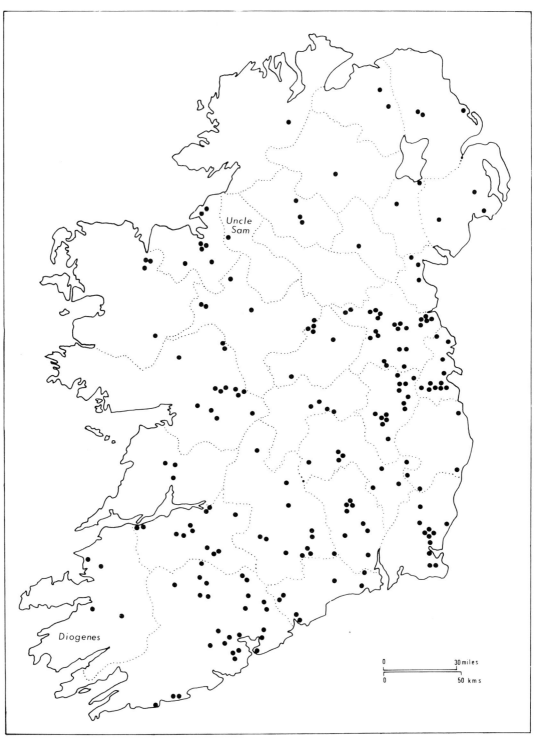

Figure 16. *The location of Registered Stallions in 1899. Stallions belonging to the Congested Districts Board are named.*

apparently, in need of a Registered Stallion. But it is hard to understand why the Society stood *Chad* and *Laurium* at the locations chosen. Obviously somebody with spatial awareness, or with the ability to couzen more money from the Government, was necessary if the Horse Breeding Schemes were to be fully effective throughout Ireland.

But the purchase of the three 'Society stallions' was a major step in the right direction. 1899 may fittingly, therefore, be known as the Year of the Trio.

CHAPTER FOURTEEN

The New Century

By the time that the midnight bells rang across the city of Dublin to announce both a New Year and a New Century, the Royal Dublin Society had already prepared its plans for the horse breeding season of 1900. As in the previous five years it had been decided that a *Register of Thoroughbred Stallions* would be issued, and that county committees should have the option of awarding nominations or premiums, or a combination of both, to mare owners. The new century therefore began in the way the old century ended. But events that were beyond the control of the Society, and that had been forseen for many years, were already casting dark and ominous shadows on the labours of the Committee of Agriculture and the Stallion Registration Committee.

The thirteen members of the Stallion Registration Committee (Major Borrowes and S. Ussher Roberts had been replaced by William Dove and Thomas Plunkett) were faced with 240 applications for the registration of stallions. The rules governing stallion registration remained the same as in 1899, '. . . after very careful inquiry' (a phrase that seemed to be included in the *Prefatory Note* to the *Register* almost as a matter of course), 201 stallions were registered. This was the lowest number since Volume One of the *Register* appeared in 1895 and was the second successive year in which there was a decrease in the number of stallions. The highest number registered, 234, had been in 1896, but there seemed no chance of such large numbers being registered again, at least not in the immediate future.

Over thirty of the stallions that had been registered in 1899 were dropped from the *Register* for 1900, whilst twenty-six 'new' stallions were admitted to the *Register*. These included such old favourites as *Condor*, who had last been registered in 1896 and continued to belong to Michael Killian of Mehambee, Athlone, and Michael Buchanan's *Middleman*. New entries included horses that had been sired by Registered Stallions, such as the three-year-old that belonged to Denis Stack of Castlehyde, Fermoy: *Rocket*. This colt was by *Canon* out of *Brown Mare* by *Tiber*, and *Canon* still stood at stud in east Cork, with Mrs. Mary O'Connell of Knockastucan, Conna. *Rocket*'s sole claim to fame at the time of registration was that he had won '. . . as a two-year-old in the Hunting Class' at Lismore Show in 1899.

In overall terms the standard of the new entries to the *Register* differed little from that of most previous years. *Court Ball* and *Curfew* were probably the best new entrants, at least if judged on racing results. *Court Ball* had been bred in England at Rahley Hall, Barnet, by R. Fossett Todd

Plate Thirty-three. Court Ball, *winner of the Rous Memorial Stakes (£1,000) at Ascot in 1894, the Doveridge Handicap (£1,000) at Derby in 1896 and other races. The horse was bred by R.F. Todd near Barnet in England and was by* Royal Hampton *out of* Polka. *Although on the small side, 15.2½ hands, Court Ball girthed 5ft 10ins and had 8ins of bone. In 1900 he was listed as a registered stallion standing with Dominick Owens at Strokestown. (Photo:* courtesy of the Royal Dublin Society)

and had a noteworthy pedigree. The horse was sired by *Royal Hampton* and his great-grand-dam was by *Parmesan*. In 1894, as a three-year-old, *Court Ball* dead-heated with *Bestman* for the Queen's Prize at Epsom, worth £1,000. Later in the season he won the Rous Memorial Stakes at Ascot (also worth £1,000) and in 1895 won the Peveral of the Peak Stakes at Derby (£1,000 also). The following season *Court Ball* won the £1000 Doveridge Handicap at Derby and, three years later, ended his racing career by winning the Leopardstown Handicap at Leopardstown. The latter race was worth only £200, but at least it showed that the horse was still able to win as an eight-year-old. *Court Ball* was therefore a hardy, useful and tried performer, and Dominick Owens of Strokestown did well to stand such a horse at stud for the Roscommon mares at a fee of only four guineas.

Curfew had been bred by Lord Lascelles and was foaled in 1887. As a two-year-old the colt did nothing outstanding, finishing third in the Hardwicke Stakes at Stockton. The following year the horse blossomed to win four races, at Thirsk, York and Gosforth Park. *Curfew* ended his account on the turf by winning the Ebor St. Leger Stakes at York. The breeders of south

Tipperary therefore had a useful stallion in their midst and John Quinlan stood *Curfew* at Carrick-on-Suir at the very reasonable fee of £3.

Of the twenty-six entrants to the 1900 *Register*, ten had won at least one race, sixteen had either won nothing or their owners were too reserved to advertise their successes. The Earl of Dunraven, who excelled himself by standing three Registered Stallions at stud, had a son of *St. Simon*: *Desmond*, in his stables. The Congested Districts Board had informed readers of the 1897 *Register* that '*St. Simon* is at present standing at a fee of 400 guineas:'[1] their horse, *St. Aidan*, was fathered by that expensive sire. *Desmond* had been bred by Dunraven and was out of *L'Abbesse de Jouarre* and foaled in 1896. Dunraven advertised the stallion at a service fee of £25, although the horse was not advertised as having done anything worthy of record on the turf. Obviously His Lordship felt that *Desmond*'s pedigree alone was enough to entice the mares of Co. Limerick to his Adare stud. His other stallions, *Atratus* and *Kirkham* stood at the far less remarkable fee of £5 for Thoroughbred mares, £3 for Half-bred mares and 'Owner's Tenants' Mares, £2.'

In fact, *Desmond* had won the Coventry Stakes and the July Stakes as a two-year-old, and in 1913 (the year in which he died), was champion race-horse sire in the British Isles.[2] *Aboyeur*,

Plate Thirty-four. Desmond, *owned by the Early of Dunraven, by* St Simon *out of* L'Abesse de Jouarre, *winner of the Coventry and July Stakes as a two-year-old and champion racehorse sire in the British Isles in 1913. (Photo:* Dublin Horse Show Magazine)

winner of the 1913 Derby, was by *Desmond* as was *Craganour*, who passed the post first but was disqualified. Another noted son of *Desmond* was *Charles O'Malley*, winner of the Ascot Gold Vase and maternal grandsire of *Blenheim*, winner of the 1930 Derby and later to be a most influential sire.

One of the most interesting entrants to the *Register*, although nothing was stated therein as to his performances on the turf or elsewhere, was Edward Mitchell's *Coylton*. Mitchell had long been a stallion owner and in 1900 he had three Registered Stallions at stud at his stables near Enniskillen. The interest in *Coylton* lay in his pedigree. His grand-dam, *Sunray*, was by *King of the Forest*, and that sire had already indelibly left his mark on half-bred horse breeding in Ireland by fathering *Heart of Oak* and *Woodreeve*, two of the leading stallions in the country in the previous decade and prominent figures in the early Horse Breeding Schemes. *King of the Forest*, as has already been noted, also figured in the pedigree of *Ground Ivy*, one of the three stallions purchased by the Royal Dublin Society in 1899.

Other stallions had far less remarkable pedigrees, and no performances credited to them to alleviate their seeming mediocrity. John Widger, the Waterford horse-man, re-registered *Snaplock* (already listed in 1896-8), by *Fetherlock* out of *Snapshot*. That was hardly an inspiring pedigree, yet even there, four generations earlier, the female line traced to *Birdcatcher*, so *Snaplock* probably had some merit. Widger was not a man to buy plain ordinary horses for stud, and he had been an architect of his brother's victory in the Grand National in 1895.

The success of the Society's schemes for horse breeding, and of its policy of including only certified and sound Thoroughbred horses of satisfactory quality in its *Registers*, was reflected in the pedigrees of some of the new stallions registered. *Lighterman*, for example, owned by John Read of Garlow Cross, Navan, was fathered by *Studley*, who was included in Volume One of the *Register* and who won the class for produce by one stallion exhibited at the Royal Dublin Society's Horse Show as long ago as 1893. *Lighterman* had won the Baldoyle Derby in 1897, as well as being second in the meagrely financed Duke of York Stakes (worth £50) at Leopardstown.

Among the names of stallion owners there appeared many changes. William Pallin remained important, with seven stallions, James Daly owned six. Francis Flannery, who was last listed as the owner of a Registered Stallion in 1894, the year when the *Register* proper apparently did not appear (only a list printed in time for the Dublin Horse Show), made a welcome reappearance. He stood *Xylophone* at his stable at Churchtown near Buttevant in north Cork. This was probably the best Registered Stallion that Flannery had owned, having won the Northumberland Autumn Plate at Newcastle in 1893, the Stansted Hurdle at Lingfield and the December Hurdle Handicap at Plumpton in 1895, the Eden Vale Handicap at Lingfield, the Egham Hurdle Handicap at Kempton and the Wickham Hurdle Handicap at Gatwick in 1896. None of these were outstanding races, but they were all fair tests of a horse and a horse that, like *Xylophone*, campaigned for five seasons and won six races, was valuable as a country sire. And it must be remembered that, in the pre-motor age, the horse was king. Nobody wanted all his horses to be Derby or Grand National winners, but most people appreciated a good riding or carriage horse. Put to a suitable half-bred mare that is exactly what one would expect a 16 hand horse and consistent performer on the race course, like *Xylophone* to produce.

Beggar's Opera and *Brayhead* were another two substantial and tested stallions. The former belonged to the Cherrywood Stud of Loughlinstown, between Dublin and Bray, and had won four races, at Newmarket and Manchester. *Brayhead* had been bred at Epsom and won six races between 1896 and 1898. As Arthur Maxwell of Lusk, his owner, advertised in the *Register*: 'With the exception of those run as a two-year-old all *Brayhead*'s races were from a mile to a mile and a half, showing he could stay as well as gallop.' For ordinary purposes, hunting, riding, cavalry use, carriage work, it was far more important that a horse should stay rather than that he should be a brilliant performer over five or six furlongs. Like *Xylophone*, *Beggar's Opera* and *Brayhead*, both standing at about 16 hands, seemed ideal horses for use on good half-bred mares.

Another good sort of horse, although by no means spectacular, was the re-registered *Zero*. He had been registered in 1894 as belonging to Francis Flannery, and in 1895-6-7 as the property of John Lynch of Latoon. In 1891 *Zero* had twice been second in Hunt Steeplechases at Abergaveny, that beautiful market town of warm old red sandstone houses that stands sentry at the exit of the Usk valley from the embracing hills of Wales onto the plains of Gwent. Latoon, Newmarket-on-Fergus (where he now stood), with its cold limestone soils and desolate salt-marshes of the Fergus estuary, must have seemed a mighty change for this son of *Monaco*. After his seconds at Abergaveny *Zero* had run twice at Cardiff and once at Cheltenham, always in Hunters' Chases, winning all three. It was no classic record, but it was solid, and not to be sneezed at. At a fee of £1. 10s., with 2s. 6d. for the groom, this 16 hand bay horse was a fair bargain for the owners of half-bred and ordinary mares in Co. Clare. Like many other sires listed in the *Register*, *Zero* was well calculated to improve the ordinary breed of horses in Ireland and produce 'Hunters and other Half-bred Horses,' which was the aim of the Society's Horse Breeding Schemes, anyway.

Among the list of stallions registered in 1899 but not in 1900 there were a number of notable names. Old *Bacchus*, for example, had made his exit and in his place the O'Donnells of the Deer Park, Lismore, were now standing *Young Speculation* at stud. At the age of sixteen the latter horse was only a youngster compared with *Bacchus*, who had been twenty-five in 1899. Another name missing was that of *Branxholme*, the 16 hand horse that had come all the way from Kelso, in Scotland, to compete at the Premium Stallion Show at Dublin in 1887 and that seems to have resided in Ireland ever since. Perhaps, having been foaled in Shropshire in 1879, it was time for the old fellow to fade from the scene.

Captain M.A. Maher's grand old horse, *Torpedo*, had also faded away. Born in Co. Wexford in 1876, *Torpedo* had won many races and sired many good offspring. He was sadly missed at Ballinkeele, Maher's mansion on his fertile Wexford farm. Lord Ashtown, too, had experienced a reduction in the number of Registered Stallions at his Woodlawn stud. *Terror*, whose grand-dam was by 'Mr. Tom Ferguson's remarkable Irish horse, *Harkaway*,'[3] (who had first run in England on 17 July 1838, coming second in the Tradesman's Cup at Liverpool), no longer figures in the *Register*. *Terror* had been foaled in 1875. The Right Hon. the Earl of Kenmare, of Killarney House, also made his and his stallion's exit from the *Registers*. *The Baron*, foaled in 1884 and second in the Derby of 1887, no longer served the nominated mares of Co. Kerry.

Of course, as in previous years, deletions from the *Register* were inevitable, but of more consequence was the overall geographical distribution of Registered Stallions. Figure Seventeen sadly shows that most of the areas deficient in Registered Stallions in previous years still continued to be so. Nothing had been done to place stallions in central west Cork and south and east Kerry. Connemara and much of Mayo were absolutely devoid of Registered Stallions, and

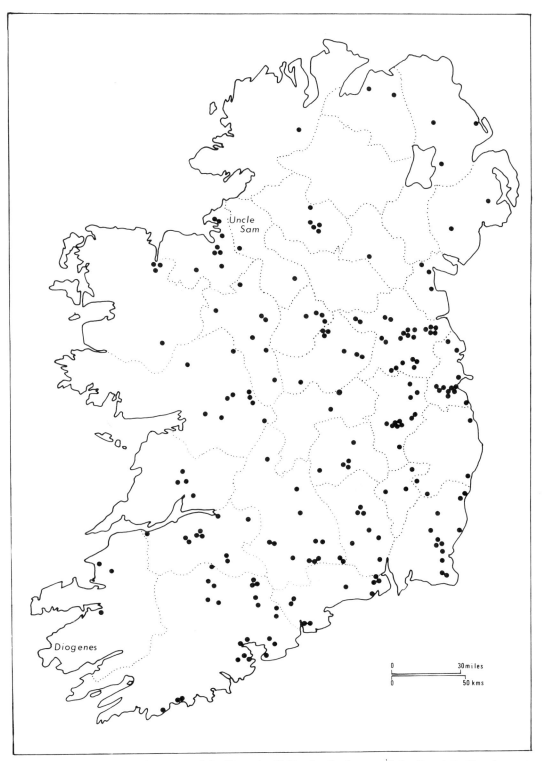

Figure 17. *The location of Registered Stallions in 1900, the final year of the Royal Dublin Society's Registration of Stallions scheme. Stallions belonging to the Congested Districts Board are named*

the Society had not replaced *Watchspring* or persuaded any private owner to stand a similar suitable little stallion in the area. *Greenfield* plodded on alone in Co. Donegal, and there were no Registered Stallions at all in Co. Tyrone.

Viewed as a national scheme for horse breeding it was apparent that the Register for 1900 had many, and serious, short-comings. The criticisms of the scheme for 1899 and the positioning of the three stallions acquired by the Royal Dublin Society: that the Society needed to be guided by '. . . somebody with spatial awareness, or with the ability to couzen more money from the Government;' held only too true for 1900. To those who pondered the matter it must have been increasingly apparent that the Society, and its Stallion Registration Committee, had made an immense contribution to the betterment of horse breeding in Ireland, but that future development needed to be guided by full-time professionals rather than by a group of cosy and respectable upper-class gentlemen, like most of the members of the Royal Dublin Society and many of its committees. The nineteenth century had, in many ways, been the heyday of the amateur, but it had also seen the rise of the professional. Telford had built his bridges, Brunel had constructed his railroads. Both had been professionals, in the true sense of the word. Now, as the twentieth century dawned, professionals were to rule supreme and the western world was to be filled with bureaucrats. Already plans were being laid, even as the *Register* for 1900 was going to press, for a meeting elsewhere in Dublin that would spell the end of the Royal Dublin

Plate Thirty-five. Duke of Portland, *owned by R.G. Nash and first registered in 1895, whose son,* Bay Duke, *won his class at Dublin in 1900. (Photo:* courtesy of the Royal Dublin Society)

Plate Thirty-six. Bay Duke, *by* Duke of Porland, *out of a mare by* Rose Sanglier, *winner of the yearling colt class at Ball's Bridge in 1900. (Photo: courtesy of the Royal Dublin Society)*

Society's *Registers of Thoroughbred Stallions* and its meetings of upper class, well-meaning and (admittedly) surprisingly efficient gentlemen.

The Report of the Chairman of the Committee of Agriculture for the year 1900, boldly stated that under the Horse Breeding Scheme, 'Each county was allowed the option of adopting the premium system, as carried out in 1895-1896, the nomination system, as in 1892-1893, or a combination of both systems. Eight Committees adopted the premium system, sixteen the nomination, and nine a combination of both systems.'[4]

Except in detail the schemes for the award of nominations to suitable mares, or premiums to mares and young stock, or a combination of both systems, differed little from those of 1899. The Committee for Co. Tipperary, for example, stated that 'No mares receiving Premiums last year will be eligible unless there is not a sufficient number of other suitable mares.' They had stated nothing of the kind in 1899. But this, and other changes, were mere trivialities, hardly worthy of discussion. Suffice it to say that the county committees each dealt with their chosen system adequately, and no complaints or problems were recorded in the printed proceedings of the Society.

Plate Thirty-seven. *R.G. Nash, Lisclogher, Athboy, owner of* Duke of Portland *and of* Bay Duke. *(Photo:* Dublin Horse Show Magazine)

Plate Thirty-eight. *Lord Langford, chairman of the Committee of Agriculture of the Royal Dublin Society and chairman of the Stallion Registration Committee. (Photo:* Dublin Horse Show Magazine)

Of far more importance was a meeting that was held, by permission of the Senate, in the Royal University Buildings, Earlsfort Terrace, Dublin, on Tuesday, May 29, 1900. Altitudinally Earlsfort Terrace lies well above the level of Ball's Bridge, and just as the porticoed buildings of the University dominate the Terrace, so did the decisions of the meeting therein on that fateful May morning dominate the activities of the Royal Dublin Society on their lowly site. The meeting at the University was 'The first meeting of the Council of Agriculture,'[5] the body newly established by the Government to take charge of agriculture in Ireland.

The meeting at Earlsfort Terrace began shortly after eleven a.m. and was chaired by the Right Hon. Horace Plunkett, M.P., P.C. From the start of the meeting it was obvious that there were many people present who held dissentient views, and some held that the meeting should not be taking place at all. The old sores and tribulations of Ireland, that still sere the country, boiled to the surface as the short-sighted and the narrowly nationalist attempted to disturb proceedings. There will always be some people who, in a metaphorical sense, wear blinkers. But Plunkett was an old campaigner, and the Council moved rapidly to business.

In his opening address Plunkett said: 'There is one remark which it occurs to me to make in connection with horse-breeding. We ought to watch very carefully the requirements of the War Office as regards remounts, and to do our utmost to anticipate a demand which the latest developments of warfare give us reason to expect. It is already in contemplation by the Department to constitute a Committee or a permanent Commission to deal with this important question of horse-breeding.'[6] The Boer War was to shake the United Kingdom and many an Irishman, like his British counterparts, left his bones to bleach under the sweltering sun of South Africa. Already, too, the growing might of Germany cast long and ominous shadows across the globe, and the thoughtful feared for the future.

Later in the meeting Mr. J.J. Molloy, J.P., stated that '. . . I feel that it is one of the first duties of this Department to make a very great effort to at once improve the breed of stock, and I refer both to cattle and sheep and to horses.'[7] His feelings echoed those of many people in Ireland, and before 1900 had ended a series of committees had been formed to guide the nascent Department of Agriculture. The first of these committees was that for horse-breeding, composed of seventeen members. On it sat men who had guided the Royal Dublin Society and some who had served on its Stallion Registration Committee: Lord Rathdonnell, for example, Captain Fetherstonhaugh, William Pallin, Percy La Touche (Hon. Secretary and Treasurer of the Society's Co. Kildare Committee in 1900) and, fittingly, the gentleman who had signed Volume One of the *Registers of Thoroughbred Stallions* with such a triumphant flourish, Frederick S. Wrench, J.P.

On February 14, 1901, Langford, Chairman of the Committee of Agriculture and Robert Bruce, Agricultural Superintendent for the Royal Dublin Society, reported to the Society that: 'The Department of Agriculture and Technical Instruction for Ireland having been established, it became necessary to reconsider schemes for the administration of the sum of £5,000, granted to the Society under the Probate Duties (Scotland and Ireland) Act, 1888 . . . The Department having adopted a horse breeding scheme practically the same as that hitherto carried out by the Society – publishing a Register of approved Stallions, and granting Nominations for Mares – it was decided that the Society discontinue compiling its annual Register of Thoroughbred Stallions. The funds from the grant to be devoted to Horses . . . will, therefore, be offered for competition, in . . . Premiums . . . at a Stallion Show to be held on the 21st February, 1901. The Premiums will be confined to Stallions registered or accepted for the Register of the Department of Agricultural and Technical Instruction for Ireland.

With a view to encourage the introduction of high-class Agricultural Stallions into the country . . . the Society will offer, from its own funds, 3 Premiums of £50 each for competition for these Stallions at the Show.'[8]

In his Report Langford also noted the numbers of mares and young stock presented for competition at the county shows of 1900. It was a routine statement of fact, and with it ended the Royal Dublin Society's involvement in mare nominations and stallion registration. From now on the task of guiding the equine destiny of the country fell, increasingly, on the newly formed Department of Agriculture, yet it was not until 1903 that the Society's involvement in the improvement of livestock (horses) scheme finally ended.

CHAPTER FIFTEEN

Loose ends

As 1900 came to an end so it became embarrassingly clear to the Society that its Horse Breeding Scheme merely duplicated the scheme of the newly formed Department of Agriculture and Technical Instruction. The obvious answer was to end the Society's scheme, but under the 1888 Probate Act the sum of £5,000 accrued to the Society annually for the improvement of livestock, and somehow it had to be spent. Thus it was that, on February 21, 1901, 109 Thoroughbred and twenty-nine agricultural stallions competed in a Stallion Show at Ball's Bridge held to award premiums to suitable stallions.

The rules governing the show were, basically, that each Thoroughbred stallion had to be registered at Weatherbys and had to be listed in the Department of Agriculture's *Register*. Furthermore, premiums were limited to stallions that had *not* already been awarded a Departmental premium. Additionally each stallion awarded a premium, Thoroughbred or otherwise, was expected to stand in a stated district and '. . . serve 50 mares nominated by the Department, if required.'[1]

Twenty-five premiums of £100 each were awarded for Thoroughbreds and three, of £50 each, for agricultural stallions. The three judges of the Thoroughbreds were P.J. Dunne of Trim, C.J. Furlong of Fermoy and Major Trocke of Parsonstown. Two judges from England, R. Brydon from Seaham Harbour and W.R. Trotter of Stocksfield-on-Tyne, helped R.M. Dowse of Carnew to adjudicate on the agricultural stallions. Competition was intense, in spite of the fact that the rules stated that: 'The place which any Stallion will be required to stand at or travel to in each district will be settled and published after a conference with the Department of Agriculture and Technical Instruction,' so that, at least in theory, stallions could be posted anywhere in Ireland. Perhaps the offer of the Society to pay '. . . all Irish Railway freights to Show of Horses entered' contributed to the large entry!

As Table Eleven shows, most of the stallions awarded premiums were already old favourites, and they were mainly allocated to districts conveniently close to their owners' stables. Pallin, however, had *Favonian* posted to Co. Clare, far from his Curragh stable. Mrs. Alexander, owner of *Connaught*, declined to comply with the posting of her horse to a '. . . station to be approved by the Committee,' and J. Mullarkey also declined to stand *Tranby Croft* at Longford. All other owners, however, seemed happy with their horses' postings, and Pallin had no compunction about sending *Favonian* to Clare.

Table Eleven[2]

Premium Stallions and Stallion Stations in 1901

Stallion	Station	Owner
1. *Thoroughbreds*		
Sir Patrick	Ballinaskea	M. Healy
Astrologer	Queen's Co.	W. Pallin
Duke of Portland	Lucan	R.G. Nash
Heligoland	Castlebellingham	A. Macan
Aconite	Clondalkin	R. Walsh
Scotch Hazel	Carlow	Messrs. Slocock
Restraint	Tullamore	T.S. Elcoate and J.M. Prior Kennedy
St. Aiden	Delgany	R.N. Thompson
Young Marden	Carrick-on-Suir	T.F. Nugent
Xylophone	Nenagh	F. Flannery
Ferdinand	Kilmallock	J.W.A. Harris
Toronto	Lismore	T. Magnier
Narellan	Ennis	Harris Brothers
Ground Ivy	Tralee	B.P.J. Mahony
Thurles	Thurles	Harris Brothers
Connaught	(declined to comply)	Mrs. J.B. Alexander
Fife	Tuam	J. Moore
Favonian	Co. Clare	W. Pallin
Court Ball	Athlone	D. Owens
Tranby Croft	Longford (declined to comply)	J. Mullarkey
Macready	Elphin	P.F. Fitzmaurice
Coylton	Cavan	E. Mitchell
St. Jude	Enniskillen	E. Mitchell
Mascarille	Larne	H.H. Smiley
Cleator	South Cavan	W.W. Kilroy
2. *Agricultural*		
Prince of Brunstane (Clydesdale)	Crossgar	T. Lindsay
Model	Drogheda	T. O'Malley
The Raider (Clydesdale)	Raheny	T. O'Malley

The posting of the stallions, or so the Society intended, complemented that of those standing under the Department of Agriculture's scheme and so, in theory, there should have been no overlap between Department and Society stallions. Unfortunately, however, duplication was sometimes unavoidable, and as 1901 progressed so the Society became increasingly unhappy about the future. As a result a Committee was appointed to report on the administration of the grant for livestock improvement.

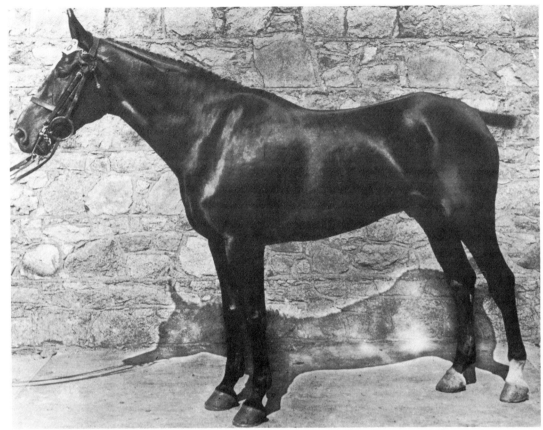

Plate Thirty-nine. Master of Hounds, *sired by* Mascarille, *winner of the five-years-old hunter class to carry up to 15 stone at the Dublin Horse Show of 1899. In 1901* Mascarille, *owned by Sir Hugh Smiley, was awarded a Royal Dublin Society premium and stood at Larne in Co. Antrim. (Photo:* courtesy of the Royal Dublin Society)

On December 12, 1901, the Committee's report was presented to the Society:[3]

'When two years ago a new department of Agriculture and Technical Instruction was formed, with very large endowments, one of their first acts was to frame schemes for the advancement of Horse and Cattle Breeding. In this they again paid your society the high compliment of practically adopting their schemes. . . .

The question now arises whether any advantage accrues to the country or to the Society from having two schemes of public money administered by two distinct bodies on nearly parallel lines. We cannot see that any advantage is thereby gained . . .

We therefore recommend that His Excellency be approached with a view to express the readiness of the Council (of the Royal Dublin Society) to co-operate in effecting a transfer of the administration of the fund to the Department of Agriculture and Technical Instruction.'

The Society accepted the recommendation of its Committee and, on January 11, 1902, sent a deputation to meet the Lord Lieutenant. Present at the meeting was the Right Hon. Mr. Horace Plunkett, Vice-President of the Department of Agriculture. The deputation argued that, in return for surrendering the £5,000 annual grant for the improvement of livestock, '. . . a capital sum, such as may be deemed adequate, might be fitly granted to the Society for the advancement of such public objects as are still forwarded by it, and by it alone.'[4] The Lord Lieutenant was favourably inclined towards the deputation's views, and on Feburary 6, 1902, the Secretary of the Department of Agriculture (T.P. Gill) wrote to the Society to state that: '. . . the Department are now . . . in a position to say that they will be prepared, in the event of the transfer in question taking place, to make a grant from their funds to the Royal Dublin Society of a sum of £5,000 to be applied by the Royal Dublin Society in the erection of an industrial Hall or annexe, and in such other improvements in their premises at Ball's Bridge as may be agreed upon between the Royal Dublin Society and the Department.'[5]

On February 20, 1902, the Council of the Royal Dublin Society 'Resolved, that the offer of £5000 to be paid by the Department of Agriculture and Technical Instruction, on the transfer of the administration of the present Government grant of £5000 a year, be accepted with the best thanks of the Society, the whole sum in question to be applied to the building and furnishing of a new Industrial Hall.'[6]

During 1902 the Government introduced a Bill into Parliament to conclude the agreement, and it was passed as the Agricultural and Technical Instruction (Ireland) (No. 2) Act, 1902. That, or so one might suppose, was the end of the matter. But it was not. Some money still existed in the Improvement of Livestock Account, so, at the 1902 Horse Show, ten premiums of £50 each were awarded to Thoroughbred sires. All competitors for these premiums (and another ten were to be awarded '. . . at established Shows in Horse Breeding Districts in Ireland to be named by the Royal Dublin Society'[7]) had to be registered at Weatherbys, be listed in the Department of Agriculture's *Register*, and must have served tenant farmers half-bred mares at fees of not more than £5. 5. 0. each during the 1902 season. The premium winners at Dublin are listed in Table Twelve.

In 1903, too, money still remained in the account, so the Society decided to award another ten premiums for Thoroughbred stallions at the 1903 Horse Show, as listed on Table Thirteen.

These were the final premiums awarded under the Improvement of Livestock (Horses) scheme, first begun in 1888. Perhaps it was appropriate, even if more than a little sad, that the grants for the improvement of horses had been succeeded by a grant for the building of an Industrial Hall. But perhaps that is what the Twentieth Century is all about. And so the horse was replaced by the machine, dominating the new Industrial Hall at Ball's Bridge. But the final comment rests, not with the machines and industries of the present century, but with the report of Mr. Simmons Harrison, an English judge[9] at the Horse Show of 1902.

'There was a magnificent class of good sires . . . I can only remark that if we had the same class of hunting sires to breed from in England we should have a very considerable improvement in our class of hunters; and I am quite confident that the good class of hunters bred in Ireland is solely due to the great care and trouble taken by those who now have had the selection of the Registered Premium Horses.'

For the future, however, the improvement of horse breeding in Ireland lay, not with the Royal Dublin Society, but with the Department of Agriculture and Technical Instruction. Eighteen years of experiment, alteration and improvement had come to an end.

Table Twelve

Premium Thoroughbred Stallions, 1902

Stallion	Owner	Stallion	Owner
Red Prince II	W. Pallin	*Favonian*	W. Pallin
Fortunio	E. Kennedy	*St. Aiden*	R.N. Thompson
Astrologer	W. Pallin	*Crotanstown*	E.K.B. Tighe
Duke of Portland	R.G. Nash	*Anklebiter*	J.C. Higgins
Xylophone	Francis Flannery	*Egerton*	W.W. Kilroy

Table Thirteen[8]

Premium Thoroughbred Stallions, 1903

Stallion	Owner	Stallion	Owner
Red Prince II	W. Pallin	*Loreto*	M.F. Neary
Sir Patrick	M. Henly	*Brayhead*	A. Maxwell
Mascarille	Sir Hugh Smiley	*Medicis*	J. Galbraith
Astrologer	W. Pallin	*Anklebiter*	J.C. Higgins
Spring Weather	J.M. Kelly	*Glenstirling*	J. Sheehy

CHAPTER SIXTEEN

Assessment

Between 1886 and 1900 there had been many changes in Ireland. Politically there had been bitter arguments that had been based on whether the country should remain a part of the United Kingdom, experience Home Rule, or even become entirely separate, politically, from the neighbouring island. There had been arguments and divisions on the vexed question of land ownership, and the estate system had crumbled dramatically. Economically there had been major developments in agriculture, with the foundation of the co-operative creamery movement and other far-sighted ventures. The Horse Breeding Schemes of the Royal Dublin Society were equally far-sighted, even if they had begun hesitantly and were eventually to prove of less importance, due to the development of motor vehicles. But the rise of the motor could hardly have been foreseen when the schemes began, and horses were not to be ousted until well after the First World War, which the British Army entered with less than eighty motorized vehicles.[1]

The first five years of the Schemes had been years of experiment, and gradual improvement. For well over a century the Royal Dublin Society had successfully used the policy of introducing premiums to encourage economic improvement in the country. The Society had found that private enterprise, once stimulated and spurred to achievement by the offer of a premium, or by the example of the high standard of a premium-winner, was invariably able to improve itself. In that way the Society had seen the development of many of the most important industries in Ireland. There is little doubt that, in 1887, when the Premium Scheme for stallions was first introduced, the Society still believed that the stimulus of a few premiums would prove effective in bettering horse-breeding.

To a limited extent the Society was right, and the Premium Stallions did improve horse-breeding. But the demand for the services of good stallions far outweighed the availability of services from the strictly limited number of Premium Stallions. When, as at Portadown in 1887, over 250 mares competed for just fifty nominations, it was obvious that something more sweeping than a Premium Stallion Scheme was necessary to cope with the demand. The early years of the Horse Breeding Scheme, in which the Society juggled with the number of premiums offered, and annually adjusted the districts in which the stallions stood, were years in which they hesitantly attempted to cope with the demand. Perhaps the most important feature of these early years was that they showed the tremendous demand for the services of quality stallions. It is easy, with the benefit of hindsight, to say that of course there must have been a demand. Yet

157

what one might have suspected could not be proved until the facts and figures of the Premium Stallion schemes were at hand. The years from 1887 until the end of 1891 may therefore be regarded as years of investigation and experiment.

During these early years the Society investigated the results of the Horse Breeding Schemes in a scientific manner. Circulars relating to foaling results were sent to most owners of mares served by the Premium Stallions, and the results were assiduously collected and catalogued. But breeding horses is not the same as breeding pigs, or most other livestock. Horses are judged on performance and temperament, and performance varies depending on the conditions under which a horse is asked to perform. Some horses race well when the ground is hard and dry, others when it is soggy and wet. Some horses race best over a mile on the flat, others over four miles across fences, as in the Grand National. Some horses are far too slow for the racecourse, but are excellent hunters. Others make fine cavalry mounts. The combinations and possibilities of horses' performances are almost endless. Pigs could be judged on the meat quality of their carcase and on their food conversion and growth rates. So could beef cattle. Dairy cattle could be judged on their milk yields and butter fat. But no such 'simple' measures could, or can, be applied to horses.

Yet the Society did look at foaling rates, and at fertility figures. But it very soon became apparent that the figures for one year often bore very little relationship to those for the next. *Paddy*, for example, had a foaling rate (expressed as a percentage on returns made by mare owners to the Society) of 56% in 1889. Two years later his rate was the almost incredible one of 79%. Was the breeding quality of the mares sent to him better in 1891 than in 1889? Was he fed or exercised differently? Was he handled at service in a more competent manner? These were the sort of questions that needed an answer if the statistics for the horse were to be at all meaningful. And to be of real value one would have had to wait ten or twelve years in order to be able to assess the true worth of his progeny. Considered on that sort of a time-scale, and with all the problems of assessment already noted, it was obviously impossible for the Society to obtain anything but a cursory impression of *Paddy*'s (or any other stallion's) success. All the Society could really do was to ensure that the stallion was free of hereditary disease, sound, and of good conformation. Furthermore, the Society could take the performance of progeny into account, where known, and it could reasonably insist that a stallion be pedigree and entered in the stud-book, since poor blood-lines were likely (for economic and other reasons) to have been weeded from the stud-book during its century or more of existence.

In 1892 the Society, wisely, dropped the Premium Stallion schemes in favour of its schemes for the registration of all suitable Thoroughbred stallions. This was a major development, and foreshadowed the registration of stallion schemes (Thoroughbred and otherwise) and the licensing of stallions that, in the latter part of the twentieth century, are considered an essential part of the Irish government's role in horse breeding. Very few people, today, question the action of the Government of Ireland when it insists that its inspectors shall examine all stallions (apart from racehorses and Thoroughbreds used exclusively for the service of Thoroughbred mares), and determine whether or not they are suitable for breeding. Yet, in 1892, the Society was breaking new ground with its registration scheme. Admittedly, it was a voluntary scheme, but it did show how necessary it was to examine stallions, and it did pave the way for the Government schemes of the twentieth century. The scheme for mare nominations, too, in a modified way, still operates in the Republic of Ireland.

But perhaps even more important was the fact that the Society's schemes brought breeders together, with their stock, annually at local venues. There they saw their stock examined and they could see, for themselves, the merits and de-merits of their own and their neighbours' animals. Furthermore, at many of the country shows, breeders could see stallions, mares *and their progeny*, and could therefore assess the value of breeding certain types of mares to certain types of stallion. Every breeder, unless he was absolutely lacking in gumption, could therefore become his own judge. Thus, unassumingly, the Society taught many thousands of farmers how to assess their equine breeding stock. It may be argued that the breeders could do that already, and perhaps they could. But now they certainly could.

Above all, the Society's *Registers of Thoroughbred Stallions* gave breeders a guarantee of the quality of the stallion to which they intended sending their mares. Previously there had been much nonsense, and not a little chicanery, in the stallion business. Now everything was above board, and a stallion's merits were there, on paper, for all to see. That was a very real advantage for the majority of breeders.

Another advantage, and not to be despised, was that breeders now knew where the stallions were, what they were, and what their services cost. And many excellent stallions, previously inaccessible to the ordinary breeder, were suddenly made available. *Hackler*, for example, was the leading Irish sire of flat racehorses in 1900 and 1903. Langan's horse, *Hominy*, winner of the Irish Grand Military Chase in 1882, was the great-grandsire of *Reynoldstown*, winner of the Grand National in 1935 and 1936. *Ascetic*, the old warrior that Mr. Purdon used for collecting the post, and that stood at a fee of £40, sired three winners of the Grand National: *Cloister*, *Drumcree* and *Ascetic's Silver*. In all probability, *Register* or not, *Ascetic* would have sired them anyway, but many other quality horses were, through the pages of the *Registers*, brought to the attention of breeders. And, through the social implications of the *Registers*, many great landowners were induced to make their stallions available to a wide circle of breeders. Many of the fine horses that one takes so much for granted in Ireland (and whose pedigrees may even be unknown), must trace back to the quality stallions first brought to breeders' notice by the *Registers*.

The main value of the Horse Breeding Schemes, however, was far more immediate. Only fourteen years after the Society issued its last *Register*, Europe was cast into the holocaust of war. Many thousands of Irishmen, like their neighbours from Britain and the Empire, and later from America (as well as already from numerous European countries), were senselessly slaughtered by the brutal and unjustifiable ambitions of the Germans. 1914-18 was a war that should not have taken place, just as 1939-45 should not, either. In it warfare depended on the stalemate of the trenches, the trundling of the tanks, and on horses. Horses, so it seemed, were needed for everything. They were needed for the cavalry, for the mounted infantry, for the artillery (to pull the guns and haul ammunition), for the ambulances, for the baggage. Horses were indispensable. As Lord Derby said in 1917, horses from Southern Ireland had proved invaluable in the muddy warfare of the French battlefields.[2] Even certain horses from the Empire owed something to Irish breeding. Mr. J. Mole of Ballagh, for example, had sold two mares to the British Government: *Duchess* and *Lady Frederick*. The former was by Maher's *Torpedo* out of a dam by *Herbertstown*, the latter was by *Cavendish*. Both had won their classes at the Queen's County Agricultural Society's Shows at Maryborough, in 1900 and 1903 respectively. Both were eventually to be sent by the Government to stud at Standerton in South Africa, to improve the

Plate Forty. Ascetic's Silver, *by* Ascetic *out of* Silver Lady, *winner of the Grand National in 1906, the third of* Ascetic's *progeny to do so. (Photo:* Dublin Horse Show Magazine)

standards of horseflesh in that area.[3] Similar exports of mares, and even of stallions, had gone to many parts of the world, and now they were to prove their value. Without horses, thousands of them, Britain (and Ireland) would have lost the war. The rebellion of 1916, that led to the eventual creation of the Republic of Ireland as a separate state, would have been to no avail had the war, the Great War, been lost. A considerable part of the Allies' success in the war must have been due to the production of worthwhile horses in Ireland, fostered by the Horse Breeding Schemes.

When the Horse Breeding Schemes began, in 1887, nobody could realistically have foreseen that the days of the horse were numbered. Travel depended, on land, on the railways and on horses. The days of total long-distance horse travel had, for the most part, gone. But it must have seemed as if horses would always be needed as feeders to and from the railway stations, and as if local travel would always depend on horses. Nobody could know that the twentieth century would be the century of the motor-car and of the motor-lorry. The Royal Dublin Society, through its Horse Breeding Schemes, was therefore attempting to improve the very heart of the economic life of Ireland.

Today it is easy to look back and be critical. One could argue that the Society were negligent in not aiding the production of draught or farm-horses. It could even be argued that they were

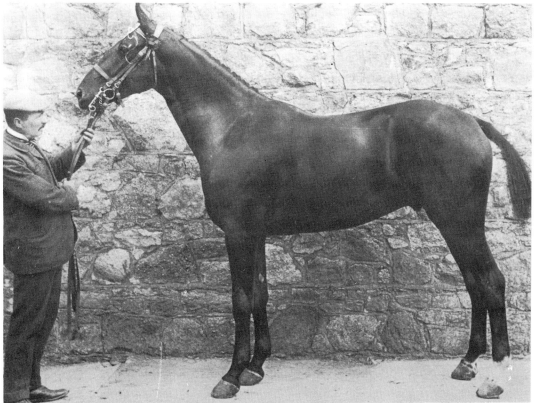

Plate Forty-one. Sportsman, *winner of the three-year-old gelding class at the 1899 Dublin Horse Show, by* Royal Charter *out of a dam by* Woodman. Royal Charter *stood with Patrick Cashman at Ballyheigue in Co. Kerry and had been second in the 1887 Yorkshire St Leger. His progeny,* Sportsman, *belonged to Captain Nickalls of Ballincollig, Cork, and stood 16.1½ hands high, girthed 6ft 2ins and had 8⅝ ins bone. (Photo:* courtesy of the Royal Dublin Society)

adopting a colonialist standpoint by aiding the breeding of the very types of horses for which there was a market in Britain, and overseas. Yet, in all fairness, what was the point in breeding horses for which there was no market? And if the local agricultural market was already catered for (and many believed that it was), why meddle with it?

But one could argue that the Society did not do enough for horse-breeding. For example, it brought only a tiny handful of stallions into the country. It did not place them in what appear to have been the most necessitous areas. But such criticisms ignore the terrible lack of finance under which the Society laboured. With only £3,200 a year at its disposal it was expected to improve the horses of Ireland, whilst Hungary allotted the equivalent of £233,333 for the task within its borders, Germany spent over £190,000 and Austria £170,000. What is remarkable is that so much was done with so little.

When the Department of Agriculture and Technical Instruction started its own horse breeding schemes, in 1901, it allocated the sum of £5,481 for mare nominations, of which £4,632 was

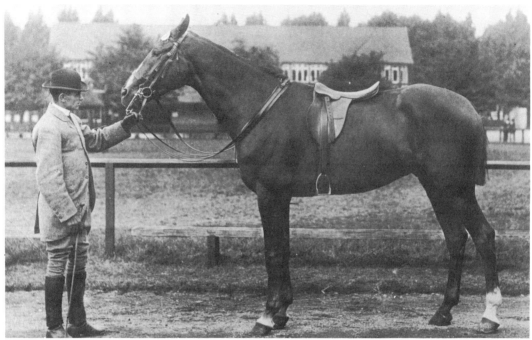

Plate Forty-two. Canon Arthur, *a five-year-old hunter gelding, winner of the class to carry 13—14 stone at the Dublin Horse Show of 1900 and the embodiment of all that the Horse Breeding Schemes stood for. Although owned by A.J. McNeile of Dollanstown, Kilcock, the gelding had almost certainly been bred in east Cork-west Waterford, for his sire was* Canon *and his dam was by* Arthur. *Both stallions were renowned getters of good hunters and* Canon *had been bred by the Rev. James Barry of Churchtown, Mallow and was later to belong to David Connell of Knockastucan, Conna.* Arthur *was a Half-bred stallion of excellent repute. McNeile's gelding typifies the Half-bred hunters for which Ireland was, and still is, rightly famous. This was exactly the type of horse that the Royal Dublin Society's schemes had been intended to produce. (Photo:* courtesy of the Royal Dublin Society)

actually spent.[4] In the years that followed even larger sums were allocated for nominations. In 1904 the Department allocated £8,371 and, in 1915, expended £11,994. Obviously the Royal Dublin Society, with its slender finances, could not have been expected to provide in such a liberal manner as this new Department of State.[5] Furthermore, in 1911, the Treasury made available £10,000 as a Development Grant, additional to the money already being expended on horse breeding by the Department of Agriculture. This grant '. . . was roughly apportioned as follows: (*a*) £4,000 in connection with the purchase of stallions; (*b*) £4,000 for additional nominations to mares; and (*c*) £2,000 for an Irish Draught Horse scheme.'[6] The Royal Dublin Society had never been so liberally treated by the Treasury and had been financially unable to purchase more than a mere handful of stallions for placement in areas where they were needed. By comparison, in 1918, 'The Department purchased . . . seven stallions and four colts, at a cost of £1,355,' and six of the stallions were '. . . resold under the terms of the Department's Scheme of Loans for the purchase of stallions.'[7] Similar purchases were made in other years.

   The acquisition of stallions by the Department was made feasible partly through the financial resources of the Department and partly because, in 1904, Chantilly Stud Farm at Shankill, Co.

Dublin, was acquired from the Congested Districts Board. The Board had, following its foundation in 1891, stood stallions at stud at nominal fees in the Congested Districts, those areas in which the rateable valuation was less than £1. 10s. per head, but its horse breeding activities ended with the 1903 season. The stallions belonging to the Board '. . . were transferred to the Department in January, 1904,' as was Chantilly, where the sires had been kept in the non-breeding season. For a number of years the Department continued to send stallions annually, for the breeding season, to the areas that had formerly been the responsibility of the Board. Thus, in 1907, four Hackneys, nine Half-bred horses, two Half-bred ponies, five Welsh cobs, one Norwegian and two Thoroughbreds were sent to the 'outlying districts' of Donegal, Leitrim, Mayo, Galway, Cork and Kerry. In addition to these sires the Department also continued the tradition of the Board in standing quality stallion asses '. . . in districts in which donkeys are largely used, and in which a demand exists for the service of suitable sires.' In 1909, for example, fifty-nine jack-asses were located in Counties Cavan, Cork, Donegal, Fermanagh, Galway, Kerry, Leitrim, Mayo, Roscommon and Sligo. This little-known aspect of the Department's activities continued until the end of the breeding season in 1914, when 'These donkeys were sold at nominal sums to suitable persons.'[8] Chantilly, outside the breeding season, must have been quite a menagerie. Nevertheless, the Department found the acquisition of the stud farm '. . . of great advantage in furthering the objects of the horse-breeding scheme,' since stallions purchased by the Department could now be '. . . kept at Chantilly Stud Farm during the period between their purchase and resale.'[9] Incidentally, the Government grant that is nowadays given

Plate Forty-three. Easter Shamrock, *a fine example of a Connemara Pony mare. (Photo:* courtesy of Mr C. Sutton)

to the Connemara Pony Society, to aid it (and, consequently, to aid the development of Connemara Ponies), may in some ways be regarded as the logical continuation of the work of the Congested Districts Board, for the homeland of the Connemara was formerly regarded as one of the major Congested Districts in Ireland.

But the Department of Agriculture's schemes for horse breeding differed from those of the Royal Dublin Society in many other ways than in being better financed. The Society, in spite of the recommendations of Lord Enniskillen's faction on the 1897 Inquiry into horse breeding (that provision should be made for the betterment of *all* sorts of horses used in Ireland, and not just Thoroughbreds and Half-breds) had steadfastly refused to register any other than Thoroughbred stallions. The Department, by comparison, recognized the need for the registration of heavy horses as well as Thoroughbreds, and from 1901 onwards Clydesdales and Shires were registered, in addition to the aristocrats of the General Stud Book. Thus, unlike the Society's schemes, the Department did much to improve the breeding of horses for agricultural and for heavy haulage work. The Society had been concerned essentially with producing horses suitable for export for light harness and riding uses, the Department was concerned with the welfare of farmers and businessmen in Ireland itself.

In 1907 the Department admitted 'medium-weight' stallions to its register, and from 1911 onwards (with the temporary exception of 1916 and 1917) divided them into two categories, Half-bred and Irish Draught.

The Irish Draught Horse was an almost mythical beast whose origins are unfathomable. R.G. Carden, who had been a prominent figure in the Royal Dublin Society's horse breeding schemes, wrote in 1907 that, prior to about the year 1850, there was a breed of horses in Ireland known as the Irish cart or draught horse. 'It must not be taken that the words "cart" and "draught" imply that these animals were purely kept for agricultural purposes, or were in any way of the same type or blood as what are known in England and Scotland at the present day as the Shire and Clydesdale, as there are many instances in which some of these "Irish draught horses" proved to be the best hunters of their time.' Carden described how Irish Draughts '. . . were a long, low build of animal, rarely exceeding 15.3 or 16 hands high, with strong, short, clean legs, plenty of bone and substance, short backs, strong loins and quarters . . . slightly upright shoulders, strong necks and a smallish head. They had good, straight, level action, without its being extravagant, could trot, canter and gallop. They were also excellent jumpers . . . No authentic information in regard to their breeding is now available, though, no doubt, many breeders carefully preserved the strain in their breeding studs for many years, but it may generally be taken that the original breeding of the "Irish draught horse" was the result of the cross of the imported thoroughbred sires on the stronger of the well-bred mares of the country, which latter must have had an infusion of Spanish or Arabian blood in their veins.'[10]

In 1904, after persistent lobbying by such men as Patrick J. Hanlon of Grangeforth in Co. Carlow, a member of the Council of Agriculture,[11] the Department decided '. . . that no new sires of the Clydesdale and Shire breeds should be registered except for the province of Ulster, the counties of Dublin and Louth, and the district comprised within a radius of ten miles of the city of Cork. The object . . . was to check the great impetus that had been given to the importation of Clydesdales and Shires; for most authorities agree that such sires, if too freely imported, will impair the reputation of Irish horses.'[12] The following year, in 1905, '. . . the Department offered to owners of stallions of the old Irish Draught type and of half-bred stallions

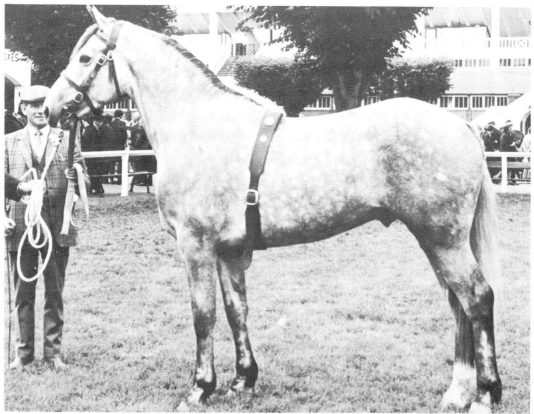

Plate Forty-four. Pride of Shaunlara (636), *a fine example of an Irish Draught, by* Milestone (498) *out of* Boston Burglar (6440). *Irish Draughts still vary considerably in conformation and some appear much heavier than the horse shown.* Pride of Shaunlara's *dam's sire was a Thoroughbred,* Prefairy, *the sire of a number of successful racehorses. It will be interesting to see whether the closure of the* Irish Draught Horse Book *as from 1978 to all but the progeny of registered Irish Draught parents will lead to increasing coarseness in the breed (which will necessitate recourse to infusions of Thoroughbred blood) or whether Irish Draughts will breed true to type. (Photo:* Ruth Rogers, courtesy of Bord na gCapall)

of the Hunter-type, a premium of £50 for selected stallions.'[13] This, in effect, meant that Irish Draught and Half-bred stallions were in future to be admitted to the Department's *Register of Stallions*, a development that was unheard of in the old Royal Dublin Society days, even though it was not until 1911 that Irish Draught Horses were accorded formal recognition by the listing of stallions under that designation in the Department's *Register*. In the same year, out of 5,040 mares inspected at 60 different exhibitions, '. . . 264 were selected as eligible for prizes and for registration' as Irish Draughts.[14] Thus, hesitantly, the Irish Draught began its official career, although Volume One of the *Irish Draught Horse Book* was not published until 1918.

The development of the Irish Draught in the years following 1918 was far slower than many had hoped, in spite of considerable initial success. 'The scheme for the establishment of an Irish Draught Horse Book, issued early in 1917, has been most successful, stated the *Annual General Report* of the Department of Agriculture in 1917–18. By 1926 the *General*

Report, which covered the strife-ridden years of 1923-26, stated of the Irish Draught Horse Scheme that 'There has been a serious set-back in horse-breeding during recent years, and the difficulty experienced by breeders in finding a market at remunerative prices for their young stock has interfered with the operation of this scheme, which has not developed to as great an extent as could be wished.'[15] In fact, it was not until 1938 or thereabouts that the Irish Draught could really have been acclaimed as a success. In that year 163 Irish Draught stallions were registered by the Department, and numbers remained high during the years of the Second World War. Following the conclusion of the War, however, the Irish Draught began to decline, and its fortunes were not to be reviewed until the formation of Bord na gCapall (The Irish Horse Board) in 1971 and the general revival of interest in the breed due to the work of the Bord and due to the formation of the Irish Draught Horse Society in 1976. Hopefully, the foundation, in 1979, of the British Irish Draught Horse Society, will, in spite of its name, further aid development of this fine type of horse. Perhaps, in view of the chequered career of the Irish Draught Horse during the twentieth century, the Royal Dublin Society was wise not to adopt the breed and include its stallions under their horse breeding schemes, although at least eleven of the sixty-nine stallions registered in the first three volumes of the *Irish Draught Horse Book*, published in 1920, had at least one Thoroughbred ancestor listed in the Society's registers. Nevertheless, the great demand for Clydesdale and Shire stallions, and the increasing demand that developed in the first seventeen years of the twentieth century for the services of Half-bred and Irish Draught stallions, showed that the Society's registers had not adequately catered for the needs of horse-breeding in general. Perhaps, after all, the Society had been colonialist and elitist in its attitudes to horse-breeding by accepting only Thoroughbred stallions for registration, and by not recognizing the grave need in Ireland for the services of stallions of other breeds. Perhaps that was inevitable, for the Society was composed essentially of members of the Ascendancy class, the Anglo-Irish, who were not always in tune with the gut needs of their country, even if it was debatable whether Ireland really was their country.

Nevertheless, the inclusion of new breeds excepted, the form of the horse-breeding schemes operated by the Department of Agriculture differed only in detail from those pioneered by the Royal Dublin Society. The Department's *Register of Stallions* appeared annually from 1901 until the partition of Ireland in 1922, even though no copies of the earlier *Registers* appear to have survived. Statistical summaries, luckily, do exist, embedded in the Annual General Reports of the Department, and, as Table Fourteen shows, they evidence the way in which the Register developed until 1918. That year, with the end of the First World War and the flooding of the market with former Army horses, saw a decline in the total number of registered stallions that continued until partition and, in fact, in the years that followed.

Fortunately at least one copy of the *Register of Stallions for 1921* still survives. From it one can reconstruct the major spatial patterns within the horse breeding industry in the fateful year that preceded the political division of Ireland into two groupings, the six counties of the north east opting to remain a part of the United Kingdom of Great Britain (and Northern Ireland) and the remaining counties forming what was eventually to become the Republic of Ireland.* In 1921 the *Register* lists a grand total of 455 stallions, of which the predominant breed was the feathery Clydesdale, as if to emphasise the transformation that had occurred in the state supported horse

---

* This designation is used hereafter.

		Table Fourteen			
		Registered Stallions, 1901–1921			
Year	Thoroughbred	Irish Draught	Half-Bred	Clydesdale	Shire	Total
1901	97	—	—	23	8	128
1902	111	—	—	35	16	162
1903	123	—	—	48	21	192
1904	140	—	—	48	23	211
1905	154	—	—	49	26	229
1906	163	—	—	50	26	239
1907	161		38	51	26	276
1908	156		50	52	24	282
1909	153		61	57	25	296
1910	167		83	63	27	340
1911	184	13	87	63	23	370
1912	192	13	105	64	22	396
1913	181	12	106	75	19	393
1914	175	12	122	83	22	414
1915	175	13	138	90	22	438
1916	176	—	149	131	29	485
1917	181	—	172	144	28	525
1918	155	44	125	135	25	484
1919	137	50	114	147	22	470
1920	136	58	109	146	22	471
1921	134	60	96	145	20	455

Sources: Annual General Reports, Department of Agriculture and Technical Instruction, Ireland, 1901–1921.

breeding industry since the days of the Royal Dublin Society's Thoroughbred dominated schemes. Figures Eighteen, Nineteen, Twenty and Twenty-two show how the registered stallion industry was organized in 1921.

Thoroughbreds (Figure Eighteen) were still dominant to the south and east of a line from Slane to Limerick, bending thence south to Cork. But major changes had occurred in Thoroughbred movement patterns since it had last been possible to map them, almost thirty years earlier, in 1893. Few Thoroughbred sires still travelled the countryside, seeking trade. Admittedly, Robert Stephens still believed that sires should travel, and his *Foxmask* visited Cahirciveen, Milltown, and Killorglin in the mountainous wilds of west Kerry. Similarly four stallions still travelled the east Cork – west Waterford region, and in north Tipperary T.A. Hogan's and P. O'Brien's stallions covered essentially the same route in their search for business. The only other areas where Thoroughbreds still travelled were in Co. Down (on a limited scale) and along the fertile coastlands of Co. Wicklow, in the garden of Ireland. Joseph

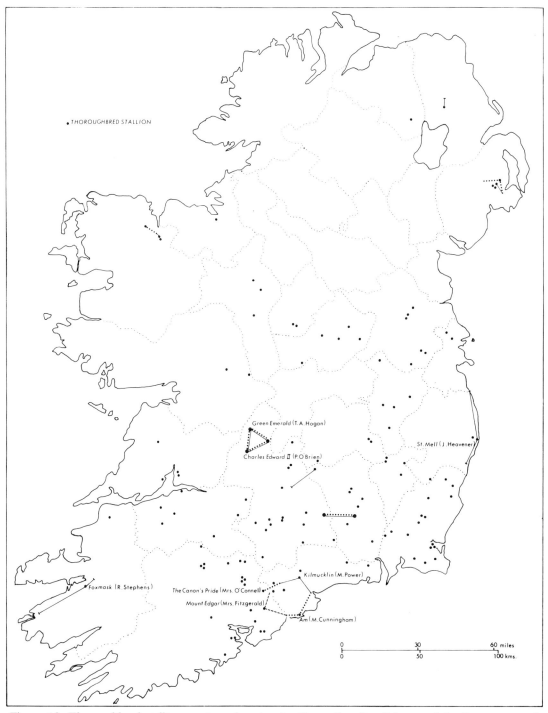

・THOROUGHBRED STALLION

Green Emerald (T.A.Hogan)

Charles Edward II (P.O'Brien)

St. Mell (J.Heavener)

Foxmask (R.Stephens)

Kilmucklin (M.Power)

The Canon's Pride (Mrs. O'Connell)

Mount Edgar (Mrs. Fitzgerald)

Am (M.Cunningham)

| 0 | 30 | 60 miles |
| 0 | 50 | 100 kms. |

Figure 18. *Thoroughbred stallions registered under the Horse Breeding Scheme of the Department of Agriculture, 1921. Notice how, by comparison with the 1893 situation (Figure 6), few of the stallions travelled for their mares*

Figure 19. *Half-bred stallions registered under the Horse Breeding Scheme of the Department of Agriculture, 1921. Note the major concentrations of stallions in south eastern Ireland, in North Tipperary and in the Hollymount region of Co. Mayo. South East Ireland remains an important Half-bred producing area in the 1970s, although North Tipperary and Mayo are less important than was formerly the case. Unlike Thoroughbreds, Half-breds still travelled extensively for their mares in 1921*

Figure 20. *Irish Draught stallions registered under the Horse Breeding Scheme of the Department of Agriculture in 1921. Notice how these sires were concentrated in the southern part of the country, and particularly in areas that had been important breeding centres under the Royal Dublin Society's schemes. Although Irish Draughts travelled extensively for their mares some, like* Zeppelin, *travelled only for fairs. The Province of Ulster was almost totally devoid of Irish Draught sires, since the northern farmers favoured the heavier Clydesdales which apparently were better suited to tillage operations in the heavy drumlin and clay soils of the north than were the lighter Irish Draughts*

Heavener of Cullen Lower, Wicklow, travelled *St. Mel* between Bray and Arklow, covering a lengthy route at the foot of the Wicklow uplands. But, for the most part, Thoroughbred sires appear to have become sedentary beasts, waiting at home for their mares to visit them, as is still the case today. Obviously, by 1921, the Thoroughbred was becoming a cossetted animal.

In marked contrast to the spatial organization of the Thoroughbred sires, Half-breds travelled extensively, although they were concentrated in Waterford, Cork, Tipperary, Galway, south Mayo, and in an interesting area in south Leitrim (Figure Nineteen). These were areas where hunter production had long been important, as the Royal Dublin Society's schemes had shown, and where there was still a need for, and appreciation of, quality riding and harness horses. A number of the Half-breds had been sired by Thoroughbreds listed on the Society's registers, such as Patrick Burke's *Breany*, by *Bergomask* out of a dam by *Ireland*, and standing at Miltown Malby in Co. Clare, emphasising the value of the Society's breeding schemes. Many Half-breds covered lengthy distances in their travels, such as *Boherscrub*, who went '. . . to Ballinrobe on Mondays, Loughgeorge, Headford, Currindullia and Aughcleggan on Wednesdays, Tuam on Saturdays, and at owner's stables on remaining days of the week.' At least it could not be said that the horse did not deserve the pleasures of his calling.

Irish Draught stallions (Figure Twenty) exhibited a less concentrated distributional pattern than that of the Half-breds, although most existed south of a line from Dublin to Galway. J. Dodd, a well-known veterinary surgeon in Sligo, owned the most far travelled horse to the north of that line, but the Dodds had long been noted horsemen and are still active in Sligo and Mayo in the late 1970s, so that it is no surprise that a member of that family should have recognized the potential of the Irish Draught for improving the local breed of horses. The greatest numbers of Irish Draughts, as Figure Twenty-one shows, existed in the southern and more fertile parts of the western counties where there was only a limited amount of tillage, and where the need was for a general purpose horse that could do relatively light farm work, such as carting, or even ploughing the generally light soils of the area, and that could also trot to market under the family trap, or carry its owner to hounds if so desired. These needs were fulfilled by the clean-legged Irish Draught, whereas the ordinary Thoroughbred was far too refined an animal for farm work, and Shires and Clydesdales were too heavy for trotting or for hunting and similar diversions.

The heavy clay lands, where tillage was highly developed, as in Co. Louth, north Co. Dublin, north Down, The Bann, the Limavaddy lowlands and the Lagan of Donegal, needed heavy horses. Here the long-standing cultural connection with Scotland was reflected by the predominance of Clydesdales. They were especially prominent in Louth and north Dublin, as Figure Twenty-two shows, and travelled extensively for their mares. The Royal Dublin Society had completely ignored the need for such heavy horses in its horse breeding schemes, and must be criticised adversely for such neglect. Even the owners of the cart-horse sires seem to have been, almost entirely, different from the Thoroughbred and Half-bred owning fraternity. In Co. Donegal James Wray of Raphoe owned four Clydesdales, which he travelled as far afield as Londonderry itself. In Louth there were fourteen registered sires, owned by such people as Dunlop and Stevenson of Louth Hall, Ardee, T.J. Clinton the vet., of Mayne, Castlebellingham, and Peter Muckian of Lurgankeel, Dundalk. In Co. Dublin Peter Bartley of Dardistown, Santry, travelled three Clydesdales, and the Wades of the White Hart in Balbriggan travelled a number of horses. William Brangan of Naul was another important owner. In the south, around Cork city, Shire stallions predominated, rather than Clydesdales, producing heavy horses for the city

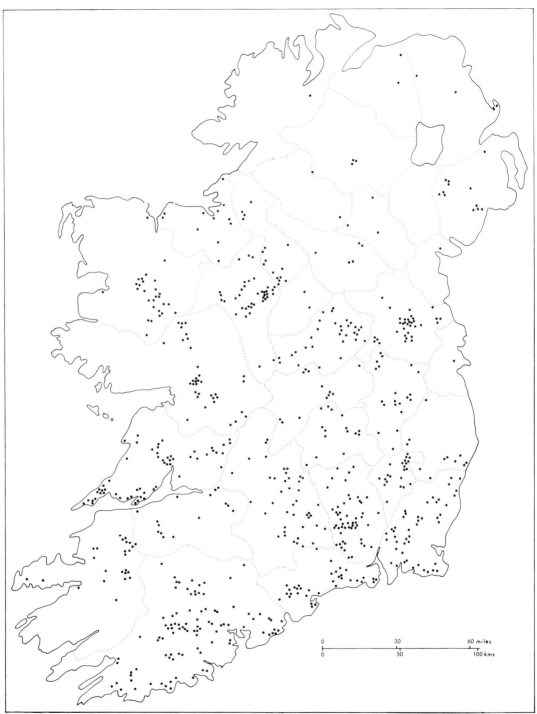

Figure 21. *The location of Irish Draught mares listed in Volumes I-III of the Irish Draught Horse Book, effectively showing all mares registered up to 1920. Analysis of heights indicates that the mare populations of Mayo and along the Cork coastlands west of Kinsale, were smaller than the national average, many mares being 15.2 hands or even less. Most registered mares were 15.3 or 16.0 hands high, although occasional mares reached 16.2. As might be expected, the distribution of mares tends to reflect the more fertile farming areas in Ireland, south of the Clydesdale dominated Province of Ulster and the Counties of Louth and Dublin*

Figure 22. *Clydesdale and Shire stallions registered under the Horse Breeding Scheme of the Department of Agriculture, 1921. Notice how, partly because of Departmental restrictions, Clydesdales were limited mainly to the Province of Ulster and to Counties Louth and Dublin. Shires were concentrated to the immediate north of Cork city, to provide draught horses for the city hauliers. Clydesdales, in particular, travelled extensively for their mares, to such an extent that it is difficult to depict the intertwining networks of Louth, Dublin, north Down, the lower Bann valley and the Lagan of Donegal. Although similar networks still existed in 1939, as the* Registers of Stallions *for that year show, farm mechanization following the end of the Second World War in 1944 rapidly ended the system. It is extremly doubtful whether any heavy draught stallions travelled regularly for their mares in Ireland after the 1960s*

Within the map legend:
CLYDESDALE
SHIRE

30 miles
60 miles
50
100 kms.

hauliers. Perhaps it was appropriate that they were Shires, an English breed, for the Cork area had much more in common with England than with the distant lands of Scotland.

Another development that occurred under the aegis of the Department of Agriculture was the licensing of stallions. This had first been mooted in 1909, when 'At a meeting of the Department's Advisory Committee on Horse-breeding held on 23 June, 1909, a resolution was adopted urging the Department to seek statutory powers to prevent stallions, other than thoroughbreds entered in the General Stud-book, from standing for public service unless licenced by the Department.'[15] Obviously the Department was in a very much stronger position to press for Government legislation in such a matter than the Royal Dublin Society would have been, but the fact remains that the Society apparently never sought Government action on licensing. As far as the Society was concerned, its horse breeding schemes and the effect of competition arising from its horse shows, appear to have been all that was contemplated for the improvement of horses in Ireland. In fact, partly because of general disruption caused by the First World War, the licensing of stallions did not become law until 1st January, 1920. There were 2,105 applications for licences that year, of which 1,718 were granted, although 159 of these licences were for one year only because '. . . the horses were unsound or . . . unsuitable, but . . . for various reasons (the) Department considered it inadvisable to refuse Licences.' 289 applications were, however, rejected.[16] The effect of the stringent application of licensing tests was immediately apparent in 1921, when it was necessary to reject only thirty-four horses for licences.

Because of political events, namely the partition of Ireland, 'On 1st January, 1922, the administration of the Act in Northern Ireland was taken over by the Northern Ministry of Agriculture.'[17] But even in the difficult year ahead strenuous efforts were made to enforce the Act, as official documents relate: 'The disturbed state of the country operated against a rigid enforcement of the provisions of the Act, and it is feared that in some cases unlicensed horses were used for stud purposes. There is, however, every reason to hope that it will be possible to take steps to ensure that no stallion will be serving without a licence during the 1924 service season.

It may be mentioned that enquiries were made through the Garda Siochana* in certain cases in which it was suspected that unlicensed sires were being used. As a result . . . several of the owners concerned took out licences . . . and in the case of each of the others it was reported that no evidence was forthcoming to justify a prosecution being instituted.'[18]

Some idea of conditions in Ireland in 1922 and 1923 is afforded by the *Annual General Report* of the Department of Agriculture for those years. 'The period covered by this Report corresponds generally to the year beginning with the 1st October, 1922, and ending on 30th September, 1923. It was a year of anxiety and struggle. The post-war depression . . . continued to weigh down Irish agriculture . . . During the greater portion of the time large areas of the country were in a disturbed condition. Railway and other travelling and transit facilities were frequently interrupted and in some instances suspended for considerable periods. Yet, notwithstanding all this, the Schemes of the Department . . . were carried out substantially as arranged.'[19]

The importance attached by the Minister for Agriculture to the licensing of stallions is amply reflected by the steps taken to ensure that the licensing regulations were enforced, as far as was

* i.e. the police

possible, even in 1922-3. Licensing has been continued ever since in the Republic of Ireland and until 1970 in Northern Ireland, and there can be little doubt but that the system has done much to improve the quality of horse-breeding throughout the country.

From 1922 onwards the registration of stallions under the official Government horse breeding schemes, like the issuing of stallion licences, became the responsibility of authorities in Northern Ireland and in the Republic of Ireland respectively. In both cases, until 1975, registration was undertaken by the Department, or by the Northern Ireland Ministry of Agriculture. In the latter year, in the Republic, Bord na gCapall (The Horse Board) assumed responsibility for the register in the Republic. In Northern Ireland horse breeding is still under the aegis of what, in the 1970s, again became called the Department of Agriculture, although since September 1979 Half-bred mares have been included in the 'Irish Horse Register.'

The immediate effect of political partition, apart from the formation of two separate registers of stallions, was reflected in an overall decrease in the number of sires registered. In the Republic, as Table Fifteen shows the total declined from 338 in 1922 to 262 in 1925, a nadir that

Table Fifteen

Registered Stallions, Republic of Ireland, 1922–78

Year	Thoroughbred	Irish Draught	Half-Bred	Clydesdale	Shire	Total
1922	120	67	71	68	12	338
1923	113	57	60	51	10	291
1924	—	—	—	—	—	277
1925	—	—	—	—	—	262
1926						270
1927	161	58	39	44		302
1928	180	67	40	44		331
1929	195	72	51	41		359
1930	210	77	66	39		392
1931	205	81	81	32		399
1932	192	84	85	38		399
1933	180	84	77	37		378
1934	166	92	72	40		370
1935	169	99	67	47		382
1936	156	114	72	47		389
1937	157	131	74	55		417
1938	162	163	78	71		474
1939	158	176	76	75		485
1940	156	187	74	81		498
1941	138	195	72	79		484
1942	123	197	64	78		462
1943	116	198	55	78		447
1944	98	187	51	76		412
1945	97	183	46	64		390
1946	92	180	40	62		374
1947	102	180	37	53	5	377

Table Fifteen (Continued)

Year	Thoroughbred	Irish Draught	Half-Bred	Clydesdale	Shire	Total
1948	105	176	35	41	6	363
1949	104	165	31	35	4	339
1950	114	165	28	32	3	342
1951	113	150	23	26	2	314
1952	106	125	19	18	1	269
1953	88	119	16	20	1	244
1954	86	126	11	16	1	240
1955	86	112	8	17	0	223
1956	72	94	6	18	0	190
1957	69	91	4	17	0	181
1958	62	91	4	18	0	175
1959	60	91	3	19	0	173
1960	60	93	3	18	0	174
1961	69	99	2	19	0	189
1962	84	104	2	15	0	205
1963	87	105	1	11	0	204
1964	88	108	1	11	0	208
1965	92	105	1	9	0	207
1966	104	103	0	3	0	210
1967*	110	100	0	3	0	213
1968*	97	96	0	0	0	193
1969*	113	97	0	0	0	210
1970*	114	109	0	0	0	223
1971*	156	119	0	0	0	275
1972*	174	110	5	0	0	289
1973*	213	97	20	0	0	330
1974*	223	77	22	0	0	322
1975*	216	65	21	0	0	302
1976*	253	66	27	0	0	346
1977*	256	63	27	0	0	346
1978*	252	62	27	0	0	341

* Based on *Register of Stallions*, the source for all other statistics is the *Annual General Reports* of the Department of Agriculture.

was not to be repeated until 1953. This mirrored the difficulties attendant upon the birth of the Irish State, and also reflected the economic depression of the post-war years. For three years, 1924-6, no register of stallions was apparently produced, and the grand total of registered stallions printed in the *General Report* of the Minister of Agriculture for the period included 'stallions entered in the Irish Draught Horse Book,' suggestive of the difficulties of proper administration and the necessity for cosmetic statistics in the official returns. Detailed returns exist, in unbroken fashion, from 1927 onwards, although the Minister's report, unlike the registers themselves, does not differentiate between Clydesdales and Shires until 1947.

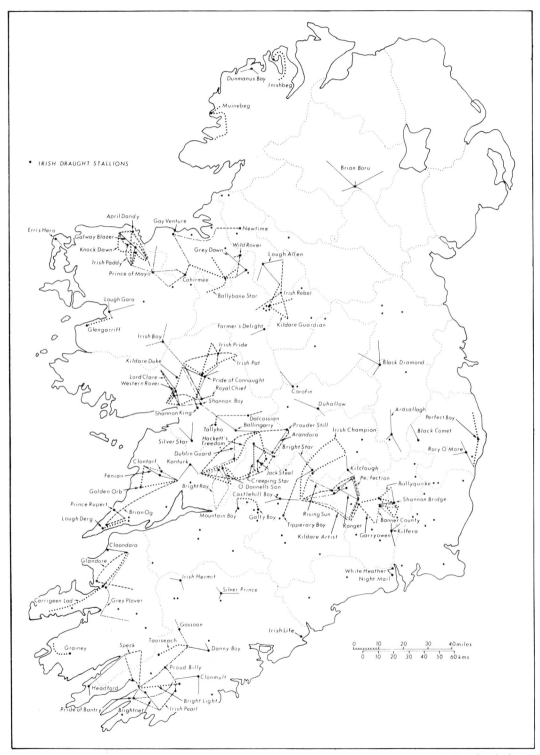

Figure 23. *The location and movement patterns of the 177 Irish Draught stallions registered under the horse breeding schemes for 1939.*

From 1927 until 1931 there was an increase in the number of stallions registered, from 270 to 399, with the greatest increase being in Thoroughbred registrations. There was thence a slight overall decline until 1937, largely because of a decline in Thoroughbred registration. In 1938 there was a marked increase in Irish Draught and heavy horse registrations, as if to foreshadow the need for work horses during the years ahead, when the Second World War made it almost impossible to get fuel for cars and tractors and made horses essential to the economy, as in former days.

That stallions still travelled the country in search of mares is shown by Figure Twenty-three, depicting the movement patterns of registered Irish Draught sires in 1939. After that year it becomes impossible to plot such patterns, for the exigensies of the war and the decrease in importance of horses to the economy in the post-war era, meant that the *Registers of Stallions* no longer recorded the necessary information. What is obvious, from comparison of Figures Twenty and Twenty-three, is that the Irish Draughts had extended their territory very appreciably between 1921 and 1939, and were extremely important in west Cork, the fertile lands of north Kerry, the Killala-Ballina lowlands and adjacent areas to the east, and in the great belt extending from Wexford-south Wicklow across Carlow, Kilkenny, north of Tipperary and thence spreading outwards to encompass much of Clare and the valuable farming areas of east Galway.

The Second World War, during which the Republic of Ireland remained neutral (if decidedly pro-British in its pattern of trade and in the number of volunteers who entered the forces of the Crown), were years of great difficulty. In July, 1942, the Emergency Powers (Control of Export) Order came into operation, and prohibited the export of horses except under licence. During 1942 'Licences were only issued for the export, through the ports, of old and useless horses and of thoroughbreds. During the period, July 1942 to March 1943, 3,543 old horses were exported through the ports.'[20] No doubt their flesh was much needed, even if not universally appreciated, in beleaguered Britain.

In 1943, 'Owing to the increased tillage operations and further deterioration in the transport position, it was found necessary to retain in the country any horses which could be utilized as workers or vanners, and licences have only been issued for the export of old and useless horses, unfit for working purposes, and of thoroughbreds.'[21] In the same year the registration of Irish Draught sires reached a peak that has never been surpassed (198), even though the total number of Clydesdales and Shires was three below its absolute peak (of 1940).

Thus, during the 1939-43 period, and continuing for a further three years, working horses played an essential, almost dominant, role in maintaining the economy of the Republic of Ireland. Yet these were the very breeds of horses, the Irish Draughts, the Clydesdales, and the Shires, that the Royal Dublin Society had neglected to include in its nineteenth century registers of stallions. Thoroughbreds were all very well, and so were Half-breds, in the days of the cavalry horse, but the twentieth century, especially from 1916 onwards (when tanks proved their value) was the era of mechanized warfare. The need now, so far as horses were concerned, was for the more lowly draught and working breeds, whose value had only been grudgingly accepted by the Royal Dublin Society towards the very end of its horse breeding schemes when, in 1901, three premiums of £50 each were awarded for agricultural stallions. In that same year, the reader might remember, the Society offered twenty-five premiums, of £100 each, for Thoroughbred stallions.

Plate Forty-five. *C. Sutton with his prize-winning team of Irish Draught geldings competing at one of the matches held by the Enniskerry Ploughing Society, Co. Wicklow, during the 1940s. (Photo:* courtesy of Mr C. Sutton)

By 1st December, 1944, conditions had sufficiently eased in the Republic of Ireland 'to relax the restrictions so as to permit the export of geldings of all types . . . during the four months ending 31st March, 1945, 713 geldings, principally hunters and riding horses, were exported to Great Britain and Northern Ireland.'[22] The flood gates had opened, and the demise of the horse as a work animal in Ireland was at hand, even though that might not have been immediately apparent, for 'The total number of horses in the country in June, 1945, was 464,520, an increase of 5,654 on the preceding year.'

The authorities in the Republic anticipated that, following the end of the war, there would be a strong demand for Irish horses so, to ensure that not too many were exported, and to be as fair as possible to potential importers, it was decided in 1945 to allocate '. . . quotas to the various countries. The numbers of horses exported on foot of these quotas were: France (quota 2,000) 1,246; Switzerland (quota 700) 735; Belgium (quota 500) 347; Sweden (quota 300) nil; Spain (quota 300) nil. Prior to the introduction of the quota system, 117 horses had been shipped to Spain and Portugal. In addition, 300 working horses were exported to Holland under the Scheme for Relief of Distress in Europe, and the Netherlands Government subsequently purchased a further 200 horses for the use of their armed forces.'[23] An important feature of these exports was that they included not only geldings but also mares standing under 15.1 hands in their shoes, the idea being that larger, and supposedly better breeding stock should be retained in Ireland. On May 1st, 1948, the final export control on horses was removed, and horses can now be freely exported from Ireland, subject to certain humane and veterinary regulations.

By the 1st June, 1946, the number of horses in the Republic '. . . was 452,354, being 12,166 or 2.6 per cent. less than on the 1st June, 1945. The most marked decrease was in the number of unbroken horses under one year which, at 28,165, was 7,024 less than in the previous year. The number of horses (15,299) being used for traffic and for manufactures in 1946 was 1,756 or 10.3 per cent. less than in the previous year . . . trade in horses was generally dull during the year.'[24] The great decline in the horse population of the Republic of Ireland had begun and, after a miniscule recovery in 1975, still continues, as Table Sixteen shows. Cart horses were, by the 1970s, becoming a rarity in Ireland, and the last listing of a Clydesdale stallion in the *Register of Stallions* was in 1967. The Shire had disappeared even earlier, the final listing being in 1954. Even the Irish Draught entered a post-war decline, from 187 stallions registered in 1944 to only 62 in 1978. That its decline was not more rapid was largely a reflection of its value as a crossing sire for hunter production and of official Government support for the beasts. Nevertheless, the recent interest in the Irish Draught, witnessed by the closing of the *Book* as from 1978 to new entries unless they are the progeny of registered parents and by the foundation and rapid growth of the Irish Draught Horse Society, has been mirrored by an upsurge in the breeding of Irish Draughts in Ireland. In 1978, for example, 79 Irish Draught colts were examined by the representatives of Bord na gCapall to decide whether they would make potential future stallions. Although it is inevitable that many of these colts will not eventually prove suitable, they provide an ample reservoir for the future continuation of the breed.

Although the Royal Dublin Society assiduously collected information on the number and sex of foals produced as a result of its breeding schemes, there was no attempt at performance or progeny testing. Bord na gCapall, however, began a testing scheme for Irish Draught stallions in

Table Sixteen

The decline in the horse population of the Republic of Ireland, 1945–76

Year	Number	Year	Number
1945	464,520	1961	207,100
1946	452,354	1962	195,900
1947	438,341	1963	190,200
1948	420,732	1964	180,300
1949	401,992	1965	172,111
1950	390,613	1966	158,400
1951	367,048	1967	142,700
1952	341,701	1968	133,600
1953	329,054	1969	124,900
1954	313,434	1970	124,300
1955	296,274	1971	117,300
1956	276,400	1972	112,100
1957	260,700	1973	103,300
1958	243,800	1974	98,100
1959	233,600	1975	99,100
1960	223,749	1976	83,200

Source: Annual General Reports of the Department of Agriculture.

1976, when it purchased *Flagmount Boy*. This colt was carefully broken before being leased to John McCarthy of Drimoleague in Co. Cork, where he covered forty mares in 1977. Like other stallions purchased even more recently, *Flagmount Boy*'s ridden and other performances, and those of his progeny, will be monitored, and it is hoped that this will indicate scientifically (and unquestionably) the value of this and other sires. Whether one could reasonably have expected the Royal Dublin Society to have undertaken such a scientific evaluation of stallions included in its registers is debatable. Show-jumping and eventing, for which the modern Irish Half-bred is particularly suited, hardly existed as serious sports during the days of the Society's horse breeding schemes. The Bord also collects information relating to the success '. . . of the progeny of Registered Stallions in show classes for young horses . . . subsidised by Bord na gCapall.'[25] The first year in which this was done was 1977, and the results were published, in table form, in the *Register of Approved Stallions, 1978*. The same *Register* contained yet another innovation, as far as the official Department of Agriculture and the new Horse Board was concerned. It listed the stud performances of Registered Sires in 1976/7 under the headings: total mares covered, live produce (by sex), dead produce at birth and since birth, barren mares, no return made, fertility in terms of live foals produced, conception fertility. This was essentially the same information as the Royal Dublin Society had collected, over eighty years earlier, which is a compliment to the Society's perspicacity.

The nadir of horse breeding in the Republic, as far as the number of stallions listed in the *Register of Stallions* was concerned, was in 1959. In that year only 173 were listed, sixty Thoroughbreds, ninety-one Irish Draughts, three Half-breds and nineteen Clydesdales. By 1966 the Half-bred, as a registered sire, had been allowed to vanish, but this was rapidly recognized as a mistake, for many Half-breds prove excellent sires for getting hunters and competition horses. Thus, in 1972, Half-breds were again listed in the *Register* and by 1976 their numbers had reached a fairly healthy level. Most of the registered sires are concentrated in the south and east of the country, especially in Wexford, Waterford and adjoining counties.[26]

Throughout the 1960s popular emphasis was placed on mechanization, as if there was no role for the horse as a working animal. Even the production of pleasure horses began to be regarded as of somewhat suspect value, and little attempt was made to ensure the registration of more than a few (sixty to a hundred) Thoroughbred sires. This development caused considerable consternation amongst horsemen, among whom were many influential members of the Irish Government, including Mr. C.J. Haughey, then Minister for Agriculture. As a result, in January 1965, Mr. Haughey appointed a Survey Team on the Horse Breeding Industry. This team reported in August 1966 and the eventual outcome was both a change of Departmental policy on horse breeding and the creation of Bord na gCapall. This Bord was set up on 8th February 1971 with the duty of developing the non-Thoroughbred horse industry in the Republic. Under the 'Bord na gCapall (Assignment of Additional Functions) Order, 1975,' the Bord became responsible for administering foaling premiums, mare nominations, the registration of Irish Draught mares, and the purchase and location of Thoroughbred sires for hunter breeding. The Bord also has certain responsibilities for developing markets for non-Thoroughbred horses.

Even before the establishment of Bord na gCapall there had been a distinct reversal of official policy on horse breeding. The Royal Dublin Society's library copy of the *Register of Stallions, 1965*, is a saddening document. In it, an unknown hand has written, in pencil, either 'dead' or 'sold for slaughter' across the names of many of the draught stallions. Seven of the Irish Draught sires are so denoted, as is the only Half-bred listed in the register. Of the total of nine Clydesdales, five have their names struck through, two are stated as 'dead', two as 'sold for slaughter,' and one as 'exported to N.I.' The day of the heavy horse had, quite obviously, ended. Indeed, the last Clydesdale to be registered for the County of Dublin had been *Dardistown Ensign (23357)*, bay, foaled in 1932, and owned by G.T. O'Reilly, M.R.C.V.S., of Air Park, Rathfarnham. From 1968 onwards no Clydesdales or Shires have been included in the Registers in the Republic, and it has been recognized that the need now is for 'fun-horse' producing sires, stallions that beget hunters, eventers, show-jumpers, even a few steeplechasers, as well as hacks and riding school horses. There is also a limited market for quality horses for private driving.

In 1971 the reversal of official policy relating to horse breeding in the Republic was witnessed by a remarkable upsurge in registration of Thoroughbred sires, from 114 in the previous year to 156. Even greater numbers have been included in more recent registers, and in 1977 Bord na gCapall included 256 in its *Register* and also printed useful information for breeders on the height, girth and bone dimensions of many of the sires. The Bord has also formed a register of Half-breds, known as the 'Irish Horse Register,' which provides a basis for the identification of all Half-bred stock. From 1978 a special passport for showjumpers, based on the Irish Horse Register and on the records of the Show Jumping Association of Ireland, provides complete documentation of animals' breeding and performances. This should prove invaluable in marketing Irish horses, since potential buyers will be able to consult verifiable information when inspecting their potential purchase. Documentation of this nature, of course, depends upon complex recording facilities and use of computer facilities, so it is hardly surprising that the Royal Dublin Society, in the days of its horse breeding schemes, did not attempt such documentary feats. Indeed, it could not have done so, because the modern emphasis on competitive-events horses had not arisen. Instead the Society was concerned with aiding the production of useful riding, hunting, cavalry and harness horses, rather than the gargantuan monsters that are beginning to tower around the show jumping arenas of the world.

By 1978 there was sufficient concern about the lack of non-Thoroughbred breeding stock on Irish farms for Bord na gCapall to launch its Mare Replacement Scheme. In 1977 only 6,681 mares had been covered under the Bord's horse breeding scheme. They produced 3,637 foals in 1978, a fertility percentage of 54, which was markedly below the percentages recorded for the Queen's Premium Stallions in 1889–91, and which should be a major cause for concern. In 1977 only 3,580 registered non-Thoroughbred foals were born and the Bord believed that this was less than the breeding industry should produce. Furthermore, as Figure Twenty-four indicates, in 1977 the distribution of mares served under the horse breeding scheme showed a concentration, if expressed in terms of mares per county per acre, in south eastern Ireland and in Co. Clare. While it was cheering to note that these areas (Clare, Kilkenny, Waterford, Wexford), that have traditionally been noted for the production of quality horses, were still important, the decline in interest in horse breeding in the western counties was worrying. As a result the Bord designated 1978 as the Year of the Breeder and did much to stimulate an increase in production. Under the Mare Replacement Scheme the Bord '. . . will offer good breeding mares to approved breeders in certain selected areas who might wish to replace an existing barren or aged mare.

The mares will be selected by the Bord and offered to breeders on favourable financial terms.' The Bord also initiated a Mare Purchase Scheme: 'Persons interested in acquiring a non-thoroughbred brood mare for the first time will be eligible for a grant of £100 provided the mare

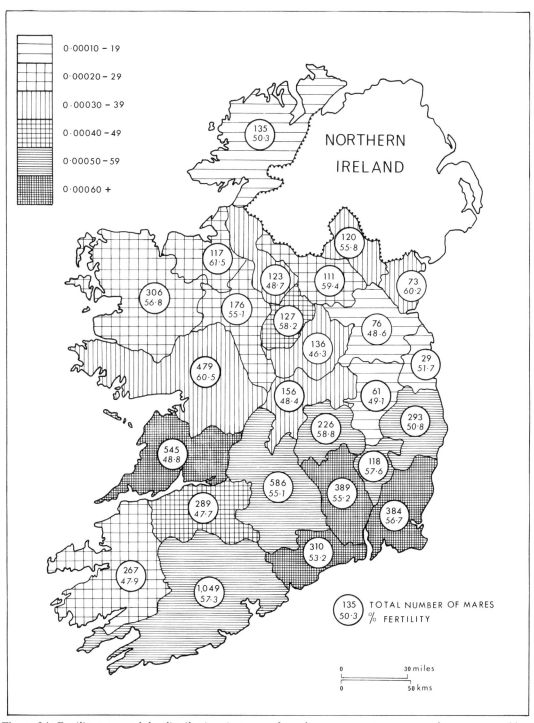

Figure 24. *Fertility rates and the distribution, in terms of numbers per county per acre, of mares covered by stallions under the breeding scheme of Bord na gCapall in 1977. (Source:* A study of the non-Thoroughbred horse industry, *Bord na gCapall, 1979).*

Plate Forty-six. El Teide *was one of some seventy Thoroughbred stallions leased to breeders by Bord na gCapall in 1978. The Bord leased three Irish Draught stallions. In 1977* El Teide *stood at stud with Walter Kent at Clearistown in Co. Wexford, but during 1978 the horse was with John Duffy of Coolarty in Co. Longford, proof that the long-standing practice of moving sires around the country at fairly regular intervals still continues.* El Teide *was foaled in 1969, by* Final Problem *out of* Bama Lough. *The horse is 17.1 hands high, girths 73ins and has 9½ins of bone. (Photo:* Ruth Rogers, courtesy of Bord na gCapall)

is suitable and approved by the Bord.'

'Both of these schemes will be operated on a pilot basis in the following areas:

(i) Donegal/Leitrim
(ii) North West Mayo
(iii) Kerry
(iv) Clare
(v) Roscommon and Galway (excluding Connemara).'[27]

Bord na gCapall has also arranged its own programme of horse sales, in an attempt to attract overseas purchasers and to raise the average level of prices so that breeders find the production of non-Thoroughbred horses financially worthwhile. The immediate stimulus to the establishment of the Bord's sales had been the sudden, dramatic and tragic decrease in sales to Britain. In 1972, for example, over 11,000 horses were sold to the United Kingdom, which was Ireland's leading customer. In 1977 the United Kingdom bought just 750 horses from Ireland.[28] This frightening decline was due to a number of factors, not least being the recession in the British economy caused by the 1973 oil crisis. Following a period of market research the Bord decided that the future hopes for the breeding industry lay in finding new markets, especially in Europe. As a result, in 1974, the Bord held sales at Cork, Gowran Park in Co. Kilkenny, and Galway. Although only 51 horses and 12 ponies were sold at these venues the Bord continued with its sales, but only at Gowran, and in 1977 sold 216 horses for £35,889. The Royal Dublin Society, which has long staged its own horse sales, continues to do so, and in October 1977 the Society's sales company sold £203,520 worth of showjumpers, eventers and hunters, in addition to Thoroughbred sales. In spite of these and other sales, in 1977 only 2,077 Half-bred horses were officially exported from the Republic, at a declared value of £1,887,027, and whilst this is derisory compared with, for example, the cattle trade, worth £57,695,000 in exports to Great Britain alone in 1977, there is obviously great scope for future development.

In Northern Ireland the decline in horse numbers was apparent even by 1930. 'The importance of horse breeding in Northern Ireland has been very much less in recent years than was the case before the war. The spread of motor transport and the great falling off in demand for horses for army purposes, especially on the part of Continental countries, has resulted in a considerable decrease in breeding. Whereas, in 1910, the number of horses used for traffic and manufacture in Northern Ireland was 13,796, by 1930 this number had declined to only 7,114. On farms . . . from 1923 to 1930 (there was) a reduction from 100,116 to 87,101 in the number of horses used for agricultural purposes.'[29] Even during the war years of 1939-44 the number of horses showed a decline, that was continuous until records of the total numbers of horses ceased to be kept annually by the Ministry, in 1953, as Table Seventeen demonstrates.

The Northern Ireland authorities appear to have placed less emphasis on horse breeding than their southern counterparts. Certainly the records of premium stallions, as printed in the *Annual* and *General Reports of the Ministry*, are less clearly presented than those of the Department of Agriculture in Dublin. For 1924 and 1925 no records are presented, and statements such as that for 1964, 'The horse still fulfills a useful place in the agricultural industry,' can hardly be accepted as jewels of precision. The greatest number of stallions registered, as if to pressage the need for horse-power during the forthcoming war, was in 1939, when 55 were listed. Once the war was over the number of registrations fell drastically, to 27 in 1949, as farm mechanization and the rapid spread of private and commercial motor vehicles ousted horses from their traditional work-horse role in the economy. Table Eighteen shows that the greatest number of premium stallions, until 1960, were Clydesdales, and that Irish Draughts, Half-breds and Shires were of little importance. Thoroughbreds, however, were reasonably popular until the Second World War and the number of registrations had remained virtually constant throughout the 1930s.

After the war the Ministry widened the base of its registration schemes by including an Arab and a 'Garron Pony' (whatever that may have been) to the *Register* for 1950. Clydesdale registrations fell away rapidly after the war, although the *Fourteenth General Report of the Ministry of Agriculture*, in 1957, recorded that 'Another form of Ministry assistance is given to a Horse Breeding Society which has operated in County Londonderry since 1946. Each year a high-class stallion from Scotland is leased for the service of pure-bred Clydesdale mares owned by members of the Society, and the Ministry's annual contribution towards the Society's working expenses is limited to a maximum of £200.'

By 1968 the Ministry were recording '. . . the virtual disappearance of the farm horse as a means of motive power,' and '. . . took the opportunity of seeking the repeal of the Horse

Table Seventeen

Total number of horses in Northern Ireland, 1939–53

Year	Number	Year	Number
1939	96,521	1949	60,664
1943	90,082	1950	54,763
1945	85,179	1951	45,462
1946	77,218	1952	39,563
1947	74,815	1953	37,038
1948	68,172		

Source: *General Reports of the Ministry of Agriculture.*

Table Eighteen

Registered Stallions, Northern Ireland, 1923–77

Year	Thoroughbred	Irish Draught	Half-Bred	Clydesdale	Shire	Other	Arab	Total
1923	8	0	0	24	0			32
1924								—
1925								—
1926	13	1	1	21	0			36
1927	13	1	1	23	0			38
1928	15	1	1	24	0			41
1929	16		4	23	0			43
1930	15	1	3	25	0			44
1931	15		4	24	0			43
1932	16		5	27	0			48
1933	15		4	29	0			48
1934	15		4	30	0			49
1939	14		2	39	0			55
1946*	7		3	32	0			42
1949	5		3	19	0			27
1950	7	1		18	0	1	1	28
1951	7		2	13	0			22
1952	6		2	13	0			21
1953	4		3	12	0			19
1954	4		4	12	0			20

Table Eighteen (Continued)

Year	Throughbred	Irish Draught	Half-Bred	Clydesdale	Shire	Other	Arab	Total
1955	4	—		8	—	5		17
1956	3	5		7	—			15
1957	3	5		6	—			14
1958	—	—		—	—			12
1959	4	3	0	6	0			13
1960	4	3	0	3	0	1		11
1961	4	3	0	3	0	0	1	11
1962	5	3	0	4	0	0	1	13
1963	5	3	0	4	0	0	1	13
1964	'The horse still fulfills a useful place in the agricultural industry.'							not stated
1965	'The usual premiums were paid for Clydesdale, Irish Draught, Thoroughbred and Arab stallions.'							not stated
1966	6	2	0	0	0	0	1	9
1967	'Sire licensing. The Ministry licences all . . . stallions intended as stock sires . . . over 70 stallions were licensed, one third being pony class.'							not stated
1968	'. . . the increased rates of subsidies and premiums announced last year aroused great interest in horse breeding especially for thoroughbreds and horses of the lighter breeds.'							
1969 1970	No information given in the Ministry's *General Reports*.							
1971	'Stallions of the Thoroughbred, Clydesdale, Arab and Connemara breeds are currently earning premiums.'							
1972	do.							
1973	do.							
1974	No information given except that the scheme '. . . has continued unchanged during the year.'							
1975	do.							
1976	No information given							
1977	'The breeding of heavy horses has declined progressively over the years but in contrast interest has increased in the breeding of thoroughbreds, hunters and ponies. The Department encourages the breeding of good quality horses through subsidies for the purchase of high quality stallions and by awarding premiums to the owners of approved stallions who keep their stallions available to serve mares in their area.'							

* Certain suspensions during the years 1940, 41, 42.

Source: *Annual* or *General Reports of the Ministry of Agriculture Northern Ireland*. N.B. *As from 1974 the title 'Ministry' has been replaced by that of 'Department'*

Breeding Acts which had made compulsory the licensing of stallions used for breeding . . . a Bill to repeal the Acts was passed by Parliament with effect from 1st January 1970.'[39]

Although no special body, comparable to Bord na gCapall, has been established in Northern Ireland to foster horse-breeding in the years ahead, the Department of Agriculture (it changed its title from being a 'Ministry' during the 1970s) continues to aid horse-breeding, after a fashion. As the *Report of the Department of Agriculture, 1978*, stated: 'The breeding of heavy horses has declined progressively over the years but in contrast interest has increased in the breeding of thoroughbreds, hunters and ponies. The Department encourages the breeding of good quality horses through subsidies for the purchase of high quality stallions and by awarding premiums to the owners of approved stallions who keep their stallions available to serve mares in their area.' While horse breeding will undoubtedly continue in Northern Ireland, it is never likely to assume the scale or the importance of that in the Republic. As the Royal Dublin Society's horse breeding schemes showed, in the 1880s and 1890s, the core of horse breeding, especially of the hunter (i.e. Half-bred) type, lay in the south of Ireland. Northern Ireland, with a few notable exceptions, was Clydesdale country, and the Clydesdale, like all heavy draught

Plate Forty-seven. *Typical Irish Half-bred hunters at a meet of the Wicklow Foxhounds during the 1970s. The aim of the Royal Dublin Society's horse-breeding schemes of the nineteenth century had been to produce useful horses of quality, such as are depicted here. The Master's horse, on the left, regularly carried over sixteen stone for many seasons. It is horses of this sort that have made Ireland famous as a horse-breeding country. (Photo:* author)

horses in Ireland (and in Britain) has well-nigh vanished, its role being usurped by the internal combustion engine.

The future of the non-Thoroughbred industry in Ireland clearly lies in the Republic, and depends heavily upon the guidance of Bord na gCapall. That there still is a non-Thoroughbred horse industry, and one that is worth developing, must largely be due to the support given to breeders through the horse breeding schemes of the Department of Agriculture during the twentieth century, to the innovatory horse breeding schemes of the Royal Dublin Society at the latter end of the nineteenth century, and to cultural factors. For many an Irishman the horse is as much a symbol of his country as the shamrock. Show jumping is a rapidly developing sport, so is eventing. Many thousands of people who never aspire to such heights of equestrianism still enjoy riding a good horse on a gentle hack for an hour or two. For others there is the sublime job of riding across country and watching a good pack of hounds hunt a fleeing fox. The role of the horse, in the century that has elapsed since the Royal Dublin Society initiated its horse breeding schemes, has changed from being an integral and essential part of the transport system of vast parts of the world, to being little more than a plaything. But even playthings, in these hectic mechanized days, have their value, especially when they are of the quality of the Irish Half-bred horse. And mention of horses still reminds people, throughout the world, of Ireland, which is itself a valuable advertisement for the country.

Perhaps the last word, however, should lie with William Pallin. He was one of the greatest supporters of the Royal Dublin Society's horse breeding schemes, and it is on the foundation of those schemes that the horse breeding activities of the Departments of Agriculture in the Republic and in the North, and of the recently formed Bord na gCapall, clearly rest, as does the development of the modern Irish Half-bred horse. Volume Six, the last volume of the Royal Dublin Society's *Register of Thoroughbred Stallions*, ended with a *Prize Essay on the Treatment of Brood Mares and Foals and the Care and Feeding of Young Stock*. The author was William Pallin, Fellow of the Royal College of Veterinary Surgeons, Prize Medallist, Examiner to the Royal College of Veterinary Surgeons, etc., Athgarvan Lodge Stud, Curragh, Co. Kildare, and, as we know, owner of Registered Stallions. The conclusion to Pallin's essay was, perhaps unwittingly, a fitting conclusion to the Royal Dublin Society's horse breeding schemes, and to our book.

'We have few more important Irish industries than horse-breeding, and those who produce good horses are benefactors to our country; and to the Royal Dublin Society all owe their deep gratitude for the way the Society has fostered and developed this great national resource of Ireland.'

Appendix One
Registered Stallions, 1892 – 1900

All Thoroughbred stallions registered by the Royal Dublin Society under their Horse Breeding Schemes are listed below. Premium stallions for the years 1887 (breeding season 1888) to 1891 are listed on Tables One, Three, Five and Seven. Premium stallions for 1901-3 are listed on Tables Eleven, Twelve and Thirteen.

1892

Stallion	Owner	Stallion	Owner
Acropolis	Major Clarke	Aintree	W. Pallin
Almoner	R.N. Talbot	Atratus	P.G. Griffin
Baldwin	T.J. Eager	Ballintrae	C. Boyd
Baron Hastings	R.H. Hayes	Bookmaker	W. Jackson
Bonnie Charlie	M.F. Neary	Bon Warrior	W.B. Powell
Buckmaster	R.N. Thompson	Campanula	Mrs Rowley
Canon	W. O'Connell	Carnage	D. Russell
Cavendish	M. Foley	Chelwood	Sir D. Brooke, Bt.
Choubra	R. Nicol	Clan-na-Gael	F. Delaney
Condor	Capt. Davis	Craigengelt	W.H. Lett
Craig Royston	R.C. Dawson	Dalhousie	D.D. Heather
Dauntless	Mrs Tuohy	Derby Dick	R.N. Talbot
Dethroned, The	T. Crowe	Double Dutch	A. Blennerhassett
Dragoon, The	P.F. Collier	Dulcimer	R.D. Lawrenson
Dyspeptic	F.P. Gervais	Earl Scroope	W. Jessop
Early Bird	A. M'Mahon	Edlington	T. Magnier
Eggflip	T.F. Sparrow	Electric Light	R. Malone
Exotic	J. Cleary	Excelsior	P. M'Nabb
Finn Ma Coul	J. Connolly	Forest King	F. Bull
Garland	Capt. Archdale	Glansdale	G. O'Gorman
Glen Art	J. Nuttall	Glen Roy	M. De Courcy
Greenfield	M. Foley	Greenfield	T. Hamilton

Harlem	R.G. Carden	*Heart of Oak*	Capt. Davis
Highflyer	W. Kilroy	*Holmby*	J. Perry
Isleworth	W. Pallin	*Jester II*	C. and J. M'Namara
John	M.F. Hussey	*Lancaster*	O.D. Coll
Lismore	J.O'Meara	*Locksley Hall*	L.M'Court
Loved One	W. Alexander	*Lynx*	M.F. Hogan
Lyric	T.P. FitzPatrick	*Marmion*	D.D. Heather
Master Mariner	W.H. West	*Master Ned*	W. Pallin
Master Pirate	R. Roe	*Marchaway*	Capt. H. de Robeck
Middleman	P.M. Saurin	*Mombasa*	F.H. Power
Monsieur	Major Dease	*Mont Cenis*	P. O'Connor
Narellan	B.B. Trench	*Nelson*	J. Barry
Novelist	Major Studdert	*Orient*	M.J. Corbally
Paddy	E.P. Ryan	*Paris II*	H. Reynolds
Pennington	F. Flannery	*Peter Gray*	W. Kilroy
Prince Alexander	O.T. Slocock	*Prince Arthur*	L.H.R. Carty
Prying	W.B. Powell	*Pursebearer*	W. Pallin
Pythias	E. Lyons	*Rattlin the Reefer*	G. Orr
Romulus	G.S. Bolster	*Runnymede*	R. Keppel
Sailor King	M. Healy	*Shinglass*	T.A. Love
Sideral	Limavady Stud Co.	*Silverstream*	B.J. Greene
Slievegullion	J. Connolly	*Stein*	J. Morton
Sterling II	W. Dimond	*Studley*	A. Maxwell
St. Paul	H. Reynolds	*Sly Boots*	J. Mahony
Thrapston	M. Quinn	*Vanderhum*	K. Mullins
Waif	B.P.J. Mahony	*Wallingford*	T.J. Eager
Warrior	F. Flannery	*Wisconsin*	T.F. Nugent
Woodman	Capt. Eccles	*Woodreve II*	R. Nicol
Young Speculation	M. O'Donovan	*Zagazig*	M.A. Maher

1893

Acropolis	Major Clarke	*Annagor*	R.C. Dawson
Appleton	J. Sheehy	*Atratus*	P.G. Griffin
Baldwin	T.J. Eager	*Ballintrae*	C. Boyd
Baron Hastings	R.H. Hayes	*Beaucourt*	W.T. Townshend
Bonnie Charlie	M.F. Neary	*Branxholme*	W. Pallin
Breach of Promise	P. Higgins	*Brooklands*	O.T. Slocock
Buckmaster	R.N. Thompson	*Cambrian*	E. Mitchell
Campanula	Mrs. S. Rowley	*Canon*	W. and D. O'Connell
Castilian	F. Flannery	*Cartago*	W.N.B. Dooley
Chicago	R. Roe	*Cavendish*	M. Foley
Chelwood	Sir D. Brooke, Bt.	*Choubra*	R. Nicol
Clan-na-Gael	F. Delaney	*Condor*	Capt. W.H. Davis

Connaught	D. Owens	*Craigengelt*	W.H. Lett
Dalhousie	D.D. Heather	*Dauntless*	Mrs M. Tuohy
Dear Boy	N. Morton	*Derby Dick*	N.J. Power
Dethroned, The	T. Crowe	*Double Dutch*	A. Blennerhassett
Dulcimer	T. Jones	*Dyspeptic*	F.P. Gervais
Earl Scroope	J.R. Salter	*Early Bird*	A.M'Mahon
Edlington	T. Magnier	*Eggflip*	T.F. Sparrow
Ellison	J.B. Atkinson	*Exotic*	J. Cleary
Excelsior	P. M'Nabb	*Finn Ma Coul*	J. Connolly
Forest King	F. Bull	*Forestay*	A. Maxwell
Garland	Capt. M. Archdale	*Glen Art*	J.W. Nuttall
Glencoe	G. Orr	*Glen Roy*	M. De Courcy
Greenfield	M. Foley	*Greenfield*	T. Hamilton
Guerilla	R.H. Falkiner	*Harlem*	R.G. Carden
Heart of Oak	Capt. W.H. Davis	*Helter-Skelter*	Major Trocke
Highflyer	W.W. Kilroy	*Holmby*	J. Perry
Jester II	C. and J. M'Namara	*John*	M.F. Hussey
Kentford	R.H. Hayes	*Lancaster*	O.D. Coll
Loved One	W. Alexander	*Lynx*	M.F. Hogan
Lyric	T.P. Fitzpatrick	*Marmion*	D.D. Heather
Mascarille	D. Russell	*Master Mariner*	W.H. West
Master Ned	W. Pallin	*Master Pirate*	R. Roe
Marchaway	Col. H. de Robeck	*Merrylegs*	W. Alexander
Molina	W. Wallace	*Mombasa*	F.H. Power
Mont Cenis	P.O'Connor	*M.P.*	J. Herdman
Narrator	D.T. Donovan	*Nelson*	J. Barry
New Laund	J. Mahony	*Novelist*	Major C.W. Studdert
Paddy	E.P. Ryan	*Paris II*	H. Reynolds
Pelican	R.D. Lawrenson	*Pennington*	F. Flannery
Prince Alexander	O.T. Slocock	*Prince Arthur*	L.H. Carty
Prince Peter	M. Quinn	*Prince Violet*	S.M. Nolan
Prying	W.B. Powell	*Pythias*	E. Lyons
Restraint	T.S. Elcoate	*Royal Duke*	T.D. Atkinson
	and J.M.P.Kennedy		
Runnymede	R. Keppel	*Sailor King*	M. Healy
Save All	B. Ryan	*Scotch Monk*	J. O'Donnell
Shinglass	T.A. Love	*Silverstream*	B.J. Greene
Sir Patrick	M. Healy	*Slievegullion*	J. Connolly
Sly Boots	J. Mahony	*Somnus*	E.P. Ryan
Stein	J. Morton	*St. Keyne*	J. Gregg
St. Paul	H. Reynolds	*Studley*	A. Maxwell
Sweetheart	T. Desmond	*Thrapston*	M. Quinn
	and W.Bateman		
Trespasser	R.J. M'Cormack	*Tunis*	C. Sherwin

Tynan	J. Brady	Vanderhum	K. Mullins
Victoricus	Lord Rathdonnell	Waif	J. Mahony
Willoughby	W.F. M'Keever	Wisconsin	T.F. Nugent
Woodman	Capt. G.M. Eccles	Woodreve II	R. Nicol
Young Speculation	M. O'Donovan	Zagazig	M.A. Maher

1894

Acropolis	Major Clarke	Annagor	R.C. Dawson
Appleton	J. Sheehy	Atratus	P.G. Griffen
Baldwin	T.J. Eager	Ballintrae	C. Boyd
Baron Hastings	R.H. Hayes	Battle Gage	T. Beatty
Blondel	P. M'Cloghery	Blue Godfrey	O.T. Slocock
Bonnie Charlie	M.F. Neary	Branxholme	W. Pallin
Breach of Promise	P. Higgins	Brooklands	R.F. Frend
Buckmaster	R.N. Thompson	Cambrian	E. Mitchell
Canon	D. O'Connell	Castilian	A. Macan
Cavendish	M. Foley	Chelwood	Sir D. Brooke, Bt.
Choubra	R. Nicol	Condor	M. Killian
Connaught	D. Owens	Dalesman	M. de Courcey
Dalhousie	D.D. Heather	Deramfield	J.T. Hinds
Derby Dick	W. Wallace	Dethroned, The	T. Crowe
Double Dutch	A. Blennerhassett	Dulcimer	O.T. Slocock
Dyspeptic	F.P. Gervais	Earl Scroope	J.R. Salter
Early Bird	A. M'Mahon	Edlington	T. Magnier
Ellison	J.B. Atkinson	Excelsior	P. M'Nabb
Experience	T.F. Sparrow	Fear Not	J. Dobson
Fife	J. Moore	Forestay	A. Maxwell
Garland	Capt. M. Archdale	Glen Art	J.W. Nuttall
Glen Roy	M. de Courcey	Glenshane	J. M'Closkey
Greenfield	M. Foley	Greenfield	T. Hamilton
Harlem	R.G. Carden	Helter Skelter	Major Trocke
Hodge	J. M'Ilroy	Isleworth	W. Pallin
John	M.F. Hussey	Kentford	R.H. Hayes
Lancaster	O.D. Coll	Loved One	W. Alexander
Lynx	M.F. Hogan	Marmion	D.D. Heather
Mascarille	D. Russell	Master Mariner	W.H. West
Marchaway	Col. de Robeck	Molina	N.J. Power
Mombasa	Mrs F.H. Power	Mont Cenis	P.J. O'Connor
M.P.	J. Herdman	Mulberry	R. Graham
Narcissus	T. M'Cordingley	Narellan	B.B. Trench
Novelist	Major Studdert	Paddy	E.P. Ryan
Pelican	R. De R. Laurinson	Pennington	F. Flannery
Prince Arthur	L. Carty	Prince Charles	T.F. Sparrow

Prince Peter	M. Quinn	*Prying*	W.B. Powell
Pythias	E. Lyons	*Raithby*	H. O'Neill
Restraint	T.S. Elcoate	*Robert Emmet*	J. Hartigan
Royal Duke	J. Ambrose	*Royal Vine*	P. Goore
Runnymede	R. Keppel	*Sailor King*	M. Healy
Save All	B. Ryan	*Scotch Monk*	J. O'Donnell
Seaport	J. Redding	*Slievegullion*	J. Connolly
Stein	J. Morton	*St. Keyne*	J. Gregg
St. Paul	H. Reynolds	*Studley*	W.T. Trench
Thrapston	M. Quinn	*Tiercel*	L.W. Hendley
Tunis	C. Sherwin	*Tynan*	J. Brady
Vanderhum	K. Mullen	*Victoricus*	Lord Rathdonnell
Waif	J. Mahony	*Willoughby*	W.F.M'Keever
Wisconsin	T.F. Nugent	*Woodman*	Capt. G.M. Eccles
Woodreve II	R. Nicol	*Young Marden*	T.F. Nugent
Young Speculation	M. O'Donovan	*Zagazig*	M.A. Maher
Zero	F. Flannery		

1895

Aconite	J. Walsh	*Acropolis*	Major Clarke
Algoa Bay	D. R. Tittle	*Almoner*	R.N. Talbot
Annagor	R.C. Dawson	*Appleton*	J. Sheehy
Ascetic	J.M. Purdon	*Astrologer*	W. Pallin
Atheling	J. Daly	*Athletic*	J.F. Bomford
Atratus	P.E. Griffin	*Bacchus*	Duke of Devonshire
Bailsman	Col. R. Thomson	*Baldwin*	T.J. Eager
Baliol	Col. R. Thomson	*Ballinafad*	J.H. Lambert
Ballintrae	H. Johnston	*Baron Hastings*	R.H. Hayes
Bel Demonio	C.J. Blake	*Belgrave*	A.T.G. Cornelius
Ben	J. Preston	*Bennitthorpe*	A. Maxwell
Bergomask	M. Ballesty	*Black Diamond*	J. Brady
Blair Hope	J.R. Webster	*Blitz*	E.M. O'Ferrall
Blondel	P.J. M'Cloghry	*Blue Godfrey*	R.P. Stakelum
Bonnie Charlie	M.F. Neary	*Bon Soir*	J.M. Purdon
Bookmaker	W. Jackson	*Boulevard*	J.C. Murphy
Branxholme	W. Pallin (lessee: P.Colfer)	*Breach of Promise*	P. Higgins
Brittanic	J.M. Purdon	*Brooklands*	R.F. Frend
Brown Prince	J.A.S. Langan	*Buckmaster*	R.N. Thompson
Cairo	J.S. Shore	*Canon*	D. Connell
Cassock	J.A.S. Langan	*Castilian*	A. Macan
Castleblaney	T. M'Mahon	*Cavendish*	J. Mahony
Chelwood	Sir D. Brooke, Bt.	*Chevy Chase*	J.R. Rennick

Choubra	R. Nicol	*Cimarron*	P. Danaher
Clan-na-Gael	F. Delaney	*Clarendon*	Capt. C. Fetherstonhaugh
Concha	P. Maynard	*Condor*	M. Killian
Connaught	D. Owens	*Controversy*	Capt. W.T. Townshend
Cornwall	J.M. Kelly	*Craig Royston*	R.C. Dawson
Dalesman	M. De Courcy	*Dalhousie*	D.D. Heather
Dauntless	Mrs M. Tuohy	*Delamont*	J. Leigh
Deramfield	J.T. Hinds	*Derby Dick*	W. Wallace
Dictator	M.A. Maher	*Doncaster*	J. Carroll
Double Dutch	A. Blennerhassett	*Double Entendre*	Marquis of London-derry
Draco	H. Dolphin	*Duke of Portland*	R.G. Nash
Dulcimer	O.T. Slock	*Dyspeptic*	F.P. Gervais
Earl Scroope	J.R. Salter	*Eary Bird*	A. M'Mahon
Edlington	T. Magnier	*Ellison*	J.B. Atkinson
Enthusiast	J. Daly	*Ethelbert*	C. O'Neill
Excelsior	A. Browne	*Explorer*	T. M'Cutchan
Falcon	J.A.S. Langan	*Favonian*	W. Pallin
Fear Not	J. Dobson	*Fife*	J. Moore
Finn Ma Coul	J. Connolly	*Fitz-Clifden*	J.C. Murphy
Florin	R. Malone	*Forestay*	A. Maxwell
Forest King	F. Bull	*Fortunio*	E. Kennedy
Fra Diavolo	J. Sheehy	*Fransiscan*	J. Widger
Garland	Capt. M. Archdale	*Glen Art*	J.W. Nuttall
Glen Roy	M. De Courcy	*Golden Orb*	Major Hickman
Golden Pippin	S.G. Williams	*Greenfield*	M. Foley
Greenfield	T. Hamilton	*Guerilla*	R.H. Falkiner
Hackler	J. Daly	*Harlem*	R.G. Carden
Heart-of-Oak	Capt. W.H. Davis	*Heckberry*	W. Pallin (lessee: Earl of Bessborough)
Hominy	J.A.S. Langan	*Ireland*	J. Daly
Isleworth	W. Pallin (lessee: J. Hutchinson)	*Isosceles*	J. Reese
Jester II	C. and J. MacNamara	*John*	M.J. Hussey
John Jones	J. Birkmyre	*Kentford*	R.H. Hayes
Keswick	J. Reese	*Koodoo*	M.J. Murphy
Lancaster	O.D. Coll	*Lasso*	D. Byrne
Lightfoot	J. Hunt	*Lismore*	P. O'Kane
Lord George	F. Mullins	*Loved One*	W. Alexander
Lyric	T.P. Fitzpatrick	*McCarthy*	J. Preston
Marchaway	Col. H. de Robeck	*Marmion*	D.D. Heather
Marmiton	C. Hannan	*Marquis of Tavora*	Capt. R.B. Irwin
Mascarille	D. Russell	*Master Mariner*	J.P. Murphy
Master Ned	W. Pallin	*Master Pirate*	W.C. Roe

Midas	Col. Thomson	*Middleman*	M. Buchanan
Mombasa	Mrs F.H. Power	*Monksman*	P. Duffy
Monsieur	Major G. Dease	*Mont Cenis*	P.J. O'Connor
M.P.	J. Herdman	*Mulberry*	R. Graham
My Lud	T. Harrison	*Narcissus*	J. Gaynor
Narellan	A.A. and G.M. Harris	*Nasr-el-din*	A.H. Davidson
New Laund	J. Mahony	*Novelist*	C.W. Studdert
Paddy	E.P. Ryan	*Passion Flower*	J. Widger
Pelican	R.D. Lawrenson	*Peter Gray*	W.W. Kilroy
Peterhof	Capt. W.J. Murphy	*Piercefield*	C. Taaffe
Play Actor	P. Maynard	*Preserver*	C.P. Kenney
Primrose League	H.E. Linde	*Prince Charles*	T.F. Sparrow
Prince Peter	M. Quinn	*Prince Violet*	S.M. Nolan
Prying	W.B. Powell	*Pythias*	E. Lyons
Red Kangaroo	S. Tanner	*Regulator*	J. Bell
Restraint	T.S. Elcoate and J.M.P.Kennedy	*Rhidorroch*	R. Graham
Ringaskiddy	J. Meany	*Robert Emmett*	J. Hartigan
Roman Emperor	J.T. Heffernan	*Royal Charter*	P. Cashman
Royal Meath	H. Steeds	*Runnymede*	R. Keppel
Sailor King	M. Healy	*St. Bavon*	P. Duffy
St. Kieran	E. Smithwick	*Saint Paul*	H. Reynolds
Save All	B. Ryan	*Scene Shifter*	J.W.A. Harris
Scotch Monk	R. Tate	*Seaport*	J. Redding
Shinglass	T.A. Love	*Slievegullion*	J. Connolly
Sly Patrick	T. Brien	*Snowdoun*	Capt. Fife (lessee: W. Pallin)
Springtime	J. Daly (lessee: W.H.West)	*Stein*	R.S. Smyth
Stratheden	T. Desmond	*Studley*	W.T. Trench
Sweetheart	Desmond and Bateman	*Tacitus*	A. Moore
Tartan	J.M. Purdon	*Terror*	Lord Ashtown
The Clown	F. Bull	*The Dethroned*	T. Crowe
The Rector	Lord Ashtown	*The Rejected*	J.J. Parkinson
The Robber	J. Preston	*The Wraith*	A. Moore
Thrapston	M. Quinn	*Tiercel*	L.W. Hendley
Toronto	T. Magnier	*Torpedo*	M.A. Maher
Touchstone	W.W. Kilroy	*Trespasser*	R.J. M'Cormack
Troubador	D. Gleeson	*Tunis*	C. Sherwin
Tynan	J. Brady	*Vanderbilt*	C.H.T. Reade
Vanderhum	F. Mullins	*Victoricus*	Lord Rathdonnell
Waif	M. Foley	*Walmsgate*	T. O'Brien
Watchspring	H.A. Robinson	*Westmoreland*	E. Kennedy
Whalebone	R. Connell	*Wild Sherry*	J.A.S. Langan

Willoughby	W.F. M'Keever	*Wisconsin*	T.F. Nugent (lessee: S.B. Weldon)
Wiseman	W. Pallin	*Woodman*	Capt. G.M. Eccles
Young Marden	T.F. Nugent	*Young Speculation*	M. O'Donovan
Zagazig	M.A. Maher	*Zanzibar*	D. M'Namara
Zero	J. Lynch		

1896

Aconite	J. Walsh	*Acropolis*	Major Clarke
Algoa Bay	J. Hutchinson	*Almoner*	R.N. Talbot
Annagor	R.C. Dawson	*Appleton*	J. Sheehy
Ascetic	J.M. Purdon	*Assassin*	T. Gleeson
Astrologer	W. Pallin (Lessee: J.Preston)	*Atheling*	J. Daly
Athletic	J.F. Bomford	*Atratus*	P.G. Griffin
Bacchus	Duke of Devonshire	*Bailsman*	Col. R. Thomson
Baldwin	T.J. Eager	*Baliol*	Col. R. Thomson
Ballinafad	J.H. Lambert	*Ballintrae*	H. Johnston
Baron Hastings	R.H. Hayes	*Beaucourt*	Capt. W.T. Townshend
Beckford	J. Hurley	*Bel Demonio*	C.J. Blake
Bendemere	T.F. Sparrow	*Ben*	J. Preston
Bennitthorpe	A. Maxwell	*Bergomask*	M. Ballesty
Black Diamond	H. Reynolds	*Blair Hope*	J.R. Webster
Blitz	E.M.O'Ferrall	*Blondel*	P.J. M'Cloghry
Bonnie Charlie	M.F. Neary	*Bon Soir*	J.M. Purdon
Boulevard	J.C. Murphy	*Branxholme*	W. Pallin (lessee: Miss Musgrave)
Breach of Promise	P. Higgins	*Brighton*	P. and T.E. Quigley
Britannic	J.M. Purdon	*Brown Prince*	J.A.S. Langan
Broxton	W. Pallin	*Bruar*	J.W.A. Harris
Bruree	J. Duggan	*Buckmaster*	R.N. Thompson
Cairo	J.S. Shore	*Canon*	D. Connell
Cassock	J.A.S. Langan	*Castilian*	A. Macan
Castleblaney	T. M'Mahon	*Cavendish*	J. Mahony
Chelwood	Sir D. Brooke, Bt.	*Choubra*	R. Nicol
Cimarron	P. Danaher	*Clarendon*	Capt. C. Fetherstonhaugh
Condor	M. Killian	*Connaught*	D. Owens
Cordelier	E. Mitchell	*Cornwall*	J.M. Kelly
Craig Royston	R.C. Dawson	*Dalesman*	P.T. Dillon
Dalhousie	D.D. Heather	*Dauntless*	Mrs M. Tuohy
David Trot	C. Hoey	*Delamont*	J. Leigh
Deramfield	J.T. Hinds	*Derby Dick*	W. Wallace
Dictator	M.A. Maher	*Doncaster*	J. Carroll

Double Dutch	A. Blennerhassett	*Double Entendre*	Marquis of London-derry
Draco	H. Dolphin	*Duke of Portland*	R.G. Nash
Dyspeptic	F.P. Gervais	*Earl Scroope*	J.R. Salter
Early Bird	A. M'Mahon	*Edlington*	T. Magnier
Elector	T. Lindsay	*Ellison*	J.B. Atkinson
Enthusiast	J. Daly	*Ethelbert*	C. O'Neill
Excelsior	A. Browne	*Experience*	T.F. Sparrow
Explorer	T. M'Cutchan	*Falcon*	J.A.S. Langan
Favoloo	W.J. Goulding	*Favonian*	J.H. Lambert
Fear Not	J. Dobson	*Fife*	J. Moore
Finn Ma Coul	J. Connolly	*Fitz-Clifden*	J.C. Murphy
Florin	R. Malone	*Forestay*	A. Maxwell
Fortunio	E. Kennedy	*Fra Diavolo*	J. Sheehy
Franciscan	J. Widger	*Garland*	P. Duff
Glen Art	J.W. Nuttall	*Glen Roy*	P. Russell
Golden Orb	Major Hickman	*Golden Pippin*	S.G. Williams
Great Briton	W. Chambers	*Greenfield*	M. Foley
Greenfield	T. Hamilton	*Guerilla*	R.H. Falkiner
Hackler	J. Daly	*Harlem*	R.G. Carden
Hartstown	J. Bell	*Heckberry*	W. Pallin
Hominy	J.A.S. Langan	*Ireland*	J. Daly
Isleworth	W. Pallin	*Isosceles*	*J. Reese*
Jester II	C. and J. MacNamara	*John*	M.J. Hussey
John Jones	J. Birkmyre	*Kentford*	R.H. Hayes
Keswick	J. Reese	*Kirkham*	Lord Dunraven
Koodoo	M.J. Murphy	*Lasso*	D. Byrne
Lentulus	Harris Brothers	*Lismore*	P. O'Kane
Lord George	F. Mullins	*Loved One*	W. Alexander, reps of
Luminary	J. Curran	*Lynx*	M.F. Hogan
Lyric	T.P. Fitzpatrick	*Marchaway*	Col. H. de Robeck
Marmion	D.D. Heather	*Marmiton*	C. Hannan
Marquis of Tavora	Major C.W. Studdert	*Mascarille*	D. Russell
Massacre	R. Henry	*Masterman*	E. Mitchell
Master Mariner	J.P. Murphy	*Master Ned*	W. Pallin (lessee: Compton Stud, Dorset
Master Pirate	Surgeon-Gen. W.C. Roe	*Matador*	R.C. Bullen
Midas	J. O'Connell	*Middleman*	M. Buchanan
Midnight	H. Reynolds	*Mombasa*	Mrs F.H. Power
Monksman	P. Duffy	*Monsieur*	Major G. Dease
Mont Cenis	P.J. O'Connor	*M.P.*	M.F. Beresford
My Lud	T. Harrison	*Narcissus*	C. O'N. Kenny

Narellan	Harris Brothers	*Nasr-ed-din*	A.H. Davidson
New Laund	J. Mahony	*Novelist*	Major C.W. Studdert
Orontes	A. M'Mahon	*Palmleaf*	J. Dely (lessee: R. St. G. Manseragh)
Passion Flower	J. Widger	*Pelican*	R.D. Lawrenson
Peterhof	Capt. W.J. Murphy	*Piercefield*	C. Taaffe
Play Actor	Major R. Galbraith	*Primrose League*	H.E. Linde
Prince Charles	T.F. Sparrow	*Prince Peter*	M. Quinn
Prince Violet	S.M. Nolan	*Prying*	W.B. Powell
Pythias	E. Lyons	*Punster*	Capt. A.W.M. Richards
Reckless	Capt. W.F. Smithwick	*Red Kangaroo*	S. Tanner
Regulator	J. Bell	*Restraint*	T.S. Elcoate and J.M.P. Kennedy
Robert Emmett	J. Hartigan	*Roman Emperor*	J.T. Heffernan
Royal Meath	H. Steeds	*Runnymede*	R. Keppel
Sailor King	M. Healy	*St. Aidan*	Congested Districts Board
St. Bavon	P. Duffy	*St. David*	C.J. Blake
St. Kieran	E. Smithwick	*Saint Paul*	H. Reynolds
Save All	B. Ryan	*Scene Shifter*	J.W.A. Harris
Scotch Monk	W. Wilson	*Shinglass*	T.A. Love
Sir Hugh	J. O'Connell	*Slievegullion*	J. Connolly
Sly Patrick	T. Brien	*Snaplock*	J. Widger
Springtime	J. Daly (lessee: W.H. West)	*Studley*	W.T. Trench
Succès	G.W. Harris	*Sun of York*	R.F. Payne
Swift	P.J. O'Connor	*Tacitus*	A. Moore
Tamerlane	M. Butler	*Tartan*	J.M. Purdon
Terror	Lord Ashtown	*The Dethroned*	T. Crowe
The Rector	Lord Ashtown	*The Rejected*	J.J. Parkinson
The Robber	J. Preston	*The Wraith*	F.G. Sikes
Thrapston	M. Quinn	*Tiercel*	L.W. Hendley
Toronto	T. Magnier	*Torpedo*	M.A. Maher
Touchstone	W.W. Kilroy	*Town Moor*	Capt. W.T. Townshend
Trespasser	R.J. M'Cormack	*Troubador*	D. Gleeson
Tunis	C. Sherwin	*Tynan*	J. Brady
Uncle Sam	Congested Districts Board	*Vanderhum*	F. Mullins
Victoricus	Lord Rathdonnell	*Waif*	M. Foley
Walmsgate	T. O'Brien	*Watchspring*	H.A. Robinson
Westmoreland	E. Kennedy	*Whalebone*	R. Connell
Wild Kilwarlin	W. Wallace	*Wild Sherry*	J.A.S. Langan
Willoughby	W.F.M'Keever	Winkfield	J.C. Sullivan

Wisconsin	J. Foley	*Wiseman*	W. Pallin
Wonderbaar	J. Brady	*Woodman*	Capt. G.M. Eccles
Young Marden	T.F. Nugent	*Young Speculation*	M. O'Donovan
Young Victor	J.W.A. Harris	*Zagazig*	M.A. Maher
Zanzibar	D. M'Namara	*Zero*	J. Lynch

1897

Aconite	J. Walsh	*Acropolis*	Major Clarke
Algoa Bay	J. Hutchinson	*Almoner*	R. N. Talbot
Ambergate	Harris Brothers	*Annagor*	R.C. Dawson
Ascetic	J.M. Purdon	*Assassin*	T. Gleeson
Astrologer	W. Pallin	*Atheling*	J. Daly
	(lessee: J.H. Lambert)		
Athletic	J.F. Bomford	*Atratus*	Lord Dunraven
Bacchus	J. O'Donnell	*Bailsman*	Col. R. Thomson
Baldwin	T.J. Eager	*Ballinafad*	J.H. Lambert
Ballintrae	H. Johnston	*Baron Hastings*	R.H. Hayes
Beaucourt	Capt. W.T. Townshend	*Beckford*	J. Hurley
Bendemere	T.F. Sparrow	*Ben*	J. Preston
Bennitthorpe	A. Maxwell	*Bergomask*	M. Ballesty
Beware	W. O'Brien	*Black Diamond*	H. Reynolds
Blair Hope	J.R. Webster	*Blondel*	P.J. M'Cloghry
Bonnie Charlie	M.F. Neary	*Bon Soir*	J.M. Purdon
Branxholme	W. Pallin	*Breach of Promise*	P. Higgins
Brighton	P. and T.E. Quigley	*Britannic*	J.M. Purdon
Brown Prince	J.A.S. Langan	*Broxton*	W. Pallin
Bruree	J. Duggan	*Buckmaster*	R.N. Thompson
Canon	D. Connell	*Castilian*	A. Macan
Castleblaney	T. M'Mahon	*Cavendish*	J. Mahony
Chelwood	Sir D. Brooke, Bt.	*Choubra*	R. Nicol
Cimarron	P. Danaher	*Clarendon*	Capt. C. Fether-stonhaugh
Connaught	D. Owens	*Cordelier*	E. Mitchell
Cornwall	J.M. Kelly	*Craig Royston*	R.C. Dawson
Dalesman	P.T. Dillon	*Dalhousie*	D.D. Heather
Dauntless	Mrs M. Tuohy	*David Trot*	C. Hoey
Delamont	J. Leigh	*Deramfield*	J.T. Hinds
Derby Dick	W. Wallace	*Dictator*	M.A. Maher
Diogenes	T. M'Mahon	*Doncaster*	J. Carroll
Double Dutch	A. Blennerhassett	*Double Entendre*	J. M'Ilroy
Draco	H. Dolphin	*Duke of Portland*	R.G. Nash
Dyspeptic	F.P. Gervais	*Earl Scroope*	J.R. Salter
Early Bird	A. M'Mahon	*Edlington*	T. Magnier

Elector	T. Lindsay	*Ellison*	J.B. Atkinson
Enthusiast	J. Daly	*Ethelbert*	G.W. Harris
Excelsior	A. Browne	*Experience*	T.F. Sparrow
Explorer	T. M'Cutchan	*Falcon*	J.A.S. Langan
Favonian	W. Pallin	*Fear Not*	J. Dobson
Fife	J. Moore	*Finn Ma Coul*	J. Connolly
Forestay	Major R.M. Marsh	*Fortunio*	E. Kennedy
Fra Diavolo	J. Sheehy	*Franciscan*	J. Widger
Garland	P. Duff	*Glen Art*	D. Byrne
Golden Orb	Major S.C. Hickman	*Golden Pippin*	S.G. Williams
Great Briton	W. Chambers	*Greenfield*	T. Hamilton
Hackler	J. Daly	*Harlem*	R.G. Carden
Hartstown	J. Bell	*Heckberry*	W. Pallin
Holloway	R.H. Clegg	*Hominy*	J.A.S. Langan
Ireland	J. Daly	*Isosceles*	J. Reese
Jester II	C. and J. MacNamara	*John*	M.F. Hussey
John Jones	J. Birkmyre	*Kendaldale*	H.L. FitzPatrick
Kentford	R.H. Hayes	*Keswick*	J. Reese
Kirkham	Lord Dunraven	*Lasso*	D. Byrne
Lismore	P.O. Kane	*Lord George*	F. Mullins
Lorikeet	T.A. Love	*Luminary*	J. Curran
Lynx	M.F. Hogan	*Marchaway*	Col. H. de Robeck
Marmion	D.D. Heather	*Marmiton*	C. Hannan
Marquis of Tavora	C.R.A. MacDonnell and J.A. Studdert	*Mascarille*	D. Russell
Massacre	R. Henry	*Master Ned*	W. Pallin (lessee: J. Preston)
Master Pirate	A. Lawrenson	*Matador*	F.G. Sikes
Midas	J. O'Connell	*Middleman*	M. Buchanan
Midnight	H. Reynolds	*Milner*	J.C. Sullivan
Mombasa	Mrs F.H. Power	*Monksman*	P. Duffy
Monsieur	Major G. Dease (lessee: E. Preston)	*Mont Cenis*	P.J. O'Connor
M.P.	Countess of Wicklow	*Mulberry*	R. Graham
Narellan	Harris Brothers	*Nasr-ed-din*	A.H. Davidson
New Laund	J. Mahony	*Novelist*	Major C.W. Studdert
Orontes	A. M'Mahon	*Palmleaf*	J. Daly (lessee: R.St.G. Manseragh)
Passion Flower	J. Widger	*Pelican*	R.D. Lawrenson
Peterhof	Capt. W.J. Murphy	*Piercefield*	C. Taaffe
Playactor	Major R. Galbraith	*Primrose League*	H.E. Linde
Prince Charles	T.F. Sparrow	*Prince Violet*	S.M. Nolan
Pythias	C.I. Kelly	*Punster*	Capt. A.W.M. Richards

Reckless	Capt. W.F. Smithwick	*Red Kangaroo*	S. Tanner
Red Prince II	H.E. Linde (lessee: W. Pallin)	*Regulator*	J. Bell
Restraint	T.S. Elcoate and J.M.P. Kennedy	*Rhidorroch*	R. Graham
Riverstown	C. Hannan	*Robert Emmet*	J. Hartigan
Roman Emperor	J.T. Heffernan	*Royal Charter*	P. Cashman
Royal Emperor	M. Gleeson	*Royal Mask*	E. Mitchell
Royal Meath	Sir J. Arnott, Bt.	*Runnymede*	R. Keppel
Sailor King	M. Healy	*St. Aidan*	Congested Districts Board
St. Bavon	P. Duffy	*St. Kieran*	E. Smithwick
Save All	B. Ryan	*Scene Shifter*	J.W.A. Harris
Sir Hugh	J. O'Connell	*Sir Patrick*	M. Healy
Sly Patrick	T. Brien	*Snaplock*	J. Widger
Studley	W.T. Trench	*Succès*	G.W. Harris
Sweetheart	Desmond and Bateman	*Swift*	P.J. O'Connor
Tacitus	A. Moore	*Tartan*	Duke of Devonshire
Terror	Lord Ashtown	*The Dethroned*	T. Crowe
The Rector	Lord Ashtown	*The Robber*	J. Preston
The Wraith	F.G. Sikes	*Thrapston*	M. Quinn
Tiercel	L.W. Hendley	*Toronto*	T. Magnier
Torpedo	M.A. Maher	*Touchstone*	W.W. Kilroy
Town Moor	Capt. W.T. Townshend	*Troubador*	D. Gleeson
Tunis	L. Sherwin	*Tynan*	J. Brady
Uncle Sam	Congested Districts Board	*Victoricus*	Lord Rathdonnell
Waif	M. Foley	*Walmsgate*	T. O'Brien
Watchspring	R. Berridge	*Westmoreland*	E. Kennedy
Whalebone	R. Connell	*Wild Kilwarlin*	J. M'Closkey
Wild Monk	H. Sparrow	*Wild Sherry*	J.A.S. Langan
Willoughby	W.F.M'Keever	*Winkfield*	J.C. Sullivan
Wisconsin	J. Foley	*Wiseman*	W. Pallin
Wonderbaar	J. Brady	*Woodman*	Major G.M. Eccles
Young Marden	T.F. Nugent	*Young Speculation*	M.O'Donovan
Young Victor	J.W.A. Harris	*Zagazig*	M.A. Maher
Zero	J. Lynch		

1898

Aconite	J. Walsh	*Acropolis*	Major Clarke
Algoa Bay	J. Hutchinson	*Almoner*	R.H. Talbot
Amber Gate	Harris Brothers	*Annagor*	R.C. Dawson
Assassin	T. Gleeson	*Astrologer*	W. Pallin

Athletic	J.F. Bomford	*Atratus*	Lord Dunraven
Bacchus	J. O'Donnell	*Bailsman*	T. Talt
Baldwin	T. Stephens	*Ballinafad*	D. Craig
Ballynoe	J. Daly (lessee: J. Bell)	*Baron Hastings*	R.H. Hayes
Beaucourt	Capt. W.T. Townshend	*Beckford*	J. M'Loughlin
Ben	J. Preston	*Bendemere*	T.F. Sparrow
Bennitthorpe	A. Maxwell	*Bergomask*	M. Ballesty
Beware	W. O'Brien	*Black Diamond*	H. Reynolds
Blair Hope	J.R. Webster	*Blondel*	P.J.M'Cloghry
Bonnie Charlie	M.F. Neary	*Bon Soir*	J.M. Purdon
Branxholme	W. Pallin	*Breach of Promise*	P. Higgins
Brighton	P. and T.E. Quigley	*Britannic*	J.M. Purdon
Brown Prince	J.A.S. Langan	*Bruree*	J. Duggan
Buckmaster	E.M. Archdale	*Bull's Eye*	C.F. Harding
Bushy Park	J. Daly	*Canon*	D. Connell
Castilian	A. Macan	*Castleblaney*	T. M'Mahon
Cavendish	J. Mahony	*Choubra*	R. Nicol
Cimarron	P. Shanahan	*Clarendon*	J. Barry
Connaught	D. Owens	*Connaught Ranger*	C. Taaffe
Cordelier	E. Mitchell	*Craig Royston*	R.C. Dawson
Dalesman	P.T. Dillon	*Dalhousie*	D.D. Heather
David Trot	C. Hoey	*Delamont*	J. Leigh
Deramfield	J.T. Hinds	*Dictator*	M.A. Maher
Diogenes	Congested Districts Board	*Doncaster*	J. Carroll
Double Dutch	A. Blennerhassett	*Double Entendre*	J. M'Ilroy
Douglas	J. Hawe	*Draco*	H. Dolphin
Duke of Portland	R.G. Nash	*Dulcimer*	A.F. Nuttall
Dyspeptic	F.P. Gervais	*Earl Scroope*	J.R. Salter
Early Bird	T. Power	*Edlington*	T. Magnier
Egerton	Col. R. Thomson	*Elector*	T. Lindsay
Ellison	J.B. Atkinson	*Enthusiast*	J. Daly
Ethelbert	Major M.J. Kenny	*Excelsior*	A. Browne
Experience	T.F. Sparrow	*Explorer*	T. M'Cutchan
Falcon	J.A.S. Langan	*Favo Loo*	W.J. Goulding
Favonian	W. Pallin (lessee: J.H. Lambert)	*Fear Not*	J. Dobson
Ferdinand	J.W.A. Harris	*Fife*	J. Moore
Fitz-Clifden	J.C. Murphy	*Fortunio*	E. Kennedy
Fra Diavolo	J. Sheehy	*Franciscan*	J. Widger
Garland	P. Duff	*Glen Art*	D. Byrne
Glen Roy	C. Magner	*Golden Orb*	E. Murphy
Great Briton	W. Chambers	*Greenfield*	T. Hamilton
Guerilla	R.H. Falkiner	*Guy Mannering*	O.T. Slocock

Hackler	J. Daly	Hartstown	J. Bell
Heckberry	W. Pallin	Hidden Treasure	Capt. W.T. Townshend
Holloway	R.H. Clegg	Hominy	J.A.S. Langan
Ireland	J. Daly	Isosceles	J. Reese
Jester II	C. and J. MacNamara	John	M.F. Hussey
Kendaldale	H.L. FitzPatrick	Kendal Royal	J.C. Murphy
Kentford	R.H. Hayes	Kentish Fire	M.A. Maher
Keswick	J. Reese	Kirkham	Lord Dunraven
Lasso	D. Byrne	Lismore	P.O'Kane
Lord George	F. Mullins	Lorikeet	T.A. Love
Luminary	J. Curran	Lyric	A. Lyons
Marchaway	W. Kavanagh and D.R. Pack-Beresford	Marmion	D.D. Heather
Marquis of Tavora	C.R.A. MacDonnell and J.A. Studdert	Mascarille	D. Russell
Master Ned	W. Pallin	Master Pirate	A. Lawrenson
Matador	F.G. Sikes	Midas	J. O'Connell
Middleman	M. Buchanan	Milner	J.C. Sullivan
Mombasa	W.J. Barry	Monksman	P. Duffy
Monsieur	Major G. Dease (lessee: E. Preston)	Mont Cenis	P.J. O'Connor
M.P.	Countess of Wicklow	Mulberry	R. Graham
Narellan	Harris Brothers	Nasr-ed-din	A.H. Davidson
Northshampton	W.F. M'Keever	Novelist	Major C.W. Studdert
Orontes	A. M'Mahon	Palmleaf	J. Daly (lessee: S. Manseragh)
Passion Flower	J. Widger	Pelican	R.D. Lawrenson
Peterhof	Capt. W. J. Murphy	Phelimfield	J.T. Hinds
Philammon	B.P.J. Mahony	Piercefield	C. Taaffe
Playactor	Major R. Galbraith	Primrose League	J.A.S. Langan
Prince Arthur	L.H.R. Carty	Prince Charles	R. Malone
Prince Violet	S.M. Nolan	Punster	Capt. A.W.M. Richards
Pythias	C.I. Kelly	Red Kangaroo	S. Tanner
Red Prince II	H.E. Linde (lessee: W. Pallin)	Regulator	J. Bell
Restraint	T.S. Elcoate and J.M. Prior Kennedy	Robert Emmet	J. Hartigan
Roman Emperor	J.T. Heffernan	Royal Charter	P. Cashman
Royal Emperor	M. Gleeson	Royal Mask	E. Mitchell
Royal Meath	Sir J. Arnott, Bt.	Runnymede	R. Keppel
Sailor King	M. Healy	St. Aidan	R.N. Thompson
St. Bavon	P. Duffy	St. Jude	E. Mitchell
St. Kieran	E. Smithwick	Save All	B. Ryan

Scene Shifter	J.W.A. Harris	*Sir Andrew*	Mrs J.B. Alexander
Sir Hugh	J. O'Connell	*Sir Patrick*	M. Healy
Sly Patrick	T. Brien	*Snaplock*	J. Widger
Springtime	J. Daly (lessee: W.H. West)	*Studley*	W.T. Trench
Succès	E.N. Power	*Sweetheart*	Desmond and Bateman
Swift	P.J. O'Connor	*Tacitus*	A. Moore
Tartan	Duke of Devonshire	*Terror*	Lord Ashtown
The Baron	Lord Kenmare	*The Dethroned*	T. Crowe
The Rector	Lord Ashtown	*The Robber*	J. Preston
The Wraith	F.G. Sikes	*Thrapston*	M. Quinn
Tiercel	L.W. Hendley	*Toronto*	T. Magnier
Torpedo	M.A. Maher	*Touchstone*	W.W. Kilroy
Town Moor	Capt. W.T. Townshend	*Tranby Croft*	J. Mullarkey
Trespasser	J.H. M'Cormack	*Troubador*	D. Gleeson
Troy II	J.S. Kincaid	*Tullagee*	T.K. Bunbury
Tunis	L. Sherwin	*Tynan*	J. Brady
Vanderbilt	C. Boyd	*Victoricus*	Lord Rathdonnell
Waif	M. Foley	*Walmsgate*	T. O'Brien
Watchspring	R. Berridge	*Westmoreland*	E. Kennedy
Whalebone	R. Connell	*Wild Kilwarlin*	J. M'Closkey
Wild Monk	H. Sparrow	*Wild Sherry*	J.A.S. Langan
Willougby	W.F. M'Keever	*Winkfield*	J.C. Sullivan
Wisconsin	R. Buckley	*Wiseman*	W. Pallin
Woodman	Major G.M. Eccles	*Young Marden*	T.F. Nugent
Young Speculation	M. O'Donovan	*Young Victor*	J.W.A. Harris
Zagazig	M.A. Maher		

1899

Aconite	R. Walsh	*Acropolis*	R.F. O'Hara
Algoa Bay	J. Hutchinson	*Amber Gate*	Harris Brothers
Annagor	R.C. Dawson	*Apollo*	A.B. Walker
Assassin	T. Gleeson	*Astrologer*	W. Pallin
Athletic	J.F. Bomford	*Atratus*	Lord Dunraven
Bacchus	J. O'Donnell	*Bailsman*	T. Talt
Baldwin	T. Stephens	*Ballinafad*	D. Craig
Ballynoe	J. Daly (Lessee: J. Bell)	*Baron Hastings*	R.H. Hayes
Beaucourt	Capt. W.T. Townshend	*Ben*	J. Preston
Bendemere	T.F. Sparrow	*Bennitthorpe*	A. Maxwell
Bergomask	M. Ballesty	*Beware*	W. O'Brien
Black Diamond	H. Reynolds	*Blair Hope*	J.R. Webster
Blâr Aodan	Dr. Cox	*Blondel*	P.J. M'Cloghry
Bonnie Charlie	M.F. Neary	*Bon Soir*	J.M. Purdon
Branxholme	J. Curran	*Breach of Promise*	P. Higgins

Brighton	P. and T.E. Quigley	*Britannic*	J.M. Purdon
Bruree	J. Duggan	*Buckmaster*	E.M. Archdale
Bull's Eye	C.F. Harding	*Bushy Park*	J. Daly
Canon	Mrs M. O'Connell	*Castilian*	A. Macan
Cavendish	J. Mahony	*Chad*	R. Malone
Choubra	R. Nicol	*Cimarron*	P. Shanahan
Clarendon	J. Barry	*Cleator*	W.W. Kilroy
Connaught	D. Owens	*Connaught Ranger*	C. Taaffe
Cordelier	E.T. Geddes	*Craig Royston*	R. Macaulay
Crotanstown	E.K.B. Tighe	*Dalesman*	P.T. Dillon
David Trot	C. Hoey	*Delamont*	J. Leigh
Deramfield	J.T. Hinds	*Derby Dick*	J. Campbell
Dictator	M.A. Maher	*Diogenes*	Congested Districts Board
Double Dutch	Knight of Glin	*Double Entendre*	J. M'Ilroy
Douglas	J. Hawe	*Draco*	H. Dolphin
Duke of Portland	R.G. Nash	*Dulcimer*	A.F. Nuttall
Dyspeptic	J.C. Dugdale	*Earl Scroope*	J.R. Salter
Early Bird	T. Power	*Egerton*	Col. R. Thomson
Elector	J. Galbraith	*Enthusiast*	J. Daly
Experience	T.F. Sparrow	*Explorer*	T. M'Cutchan
Falcon	J.A.S. Langan	*Favo Loo*	W.J. Goulding
Favonian	W. Pallin (lessee: J. Craig)	*Fear Not*	J. Dobson
Ferdinand	J.W.A. Harris	*Fife*	J. Moore
Fitz-Clifden	J.C. Murphy	*Fortunio*	E. Kennedy
Fra Diavolo	J. Sheehy	*Garland*	P. Duff
Glen Roy	C. Magner	*Glenvannon*	Mrs Cowhy
Great Briton	W. Chambers	*Greenfield*	T. Hamilton
Guerilla	R.H. Falkiner	*Guy Mannering*	O.T. Slocock
Hackler	J. Daly	*Hartstown*	J. Bell
Heckberry	W. Pallin	*Hidden Treasure*	Capt. W.T. Townshend
Holloway	R.H. Clegg	*Hominy*	J.A.S. Langan
Horoscope	C. Friery	*Jester II*	C. and J. MacNamara
John	M.F. Hussey	*Kendal Royal*	J.C. Murphy
Kentford	R.H. Hayes	*Kentish Fire*	M.A. Maher
Keswick	J. Reese	*Kirkham*	Lord Dunraven
Lasso	D. Byrne	*Laurium*	J.H. Lambert
Lord George	F. Mullins	*Lorikeet*	T.A. Love
Luminary	J. Curran	*Lyric*	A. Lyons
Marmion	Capt. D.D. Heather	*Marquis of Tavora*	C.R.A. MacDonnell
Mascarille	H.H. Smiley	*Master Ned*	M.F. Neary
Master Pirate	A. Lawrenson	*Matador*	F.G. Sikes
Midas	E. Rohan	*Milner*	J.C. Sullivan

Mombasa	W.J. Barry	*Monksman*	P. Duffy
Monsieur	Major G. Dease (lessee: M. Murphy)	*Mont Cenis*	P.J. O'Connor
M.P.	Countess of Wicklow	*Mulberry*	R.T. Graham
Narellan	Harris Brothers (lessee: T. Lindsay)	*Nasr-ed-din*	A.H. Davidson
North Mayo	C.L. Ellison	*Northshampton*	W.F. M'Keever
Novelist	Major C.W. Studdert	*Orontes*	A. M'Mahon
Palmleaf	J. Daly (lessee: S. Manseragh)	*Passion Flower*	J. Widger
Pelican	R.D. Lawrenson	*Peterhof*	Capt. W.J. Murphy
Phelimfield	J.T. Hinds	*Piercefield*	C. Taaffee
Playactor	J. Flanagan	*Primrose League*	J.A.S. Langan
Prince Arthur	L.H.R. Carty	*Prince Charles*	H. Sparrow
Prince Violet	D.R. Kares	*Punster*	Capt. A.W.M. Richards
Pythias	C.I. Kelly	*Quebec*	H. Delany
Red Kangaroo	S. Tanner	*Red Heart*	Capt. D.D. Heather
Red Prince II	H.E. Linde (lessee: W. Pallin)	*Regulator*	J. Bell
Restraint	T.S. Elcoate and J.M. Prior Kennedy	*Robert Emmet*	J. Hartigan
Roman Emperor	J.T. Heffernan	*Royal Charter*	P. Cashman
Royal Emporor	M. Gleeson	*Royal Mask*	E. Mitchell
Royal Meath	Sir J. Arnott, Bt.	*Runnymede*	R. Keppel
St. Aidan	R.N. Thompson	*St. Bavon*	P. Duffy
St. Jude	E. Mitchell	*St. Kieran*	E. Smithwick
St. Michael	M.J.J. Saurin	*Save All*	B. Ryan
Scene Shifter	J.W.A. Harris	*Sir Andrew*	Mrs J.B. Alexander
Sir Hugh	J. O'Connell	*Sir Patrick*	M. Healy
Skeddaddle	T.J. Studdert	*Sly Patrick*	M. Brien
Springtime	J. Daly (lessee: W.H. West)	*Sternchaser*	T. M'Cutchan
Succes	E.N. Power	*Tacitus*	A. Moore
Tartan	Duke of Devonshire	*Terror*	Lord Ashtown
The Baron	Lord Kenmare	*The Dethroned*	T. Crowe
The Rector	Lord Ashtown	*The Wraith*	J. Merrick
Thrapston	M. Quinn	*Thurles*	Harris Brothers
Tiercel	L.W. Hendley	*Toronto*	T. Magnier
Torpedo	M.A. Maher	*Touchstone*	W.W. Kilroy
Tramore	J. Barry	*Tranby Croft*	J. Mullarkey
Trot On	A. M'Mahon	*Trespasser*	J.H. M'Cormack
Troubador	D. Gleeson	*Troy II*	J.S. Kincaid
Tunis	L. Sherwin	*Tynan*	J. Brady

Uncle Sam	Congested Districts Board	*Vanderbilt*	C. Boyd
Victoricus	Lord Rathdonnell	*Waif*	M. Foley
Walmsgate	T. O'Brien	*Westmoreland*	E. Kennedy
Whalebone	R. Connell	*Wild Kilwarlin*	J. M'Closkey
Wild Monk	H. Sparrow	*Wild Sherry*	J.A.S. Langan
Willoughby	W.F. M'Keever	*Winkfield*	J.C. Sullivan
Wiseman	W. Pallin	*Wonderbaar*	R. Macaulay
Woodman	Major G.M. Eccles	*Young Marden*	T.F. Nugent
Young Speculation	M.O'Donovan	*Zagazig*	M.A. Maher

1900

Aconite	R. Walsh	*Acropolis*	R.F. O'Hara
Aerolite	R.G. Wordsworth	*Algoa Bay*	J. Hutchinson
Amber Gate	Harris Brothers	*Annagor*	J.S. Langan
Apollo	A.B. Walker	*Ashbough*	Lord Crofton
Assassin	T. Gleeson	*Astrologer*	W. Pallin
Athletic	J.F. Bomford	*Atratus*	Lord Dunraven
Bailsman	T. Talt	*Baldwin*	T. Stephens
Ballinafad	D. Craig	*Ballynoe*	J. Daly (lessee: J. Bell)
Baron Hastings	R.H. Hayes	*Beaucourt*	Capt. W.T. Townshend
Beggar's Opera	Cherrywood Stud	*Ben*	J. Preston
Bendemere	T.F. Sparrow	*Bergomask*	M. Ballesty
Beware	W. O'Brien	*Black Diamond*	H. Reynolds
Blair Hope	J.R. Webster	*Blâr Aodan*	Dr Cox
Blondel	P.J. M'Cloghry	*Bon Soir*	J.M. Purdon
Brayhead	A. Maxwell	*Broxton*	W. Pallin
Breach of Promise	P. Higgins	*Brighton*	P. and T.E. Quigley
Britannic	J.M. Purdon	*Bruree*	J. Duggan
Buckmaster	E.M. Archdale	*Bull's Eye*	C.F. Harding
Bunbury	W. Pallin	*Bushy Park*	J. Daly
Canon	Mrs M. O'Connell	*Cavendish*	J. Mahony
Chad	R. Malone	*Choubra*	D. Owens
Cimarron	P. Shanahan	*Clarendon*	J. Barry
Cleator	W.W. Kilroy	*Condor*	M. Killian
Connaught	Mrs J.B. Alexander	*Connaught Ranger*	C. Taaffee
Cordelier	E.T. Geddes	*Court Ball*	D. Owens
Coylton	E. Mitchell	*Craig Royston*	R. Macaulay
Crotanstown	E.K.B. Tighe	*Curfew*	J. Quinlan
Dalesman	P.T. Dillon	*David Trot*	C. Hoey
Delamont	J. Leigh	*Deramfield*	J.T. Hinds
Desmond	Lord Dunraven	*Dictator*	M.A. Maher

Diogenes	Congested Districts Board	*Double Entendre*	J. M'Ilroy
Douglas	J. Hawe	*Draco*	H. Dolphin
Duke of Portland	R.G. Nash	*Dulcimer*	A.F. Nuttall
Dyspeptic	J.C. Dugdale	*Earl Scroope*	J.R. Salter
Early Bird	T. Power	*Egerton*	Col. R. Thomson
Elector	J. Galbraith	*Enthusiast*	J. Daly
Explorer	T. M'Cutchan	*Falcon*	J.A.S. Langan
Favonian	W. Pallin (lessee: T. Lindsay)	*Ferdinand*	J.W.A. Harris
Fife	J. Moore	*Fitz-Clifden*	J.C. Murphy
Fortunio	E. Kennedy	*Fra Diavolo*	J. Sheehy
Garland	P. Duff	*Gay Lumley*	E. Mitchell
Glen Roy	C. Magner	*Great Briton*	W. Chambers
Greenfield	T. Hamilton	*Ground Ivy*	B.P.J. Mahony
Guerilla	R.H. Falkiner	*Hackler*	J. Daly
Hartstown	J. Bell	*Heckberry*	W. Pallin (lessee: D. Craig)
Heligoland	A. Macan	*Hidden Treasure*	Capt. W.T. Townshend
Hominy	J.A.S. Langan	*Horoscope*	C. Friery
Ignus Fatuus	W.F. M'Keever	*Kendal Royal*	J.C. Murphy
Kentford	R.H. Hayes	*Kentish Fire*	M.A. Maher
Kirkham	Lord Dunraven	*Lasso*	D. Byrne
Laurium	J.H. Lambert	*Le Noir*	A. Lowry
Lighterman	J. Read	*Little John*	P.J. O'Connor
Lord George	F. Mullins	*Lorikeet*	T.A. Love
Luminary	J. Curran	*Marmion*	Capt. D.D. Heather
Marmiton	C. Hannan	*Marquis of Tavora*	C.R.A. MacDonnell
Mascarille	H.H. Smiley	*Master Ned*	M.F. Neary
Master Pirate	A. Lawrenson	*Matador*	F.G. Sikes
Midas	E. Rohan	*Middleman*	M. Buchanan
Milner	J.C. Sullivan	*Minor Canon*	F. Daly
Mombasa	W.J. Barry	*Monksman*	P. Duffy
Monsieur	Major G. Dease (lessee: M. Murphy)	*Mont Cenis*	P.J. O'Connor
M.P.	Countess of Wicklow	*Mulberry*	R.T. Graham
Narellan	Harris Brothers	*Nasr-ed-din*	A.H. Davidson
North Mayo	C.L. Ellison	*Northshampton*	W.F. M'Keever
Novelist	J. Widger	*Orontes*	A. M'Mahon
Palmleaf	J. Daly (lessee: R.S. Manseragh)	*Passion Flower*	J. Widger
Pelican	R.D. Lawrenson	*Peterhof*	Capt. W.J. Murphy
Phelimfield	J.T. Hinds	*Playactor*	J. Flanagan
Primrose League	J.A.S. Langan	*Prince Arthur*	L.H.R. Carty

Prince Charles	J. Curran	*Prince Violet*	D.R. Kayes
Punster	Capt. A.W.M. Richards	*Pythias*	C.I. Kelly
Quebec	H. Delany	*Quidnunc*	P. Rogers
Red Kangaroo	S. Tanner	*Red Heart*	Capt. D.D. Heather
Red Prince II	W. Pallin	*Regulator*	J. Bell
Restraint	T.S. Elcoate and J.M. Prior Kennedy	*Riverstown*	C. Hannan
Robert Emmet	C. Mahon	*Rocket*	D. Stack
Roman Emperor	M. Gleeson	*Royal Charter*	P. Cashman
Royal Emperor	M. Gleeson	*Royal Mask*	E. Mitchell
Royal Meath	Sir J. Arnott, Bt.	*Runnymede*	R. Keppel
St. Aidan	R.N. Thompson	*St. Jude*	E. Mitchell
St. Kieran	E. Smithwick	*Scene Shifter*	J.W.A. Harris
Sir Hugh	J. O'Connell	*Sir Patrick*	M. Healy
Sly Patrick	M. Brien	*Snaplock*	J. Widger
Springtime	J. Daly (lessee: W.H. West)	*Sternchaser*	T. M'Cutchan
Succès	E.N. Power	*Sun of York*	R.F. Payne
Tacitus	A. Moore	*Tartan*	Duke of Devonshire
The Dethroned	T. Crowe	*The Rector*	Lord Ashtown
The Wraith	J. Merrick	*Thrapston*	J. Sufferin
Thurles	Harris Brothers	*Toronto*	T. Magnier
Touchstone	W.W. Kilroy	*Tramore*	J. Barry
Tranby Croft	J. Mullarkey	*Trot On*	A. M'Mahon
Tunis	L. Sherwin	*Tynan*	M. Healy
Uncle Sam	Congested Districts Board	*Vanderbilt*	C. Boyd
Victoricus	Lord Rathdonnell	*Waif*	J. Cummins
Whalebone	R. Connell	*Wild Kilwarlin*	J. M'Closkey
Wild Monk	T.F. Sparrow	*Wild Sherry*	J.A.S. Langan
Winkfield	J.C. Sullivan	*Wiseman*	W. Pallin
Wonderbaar	R. Macaulay	*Woodman*	Major G.M. Eccles
Xylophone	F. Flannery	*Young Marden*	T.F. Nugent
Young Speculation	T. O'Donnell	*Zagazig*	M.A. Maher (lessee: J.L. Handcock)
Zero	J. Lynch		

Note: The names of stallions are printed as in the lists of stallions in the *Registers*. Obviously various spelling errors occurred!

Appendix Two

The following table, showing the names, breed and location of stallions owned by the Congested Districts Board and standing at stud in 1892, gives a good idea of the way in which the Board operated its horse breeding schemes. Stallions were located under the charge of District Inspectors of the Royal Irish Constabulary during the stud season but for the rest of the year they were kept at a farm belonging to the Board and located at Shankill, between Dublin and Bray. In addition to horse stallions the Board also kept jack-asses at stud, and in 1892 the Board reported that '. . . through the instrumentality of the War Office we are now importing six other Spanish Jacks direct from Spain.'

Place	County	Breed	Name
Carndonagh	Donegal	Hackney	*Lord Tennyson*
Dungfanaghy	Donegal	Hackney	*Real Gentleman*
Glenties	Donegal	Arab	*Tarassan*
Dungloe	Donegal	Hackney	*Zeus*
Swinford	Mayo	Hackney	*Fireaway 2nd*
Belmullet	Mayo	Hackney	*Lord Derwent 2nd*
Belmullet	Mayo	Arab	*Ali Baba*
Achill Sound	Mayo	Arab	*Desert Born*
Achill Sound	Mayo	Hackney	*Callis Fireaway*
Newport	Mayo	Hackney	*Beau*
Clonbur	Galway	Hackney	*Fashion 3rd*
Letterfrack	Galway	Hackney	*Lord Go Bang*
Cashel	Galway	Barb	*Awfully Jolly*
Oughterard	Galway	Hackney	*King Fireaway*
Schull	Cork	Hackney	*North Riding*
Kilmorna	Kerry	Cleveland Bay	*Bay Benedict*
Ballinamore	Leitrim	Hackney	*Rokeby*

Source: *First Report of the Congested Districts Board for Ireland*, 1893, 39.

Appendix Three

AN ROINN TALMHAIOCHTA AGUS IASCAIGH

HORSE BREEDING ACT, 1934

LICENSING OF STALLIONS

Under the Horse Breeding Act, 1934, the owner of every entire horse two years of age or upwards, which is not eligible for entry in the List of Exempted Stallions, must obtain a licence or permit to retain it.

A stallion becomes of age, for the purposes of the Act, on the 1st of January in the second year following that in which it was foaled. For example, a colt foaled in 1974 would become of age on the 1st January, 1976.

Date for Lodging Applications for Licences

Applications for licences must be lodged with the Department of Agriculture and Fisheries, Dublin, not later than the 31st December of the year preceding that for which the licences are required. Applications lodged after the 31st December must each be accompanied by a special late fee of £3 in addition to the ordinary licence fee. *The special fee is statutory and must be paid before a late application can be considered.*

Licences are valid for one calendar year.

Fees for Licences

   (a) £1.50p in respect of a stallion over 14 hands high.
   (b) 53p in respect of a pony stallion not exceeding 14 hands high.
   (c) 53p in respect of a stallion which has attained the age of seven years and for which a licence has been granted for each of the three preceding years.

Permits

Permits, which are issued in special cases only, are valid for a period not exceeding eleven months.

The fee for a permit is 25p.

Exemptions

Thoroughbred stallions in training for racing, or used exclusively for the service of Thoroughbred mares, are eligible for entry in the List of Exempted Stallions.

The entry fee for exemption is 13p.

Appeals

If the Minister refuses to grant a licence, the owner of the stallion is entitled to appeal and to have the horse inspected by an independent referee selected by the Minister from the panel of referees set up under the Act. The appeal, which must be lodged within twenty-one days of the date of rejection must be accompanied by a fee of £5.25p which will be returned if the appeal is successful.

Appendix Four

This is an illustratory excerpt from the progeny performance tables now being produced by Bord na gCapall.

The following is a survey of the performance of the progeny of Registered Stallions in show classes for young horses which were subsidised by Bord na gCapall in 1977

THOROUGHBRED

Stallion	No. of winning progeny	Prizes Won								
		Foals			Yearlings			2 year olds		
		1st	2nd	3rd	1st	2nd	3rd	1st	2nd	3rd
Alchopal	1			1						
Amalric	1					1	1			
Amazon	2			1		1	1			
Arctic Que	3				3	3	1		1	
Athenius	2				2	1	2		1	2
Awkward Brief	12	1	1	3	8	6	1	2	1	4
Bahrain	4	2	1		1	3	1			
Ballinamona Boy	4	1		1			1		3	1
Barney Crookey	1				1					

Bassompierre	4	1	1		1	1			
Beau Tudor	1								1
Belgrave	5		2					2	4	1
Birkenhead	2	1		1					
Bliss	7	1	1	2	1		4	1	1
Blue Cliff	5	6			1	1		5	1	1
Blue Laser	2	1	3						
Bob's Vision	11	4	1	2	2	4		3	2	2
Bright Will	3	3						2	1
Campaigner	3	3		1	2		1		
Carnival Night	3		1					1	1	2
Cassanant	2							1	5	3
Ceredigion	2	4	1						
Chair Lift	4							7	4	3
Chilon	4	2		2	1				3
Chou Chin Chow	7	1	5	1	6	2	3	1	
Coevers	3		1		3	1			
Colinstable	2			1				8	4	
Column	4	1	1	2					
Cornelscourt	2	1							1
Crafty Codger	1		2						
Crespino	4	2	2	1			1		
Darantus	13	1	2	2	8	2	3	14	4	2
Dangan Slippered	3	2	1					1	1	1

References

Note. In many cases the source of reference is obvious from the text, e.g. '. . . as the *Schedule* for the 1889 show states.' The reference is to that *Schedule*. To avoid duplication such references are not listed hereunder.

Introduction
1. MacCormac, M., 1978, *The Irish racing and bloodstock industry*, 222.

Chapter One
1. Van Wijngaarden-Bakker, L.H., 1974, 'The animal remains from the Beaker settlement at Newgrange, Co. Meath: first report, '*Proc. Roy. Irish Acad.*, 74,C,313-83.
2. Lewis, C.A., 1975, *Hunting in Ireland,* 24.
3. Dent, A. and Goodall, D.M., 1962, *The foals of Epona*, 38.
4. Furlong, N., 1973, *Dermot King of Leinster and the Foreigners*.
5. *ibid.*, 127.
6. Hore, P.H., 1904, *History of the town and county of Wexford,* 9.
7. *ibid.*, 16.
8. *ibid.*, 35.
9. *ibid.*, 38.
10. *ibid.*, 275.
11. Dent and Goodall, *op. cit.*, 108.
12. Hore, *op cit.*, 275.
13. Watson, S.J., 1969, *Between the flags: a history of Irish steeplechasing*, 3.
14. Mackay-Smith, A., (in press), *The Colonial Quarter-horse*, ch.6.
15. Cox, M.F., 1897, *Notes on the history of the Irish horse*, 28.
16. *ibid.*, 28.
17. Spencer, E., quoted from Morton, G., 1971, *Elizabethan Ireland*, 141.
18. Cox, *op. cit.,* 71.
19. Watson, *op. cit.*, 4.
20. *Carte Papers*, 3 April 1668.
21. Cox, *op. cit.*, 94.
22. de Breffny, B. and ffolliott, R., 1975, *The houses of Ireland*, 95ff.
23. Bianconi, M.O'C., and Watson, S.J., 1962, *Bianconi*, 57.
24. *ibid.*, 168.
25. *Proceedings of the Royal Dublin Society* (henceforth *PRDS*), 139,190,5-12.
26. Berry, H.F., 1915, A history of the *Royal Dublin Society*, 315.

Chapter Two

1. *PRDS*, 123,1887,4.
2. *Carte Papers*, 3,186, letter of June 9,1668.
3. *PRDS*, 122,1886.
4. *PRDS*, 124,1888, 4-6.
5. *ibid.*, 16.
6. Lewis, C.A., *op.cit.*, 55.
7. *Reports by the Commissioners appointed to inquire into the horse breeding industry in Ireland*, 1897, paragraph 9437.
8. Bowen, M., 1954, *Irish Hunting*, 126.
9. *PRDS*, 125,1889,6.

Chapter Three

1. Chivers, K., 1976, *The Shire Horse*, 140.
2. *PRDS*, 125,1889,7.
3. *PRDS*, 127,1890,98.
4. Bowen, *op.cit.*, 42.
5. *PRDS*, 126,1889,41.
6. *PRDS*, 127, op.cit., 98.
7. *ibid.*, 99.
8. *Register of Thoroughbred Stallions, 1895,* Royal Dublin Society, 89.

Chapter Four

1. *PRDS*, 126,1889,48.
2. *ibid.*, 38-9.
3. Leicester, C., 1957, *Bloodstock breeding*, 246.
4. *PRDS*, 126,1889,46.
5. Lewis, C.A., *op.cit.*, 65.
6. *PRDS*, 128, 1891.

Chapter Five

1. *PRDS*, 127,1891,100.
2. *PRDS*, 124,1888,16.
3. PRDS, 128,1891,360.
4. *ibid.*,369.
5. Bowen, *op.cit.*, 190.
6. *ibid.*, 210.
7. PRDS, 129,1892,12
8. Cox, *op.cit.,* 102.

Chapter Six

1. *PRDS,* 129,1892,55ff.
2. Lyon, W.E., 1950, *First aid hints for the horse owner,* 54.
3. *ibid.*, 117.
4. *ibid.*, 112.
5. *First Report of the Congested Districts Board for Ireland*, 1893,39.
6. *PRDS*, 130,1894,123ff.

Chapter Seven

1. Foley,D., 1977, personal communication.
2. *Baily's Hunting Directory*, *1928-9*, 193.
3. Bowen, *op.cit.*, 69.
4. *ibid.*, 70, (quoting from Lever,C.).

Chapter Eight

1. PRDS, 131,1894,89.
2. *Register of Thoroughbred Stallions*, 1897,3,97.
3. *PRDS*, 131,1894,89.

Chapter Nine

1. *Register of Thoroughbred Stallions, 1895*,67.
2. *ibid.*, vii.
3. Kavanagh, P., 1938, *The Green Fool*, ch.7.
4. McDowell, R.B., 1975, *The Church of Ireland, 1869-1969*,47.
5. *Reports* etc., *op.cit.*, paragraph 7448.
6. Bowen, *op.cit.*, 194ff.
7. *Register of approved stallions*, 1977.
8. Bowen, *op.cit.*, 195.
9. Micks, W.L., 1925, *An account of the constitution, administration and dissolution of the Congested Districts Board for Ireland from 1891 to 1923*, 19.
10. Freeman, T.W., 1965 (third ed.), *Ireland*, 144.
11. Bowen, *op.cit.*, 208.
12. *PRDS*, 132,1896, 99ff.
13. *Reports* etc., *op.cit.*, 18.

Chapter Ten

1. Bowen, *op.cit.*, 125.
2. Sassoon, S., 1968, *Selected Poems*, (The Old Huntsman).
3. *Reports*, etc., *op.cit.*, 37ff.
4. Lewis, C.A., *op.cit.*, 156.

Chapter Eleven

1. *Register of Thoroughbred Stallions, 1897*, prefatory note.
2. Leicester, *op.cit.*, 158.
3. Casserley, H.C., 1974, *Outline of Irish railway history*, 98.
4. Dent and Goodall, *op.cit.*, 283.
5. *Reports*, etc., *op.cit.*, 8.
6. *ibid.*, 13-48.
7. *Register of Thoroughbred Stallions*, 1897,27.
8. Somerville, E.OE. and Ross, V.M., 1928, *The complete experiences of an Irish R.M.*, 270.

Chapter Twelve

1. Lowe, C.B., edited by W. Allison, 1895, *Breeding racehorses by the Figure system*, 25.
2. Freeman, *op.cit.*, 126.
3. *PRDS*, 136,1899, 86.

Chapter Thirteen

1. Ryder, T., 1961, *The high stepper*, 11
2. *Register of Thoroughbred Stallions, 1899*, v.
3. *PRDS*, 136,1899,92.
4. Watson, *op.cit.*, 121.
5. *ibid.*, 118.
6. Dalesman (C.N. de Courcy-Parry), 1964, *Here lies my story*, 135.

Chapter Fourteen

1. *Register of Thoroughbred Stallions, 1897*, 28.
2. Browne, T.H., 1931, *History of the English turf, 1904-30*, 237.
3. Watson, *op.cit.*, 64.
4. *PRDS*, 137,1901, 81.
5. *Journal*, Department of Agriculture, 1,1900, 1.
6. *ibid.*, 11.
7. *ibid.*, 23.
8. *PRDS*, 137,1901,81-2.

Chapter Fifteen

1. *Stallion Show Catalogue, 1901*, 2.
2. *PRDS*, 138,1901,68.
3. *PRDS*, 139,1902,6.
4. *ibid.*, 10.
5. *ibid.*, 11.
6. *ibid.*, 12.
7. *Catalogue of the Horse Show, 1902*, 2.
8. *Catalogue of the Horse Show, 1903*, results appendix.
9. *PRDS*, 139,1902,82.

Horse Breeding in Ireland – Job 188
Galley 146

Chapter Sixteen

1. Hoctor,D., 1971, *The Department's story: a history of the Department of Agriculture*, 108.
2. *Irish Draught Horse Book*, 1,19.
3. *British Hunts and Huntsmen*, 4,1911,471.
4. *Annual General Report of the Department of Agriculture and Technical Instruction, Ireland*, (henceforth *AGR*), 1902-3, 26.
5. *ibid.*, 1918-19, 38.
6. *ibid.*, 1910-11, 58.
7. *ibid.*, 1917-18, 42.
8. *ibid.*, 1914-15, 45.
9. *ibid.*, 1903-4, 37.
10. Carden, R.G., in de Trafford, Sir Humphrey (ed.), 1907, *The horses of the British Empire*, 231.

11. *Irish Draught Horse Book*, Vol.I, 6.
12. *AGR*, 1903-4, 35.
13. *ibid.*, 1904-5, 27.
14. *ibid.*, 1910-11, 59.
15. *ibid.*, 1908-9, 37.
16. *ibid.*, 1919-20, 40.
17. *ibid.*, 1921-2, 32.
18. *ibid.*, 1922-3, 37.
19. *ibid.*, 1922-3, 2-3.
20. *ibid.*, 1942-3, 23.
21. *ibid.*, 1943-4, 80.
22. *ibid.*, 1944-5, 19.
23. *ibid.*, 1945-6, 82.
24. *ibid.*, 1946-7, 14.
25. *Register of Approved Stallions, 1978*, 75.
26. Lewis, C.A. and McCarthy, M.E., 1977, 'The horse breeding industry in Ireland,' *Irish Geogr.*, 10, 72-89.
27. *Register, op.cit.*, 6.
28. *Irish Draught Horse Yearbook, 1978*, 16-7.
29. *Annual Report, Ministry of Agriculture, 1929-30, N.I.* 21.
30. *29th General Report of the Ministry of Agriculture, 1970, N.I.*, 71.

Index

For ease of reference the index is divided into two parts. Part One lists horses under four headings: Thoroughbreds, Half-breds, Irish Draughts, Other Breeds. Part Two lists people. Horses and people named in the Appendices are not indexed therefrom since horses are already listed alphabetically in Appendices One, Two and Four and the people named therein are their owners.

Part One: Horses

A. Thoroughbreds

Note. A few of the horses listed above as Thoroughbreds did not qualify for the General Stud Book and may, in fact, have been Half-breds.

B. Half-breds

Part Two: People